SHATTERED SPHERE™

FASA CORPORATION

TABLE OF CONTENTS

CREDITS

Writing
Diane Piron-Gelman

Additional Material
Michael A. Stackpole (A Brief History of the Inner Sphere)
Dan "Flake" Grendell (Twilight of the Clans)

Project Development
Randall N. Bills
Development Assistance
Bryan Nystul

Project Editing
Sharon Turner Mulvihill

BattleTech Line Developer
Bryan Nystul

Editorial Staff
Editorial Director
Donna Ippolito
Managing Editor
Sharon Turner Mulvihill
Assistant Editor
Robert Boyle

Production Staff
Art Director
Jim Nelson
Cover Art
Chris Moeller
Cover Design
Fred Hooper
Illustrations
Clint Langley
Scott James
Jim Nelson
Matthew Plog
Steve Prescott
Loston Wallace
Maps
John Bridegroom
Layout
Jim Nelson

Acknowledgements
The author would like to acknowledge the following writers, on whose material much of this book is based:
Michael A. Stackpole, Loren L. Coleman, Chris Hartford, Thomas S. Gressman, Blaine Lee Pardoe, Chris Hussey, Randall N. Bills, Dan "Flake" Grendell, Rodney Knox, Christoffer Trossen, Bryan Nystul, Herbert Beas III, and Patrick Kirkland.
Thanks also to Bryan Nystul, for giving me my first-ever shot at a whole book (!); to Randall N. Bills, for his invaluable guidance, timely suggestions and boundless font of patience; to Sharon Turner Mulvihill, for frequent words of encouragement; and to Stephen Gelman, outstanding husband and father, who took over the child care every evening so that I could write this opus.

Thanks
The development staff would like to thank the art staff for the extra effort they gave to this and many recent products—thanks for going the extra mile, guys!

Published by FASA Corporation • 1100 W. Cermak Road • Suite B305 • Chicago, IL 60608

FASA Corporation can be reached on America OnLine at FASAInfo (General Information, Shadowrun, BattleTech) or FASA Art (Art Comments) in the Online Gaming area (Keyword "Gaming"). Via InterNet use <AOL Account Name>@AOL.COM, but please, no list or server subscriptions. Thanks!

Visit our World Wide Web site at http://www.FASA.com

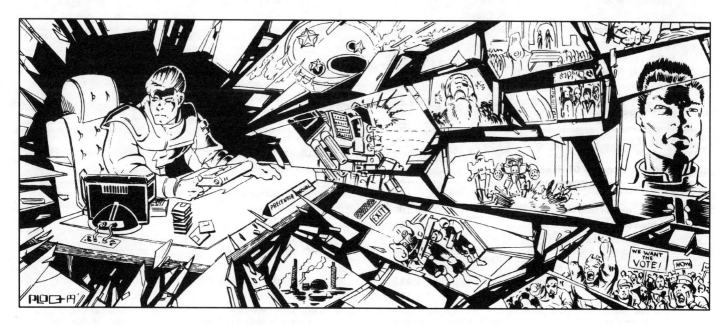

INTELLIGENCE COMMAND CLASSIFIED REPORT
ALPHA LEVEL CLEARANCE

FROM: Lieutenant General Jerrard Cranston, SLDF Intelligence Command
TO: Victor Steiner-Davion, Precentor Martial, ComStar/Commanding General, Star League Defense Force
DATE: 1 January 3062

Victor—

Here it is, in all its ugly glory—the intelligence report you requested on the current state of the Inner Sphere and the Periphery realms. The attached files contain the latest information on all the potential trouble spots we're likely to be facing over the next several months, as well as general information about affairs in our newborn Star League. I'm afraid most of it doesn't make pretty reading—but then, I'm sure you expected that. Some of what's in these files may disturb you, but I doubt any of it will surprise you.

My agents have collected the following documents from various sources throughout the Inner Sphere and Periphery—some from those working with us, some intercepted on their way to other destinations. As time is of the essence, these files contain raw intelligence—post-battle reports, news transcripts, decoded civilian and military transmissions, political pamphlets, personal diary entries and so on—rather than the synthesized analysis of such bits and pieces typical of the usual intelligence report. I've imposed a rough organization on the data, separating it by region and offering my own comments and interpretations where useful or appropriate, but beyond that, you're seeing it pretty much as it crossed my desk.

As a way to put recent developments into context—and also just because I know you'll appreciate it, as a student (so to speak) of both the Clans and history—I've included a brief historical overview of the Inner Sphere up to the present day. Following that are files covering each of the Star League member-states, the Clan occupation zones—as well as information on the "Home Clans"—ComStar and the Word of Blake, and the Periphery nations. Each of these files begins with an account of a recent event that, in my opinion, either set the stage for or has most influenced that region's current situation and its likely course of action in the immediate future. The information in the rest of each file should give you an accurate sense of what's going on now, how things got that way, where trouble is most likely to crop up, and who to watch for or depend on in the coming months and years.

The Federated Commonwealth and Lyran Alliance files also contain troop deployments, including assessments of which units you can and cannot count on should military action against Katherine Steiner-Davion become necessary. I know you don't want a war, but I believe Katherine will give you no choice. Sooner or later, war will come—either you will be forced to use military action to bring Katherine to justice, or she'll fall prey to her paranoia and make a pre-emptive strike against you. That's not what you'd like to hear, I know—but you've always valued my honest opinion, and I owe you nothing less.

I'd say happy reading, but I doubt it will be. We have a functioning Star League and a sort of stability for the moment, and against all odds we've beaten the threat of organized invasion from the Clans—all things to be grateful for. As usual, however, there are enough dark clouds on the horizon to make for a nasty storm when something finally breaks. Hopefully, the information in this report will help us to weather it.

A HISTORY OF THE INNER SPHERE

[Your cousin Phelan sent me the following, with the comment that you and I both might find it a useful gauge of just how well Clan Wolf knows Inner Sphere history, especially the plots, events and fallout of those events that occurred after the Exodus. This document was originally created by Gus Michaels, Archivist to Natasha Kerensky, in December of 3057, and Phelan has updated it. Given the ongoing threat from the Wolf Clan, their level of knowledge is disturbing; they may well be a damn sight better at predicting how Inner Sphere leaders are likely to think and act than is good for anyone in this region of space. —JC]

The history of human life among the stars, the creation of the great star empires and the formation of the human society known as the Clans begins with humanity's long-ago first steps into space. Among the ancient nations of Terra, the dissolution of traditional alliances and enmities in the late twentieth and early twenty-first centuries created an era of unprecedented peace and cooperation, in which all human societies turned their energies toward the advancement of the human race. By 2020, the groundbreaking research of two scientists—Thomas Kearny and Takayoshi Fuchida—led to the development of a fusion reactor capable of powering a starship. In 2027 the Alliance starship *Columbia*, powered by the first Kearny-Fuchida fusion engine, made its historic journey to Mars. With that brief voyage, Man's migration from Terra began.

In 2102, the scientific community paid new attention to pan-dimensional gravitational mathematics, a breakthrough discovery made eighty years earlier by Kearny and Fuchida. Though twenty-first-century scientists had scoffed at this theory, twenty-second-century physicists used Kearny and Fuchida's work to develop the first faster-than-light ship in an intensive research effort known as the Deimos Project. Deimos produced the first Kearny-Fuchida drive, which created a space warp around a starship through which the craft could "jump" distances of up to thirty light years from its starting point. On 5 December 2108, Terra launched the first so-called JumpShip, the TAS *Pathfinder*, on its famous round trip between Terra and the Tau Ceti system.

The ability to travel between star systems in the blink of an eye led to an unparalleled expansion of human colonies to other worlds. The first human colony of New Earth, established on Tau Ceti IV in 2116, paved the way for hundreds of others. Under the banner of the Terran Alliance, man spread throughout the galaxy as his ancestors had once swarmed over Terra. By the year 2235, an Alliance survey had counted more than six hundred human colonies scattered across a sphere roughly eighty light years in diameter. In an eerie parallel to earlier human history, however, this colonial expansion carried within it the seeds of its own destruction. Self-sufficient colonies far from their founding worlds began agitating for home rule; in 2236, a group of worlds at the edge of human-explored space declared independence from Terra. The Colonial Marines, dispatched from Earth to quell the rebellion, failed miserably. Within six years, the Alliance government had granted independence to all colonies that lay more than thirty light years from Terra.

RISE OF THE HEGEMONY

Over the next several decades, a combination of political infighting and the severe economic strain of supporting Terran colonies ate away at the fabric of the Terran Alliance. Tales of colonists starving to death sparked riots among sympathetic Terrans, while the ranks of the poor, dispossessed and angry grew. In 2314, civilian riots and political polarization erupted into Alliance-wide civil war. The Alliance Global Militia, which had remained uneasily neutral throughout the long years of unrest, stepped in to stop the violence at the behest of James McKenna, an admiral in the Alliance Global Navy. Using his newfound authority as the Alliance's military savior, McKenna tore down the corrupt Alliance government and established the Terran Hegemony in its place. In 2316, a grateful public elected him the Hegemony's first Director-General.

During McKenna's twenty-three-year term of office, he launched three military campaigns to bring independent colony worlds back under Hegemony control. The first two campaigns, though hard-fought, were largely successful; the third, launched in 2335, was not. The aging McKenna left control of the final campaign to his son Konrad, whose persistent refusal to follow standard procedure eventually ended in disaster for the Hegemony Navy. In 2338 Konrad led his naval convoys blindly into the heavily mined Syrma system, losing all but two of his twenty-nine troopships. This failure also gave heart to the worlds opposing the Hegemony, who had begun to ally with each other in order to protect themselves from the expanding Hegemony influence. Konrad's disgrace left the Hegemony without an heir to fill McKenna's place; upon James McKenna's death in 2339, the Hegemony's High Council passed the leadership of the Hegemony to James McKenna's third cousin, Michael Cameron. The new Director-General immediately began efforts to cement good relations with the allied colony worlds that had by this time formed independent nations.

In 2351, Michael Cameron took an action whose cultural repercussions would echo for centuries. He created the Peer List, establishing the equivalent of a feudal nobility whose members owed their exalted rank to their achievements. Among the first to receive a title was Dr. Gregory Atlas, lauded for his work on refining myomer bundles. These incredibly powerful synthetic muscles were an integral part of early WorkMechs; when powered by a fusion reactor, myomer bundles give a BattleMech its strength and mobility. Though Dr. Atlas would not live to see the first BattleMech—used in action on 5 February 2439—his work ultimately changed the face of war.

TERRAN ALLIANCE

FUTURE BOUNDARY FOR SCALE

2235

military expansion, the presence of Terra at its heart gave it a certain credibility as a peacemaker in the eyes of other nations. Ian Cameron, who became Director-General in 2549, expanded the Hegemony's peacemaking role and negotiated an end to a number of conflicts. In 2556, Ian persuaded the leaders of the Free Worlds League and the Capellan Confederation to sign the Treaty of Geneva; this famous document laid the groundwork for the formation of the Star League, the glorious interstellar alliance that all too briefly ended wars and advanced the welfare of all humanity. The Lyran Commonwealth signed the treaty in 2558, the Federated Suns in 2567. With the inclusion of the Draconis Combine in 2569, Ian Cameron achieved his dream of uniting virtually all humanity under one ruler.

Led by the enlightened Cameron dynasty, the Star League gave its citizens peace and prosperity for two hundred years. Though even the Star League could not completely wipe out the human need for conflict, it kept disputes between its member-states under firm control. After Lord Simon Cameron's tragic death in 2751, the rulers of all the member-states served as regents for Simon's young son, Richard Cameron, but unfortunately abused their positions to jockey for personal power. The lonely Richard turned to Stefan Amaris, ruler of the Rim Worlds Republic in the far-off Periphery, for friendship and advice. Amaris hated the Camerons, and used his false friendship with Richard to destroy the Star League from within. On 27 December 2766, Stefan Amaris murdered Richard and took control of the Star League.

Within weeks of his coup d'etat, Amaris tried and failed to gain the support of General Aleksandr Kerensky, commander of the Star League Defense Forces. The honorable Kerensky despised the usurper Amaris, and launched a bitter, thirteen-year war to liberate the Terran Hegemony from his grasp. On 29 September 2779, Kerensky led the assault against Amaris's final stronghold on Terra. In the face of overwhelming force, Amaris surrendered. By order of General Kerensky, Amaris, his family and his closest aides were summarily executed by SLDF troops for their crimes against humanity. This act of vengeance closed the book on the Star League.

In late 2780, the Council Lords stripped General Kerensky of his title as Protector of the Realm and ordered him to disperse all SLDF units to their peacetime locations. Bereft of cen-

Inevitably, Cameron's Peer List led to the creation of feudal ruling families in the various independent states surrounding the Hegemony. In the latter half of the twenty-fourth and the early twenty-fifth centuries, tensions between these fiefdoms escalated into open war. Humanity's interstellar nations fought battle after battle against each other, each more savage than the last, culminating in the unspeakable massacre of civilians on the world of Tintavel in the Capellan Confederation. The Confederation's leader, Chancellor Aleisha Liao, responded to the tragedy by devising the Ares Conventions—a set of rules for warfare intended to keep such atrocities from ever happening again. On 13 June 2412, the Hegemony and all other nations signed the Ares Conventions, agreeing to limit their use of nuclear weapons and cease assaulting civilian targets. Though hailed as an act of peace, the Ares Conventions in effect made war legal. Many of the signatory states wasted little time in abusing their legal right to wage warfare.

THE STAR LEAGUE ERA

The Hegemony engaged in its share of battles over the next century or so, but equally as often served as a neutral mediator between warring parties. Despite the Hegemony's history of

tral leadership, the member-states of the Star League vied with each other for power. Unable to agree on which of them should become the new First Lord of the Star League, the lords officially dissolved the High Council in August of 2781. Each lord then left Terra for home, and began to build his own power base. When the various lords attempted to persuade SLDF units to back their personal bids for power, General Kerensky took drastic action. On 14 February 2784, Kerensky proposed to his troops that the SLDF should leave the Inner Sphere and found a new society beyond known space, basing that society on the dearly held ideals of the Star League. In late November of 2784, Kerensky's Operation Exodus became a reality; more than 80 percent of the SLDF departed with Kerensky. The bewildered people of the Inner Sphere, mourning the loss of their hero, comforted themselves with the belief that Kerensky and his people would return when humanity needed them.

CENTURIES OF WAR

In the resulting power vacuum, the rulers of the realms now called the Successor States fought endless, brutal wars, each seeking to re-establish the Star League under his own leadership. In three hundred years of conflict, the Successor Lords accomplished little save to blast humankind virtually back to the Stone Age. By the time the third of the so-called Succession Wars ended, humanity had lost nearly every technological advance that the Star League had made possible; only stringent restrictions on destroying JumpShips, DropShips, BattleMechs and other irreplaceable technologies of war allowed interstellar combat to continue. As the Successor States battered each other senseless, the fighting ground down to endless border skirmishes in which no combatant gained significant advantage.

As the Inner Sphere warred, so did the descendants of the SLDF. Within two decades of planetfall, the men and women who had followed Kerensky in order to preserve the ideals of the Star League had betrayed those ideals and degenerated into vicious, fratricidal conflict. Determined to salvage something from the wreckage of his father's dream, Kerensky's son Nicholas led eight hundred loyal followers to a safe haven, where together they forged the society later known to history as the Clans. Though the Clans would not arrive in force in the Inner Sphere until 3049, they did send one unit as a vanguard

in 3005—Wolf's Dragoons. This famed mercenary unit fought for each of the Successor States in turn, testing the strength of their militaries. Ultimately, the Clan-born Dragoons would become one of the strongest units fighting against the Clans on the side of the Inner Sphere.

STEPS TOWARD PEACE

By the turn of the thirty-first century, common wisdom among Successor State militaries held that conquest of the Inner Sphere through conventional warfare was impossible. Those who wished to found a second Star League had to find another way. In 3020, Archon Katrina Steiner of the Lyran Commonwealth sent a peace proposal to her fellow Successor Lords, but only Prince Hanse Davion of the Federated Suns showed any interest. In 3022, the Archon and the Prince concluded a secret alliance that would bind their realms together through Hanse Davion's marriage to Katrina's daughter and heir, Melissa Steiner. This union joined two families and two nations into a single strong realm, combining the prosperous Lyran Commonwealth with the militarily powerful Federated Suns. The union of these states put the Draconis Combine in an uncomfortable position between two of its greatest enemies,

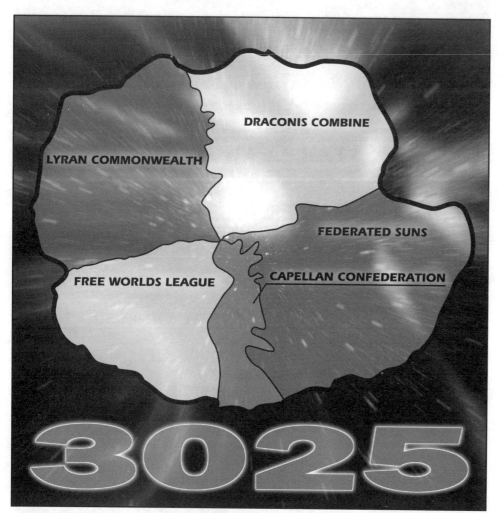

LYRAN COMMONWEALTH

DRACONIS COMBINE

FEDERATED SUNS

FREE WORLDS LEAGUE

CAPELLAN CONFEDERATION

3025

numbers of troops swiftly to distant battlefields. He had also reorganized his army, regrouping battalions and regiments into Regimental Combat Teams consisting of one or more regiments of BattleMechs plus armor, infantry and artillery support. This organization gave Davion troops overwhelming advantages in numbers. The RCTs poured into the Capellan Confederation in seven successive waves, cutting it in half.

Such large-scale mobilization by the Federated Suns did not come without cost. The vast demand for JumpShips and DropShips to ferry troops across space reduced commerce between worlds to essential items only, inflicting economic hardship on many planets. In addition, the Holy Order of ComStar, whose members had preserved the technology of interstellar communications ever since the fall of the Star League, opposed Hanse Davion's war and placed the Federated Suns under Interdiction. ComStar's hyperpulse generators would relay no messages to, from or between any Federated Sun worlds. Hampered by the Interdiction and pleased with his conquests, Hanse Davion sued for peace in 3029. The battered Capellan Confederation agreed willingly to the Federated Suns' terms, desperate to free its scant military resources for use against other enemies. The Free Worlds League had exploited the Confederation's weakened state, taking more than a few worlds for itself; the Confederation's leadership could no longer afford war with House Davion if he hoped to preserve his nation.

and led the smaller Capellan Confederation and Free Worlds League to fear conquest by the emerging Federated Commonwealth.

After months of secret negotiations between the Capellan Confederation, Draconis Combine and Free Worlds League, all three of those nations signed the Concord of Kapetyn in 3024. Intended as a counter to the Lyran Commonwealth–Federated Suns alignment, this triple alliance provided for mutual support and defense. It also guaranteed that any renewed war would engulf the entire Inner Sphere.

FOURTH SUCCESSION WAR

On 20 August 3028, Hanse Davion and Melissa Steiner held their wedding on Terra in the presence of their fellow Successor Lords. At the reception following the wedding, Hanse Davion offered a gift to his bride. As he fed Melissa a piece of wedding cake, Prince Hanse announced, "Wife, in honor of our marriage, in addition to this morsel I give you a vast prize. My love, I give you the Capellan Confederation!" With those words, Hanse Davion launched the Fourth Succession War.

In a series of military exercises held between 3026 and 3028, Hanse Davion had discovered that he could move vast

SKIRMISHES AND PLOTS

Between 3029 and 3039, the Successor States jockeyed for power through covert dealings and small skirmishes in lieu of outright war. The Federated Commonwealth completed the integration of its militaries, governments, economies and conquered worlds, forming the largest and most powerful realm in the Inner Sphere. Meanwhile, the Draconis Combine took one lesson from the Fourth Succession War to heart, and overhauled its military in response to Hanse Davion's "lightning war." In his role as the Combine's *Gunji-no-Kanrei*, or Deputy of Military Affairs, Theodore Kurita took several steps to ensure his nation's safety. He revamped the Draconis Combine Mustered Soldiery, upgrading their training and loosening the command structure to reward personal initiative. In his most controversial act, Theodore signed a compact with ComStar, granting independence to several Combine worlds in exchange for ComStar's Star League-era BattleMechs. As a result, on 13 March 3034, the Free Rasalhague Republic announced its independence from the Draconis Combine.

The declaration of independence touched off a minor rebellion within the Combine, as reactionary commanders refused to pull their military units from the new republic. Theodore declared the reactionaries *ronin*, lordless, and sent his own units to drive them from Free Rasalhague. Theodore's troops and various mercenary groups joined the Republic's Kungsärmé in battle against the ronin, but poor contracts negotiated in haste with the mercenaries paid most too much money for too little fighting. Free Rasalhague won the freedom it had claimed, but its citizens learned to loathe the mercenary MechWarrior.

In April of 3039, Hanse Davion set in motion the second great wave of his war to unite the Inner Sphere. Selecting the Draconis Combine as his target, he launched a two-front attack on the Dieron district. The first assault wave succeeded brilliantly; Davion's military advisors believed they had taken the Combine by surprise. Before Federated Commonwealth forces could launch their second wave, however, the Combine counterattacked and threw the Commonwealth on the defensive. Aided by the Star League 'Mechs he had received from ComStar, Theodore Kurita gambled with the fate of his nation and won. By attacking in the teeth of the Davion onslaught, Theodore made Hanse Davion believe the DCMS stronger than it actually was. Also, Hanse Davion saw no reason to grind his troops down against soldiers armed with superior, Star League-era technology. By October of 3039, Davion chose to cut his losses and make peace.

The War of 3039 accomplished little for those who fought it, save to remind the Successor States of the severe cost of war. A few worlds changed hands, but the balance of power remained the same. Aside from an assault in 3041, in which the Tenth Lyran Guards took the world of Skondia from the Combine, the states of the Inner Sphere seemed content to rebuild their realms in peace. Military readiness and overcharged rhetoric still ruled the day, but the Successor States had—at least temporarily—grown tired of war. The Inner Sphere

rebuilt during ten years of peace, which ended abruptly on 13 August 3049.

ENEMIES FROM BEYOND

In that year, while hunting pirates in the Periphery near the Free Rasalhague Republic, a detachment of the famed Kell Hounds mercenary unit met and succumbed to a mysterious fighting force on a godforsaken planet known as The Rock. Casualties included Phelan Kell, only son of the Hounds' founder Morgan Kell and cousin to Victor Steiner-Davion, Hanse and Melissa's eldest son. Phelan was listed as missing, presumed killed, but the Inner Sphere did not learn his true fate until several months later. The Kell Hounds' defeat marked the first of many battles lost to the Clans, mighty warriors descended from the long-vanished Star League Army. The Clans invaded the Inner Sphere in order to conquer it and restore their version of the Star League.

In March of 3050, the Clans struck in force, hammering the Draconis Combine, the Free Rasalhague Republic and the Lyran side of the Federated Commonwealth. Wave after wave of Clan attacks followed, executed with blinding speed and ruthless efficiency. Using their technologically superior OmniMechs and

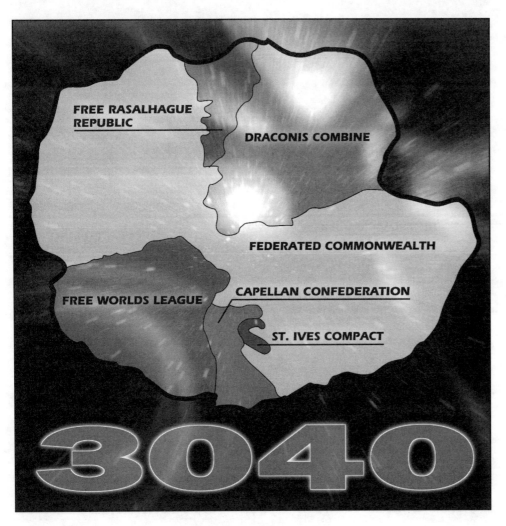

FREE RASALHAGUE REPUBLIC

DRACONIS COMBINE

FEDERATED COMMONWEALTH

FREE WORLDS LEAGUE

CAPELLAN CONFEDERATION

ST. IVES COMPACT

3040

the world of Outreach. There, Wolf revealed that he and his fellow Dragoons were actually Clan warriors—and that they were prepared to aid the Inner Sphere against their own people. The Inner Sphere leaders spent the better part of that year formulating a combined response to the overwhelming Clan threat. Setting aside centuries' worth of mistrust between their two nations, Hanse Davion and Theodore Kurita sealed a non-aggression pact. Davion also extorted material aid from the Free Worlds League by promising its leader, Thomas Marik, that he would devote all the resources of the New Avalon Institute of Science toward curing Thomas's son Joshua of leukemia.

In November of 3051, the Clans renewed their invasion of the Inner Sphere. In January 3052, Clans Smoke Jaguar and Nova Cat attacked the Combine capital of Luthien. In an act of unexpected political courage that sealed the loose alliance between the Federated Commonwealth and the Draconis Combine, Hanse Davion sent the Kell Hounds and Wolf's Dragoons to help defend his age-old enemy's homeworld. The trust engendered between the two nations by Davion's action enabled both to devote all their efforts to fighting the Clans.

tenacious armored infantry known as Elementals, Clan warriors cut down their Inner Sphere opponents like wheat before a scythe. Four Clans rolled across the Inner Sphere in the first wave: Clans Smoke Jaguar, Ghost Bear, Jade Falcon and Wolf. All took their share of planets, but Clan Wolf conquered more worlds than all its compatriots. Inner Sphere forces launched a few successful counterattacks, but those strikes came too little and too late. The Clan juggernaut thundered on, halted only when catastrophe struck.

On 31 October 3050, a Rasalhagian pilot named Tyra Miraborg crashed her *Shilone* fighter into the Clan flagship *Dire Wolf*, killing the Clans' war leader. The death of the ilKhan accomplished what six months of desperate fighting had not; the Clans ended their assaults, garrisoned the worlds they had conquered and pulled much of their military strength out of the Inner Sphere. For several months, later dubbed the Year of Peace, the leaders of each Clan debated the question of who should be the new ilKhan. In mid-3051, they chose Khan Ulric Kerensky of Clan Wolf to lead a renewed assault against the Inner Sphere.

In this year of peace, Colonel Jaime Wolf of Wolf's Dragoons summoned the leaders of the Successor States to

Despite the close cooperation between the Federated Commonwealth and the Draconis Combine, the Inner Sphere's unity remained largely an illusion. ComStar had negotiated with the Clans soon after the initial invasion, and upon their return to the Inner Sphere the Order offered to administrate the Clans' conquered worlds. ComStar's leader, Primus Myndo Waterly, intended to use the Clan conquest to bring about the collapse of civilization; ComStar would then step in as humanity's savior, thus gaining power over all of human-occupied space. When Waterly discovered that the Clans intended to conquer Terra, ComStar's homeworld and the cradle of humanity, she abruptly changed her tactics. At the urging of her Precentor Martial, Anastasius Focht, Waterly struck a deal with the invaders and sent the Com Guards to fight the Clans on the backwater world of Tukayyid. If the Clans won, ComStar would give them Terra. If they lost, the Clans would halt their advance toward Terra for fifteen years. Unknown to the Precentor Martial, Waterly also set secret plans in motion to strike at the Clans and the Inner Sphere simultaneously.

The Com Guards defeated the Clans on Tukayyid in May of 3052, in a horrific blood bath that cost ComStar's forces dearly. While the Com Guards fought and died on Tukayyid to save the Inner Sphere, Primus Waterly gave the word to her agents. They launched Operation Scorpion, making a series of covert attacks on worlds in the Clan occupation zones and striking at communications sites across the Inner Sphere. By this bold gambit, Waterly hoped to cripple both the Inner Sphere and the Clans in the same blow, enabling her ComStar loyalists to seize power. The strikes failed; upon Focht's return to Terra, he deposed Primus Waterly and began a massive reform of ComStar.

VICTORY AND CHANGE

The end of the Clan invasion brought other changes in its wake. Hanse Davion died of a massive heart attack at the end of the war; Chancellor Romano Liao of the Capellan Confederation died at the hands of an assassin, leaving her son Sun-Tzu on the Celestial Throne. Sun-Tzu immediately began to build a power base, allying himself to House Marik through an engagement to Thomas Marik's illegitimate daughter, Isis. Within a few short years, Theodore Kurita succeeded his father Takashi as Coordinator of the Draconis Combine. Ryan Steiner, perennial thorn in the side of the Federated Commonwealth's rulers, began agitating for an independent Isle of Skye. ComStar, meanwhile, split into two factions over Precentor Focht's reforms. The reactionary group, calling itself Word of Blake, emigrated to the Free Worlds League planet of Gibson with Thomas Marik's blessing.

On 19 June 3055, a bomb blast at a charity event on Tharkad killed the Federated Commonwealth's beloved Archon, Melissa Steiner. Authorities failed to apprehend a suspect. Ryan Steiner, riding the crest of anti-Davion sentiment he had spent years creating, accused Archon Prince Victor Steiner-Davion of engineering Melissa's death in order to ascend her throne. Ryan's native Isle of Skye, already seething with secessionist fever, erupted in open rebellion. Victor's sister Katherine tried to mediate between her brother and the rebel faction, with little success.

In April of 3056, Victor's aide and Katherine's lover, Galen Cox, fell victim to a bombing attack in a Solaris hotel that nar-

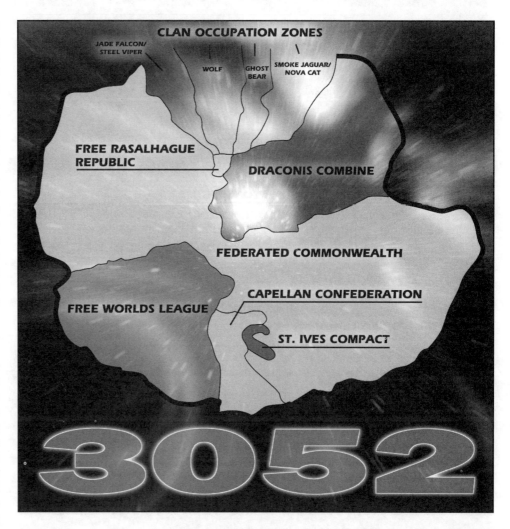

rowly missed Katherine. Four days later, an unknown assassin shot Ryan Steiner dead. Suspicion centered on Sven Newmark, an expatriate Rasalhagian who served as Ryan's aide. Many people, however, suspected that Victor ordered Ryan's death to silence his allegations about the death of Archon Melissa. In an effort to defuse the hostilities in the Lyran half of the Federated Commonwealth, Victor declared the Lyran world of Tharkad and the Davion world of New Avalon co-capitals. He then shifted his government to New Avalon and left Tharkad in Katherine's hands, naming his sister as his official regent. This move, coupled with Ryan's death, quelled the rebellion—but the brief peace could not last.

Victor arrived on New Avalon, only to be faced with the disturbing news that Joshua Marik was dying of leukemia despite the best efforts of the NAIS to save him. Knowing that his realm still desperately needed war materiel that only the Free Worlds League could provide, Victor could not afford to lose the only hold he had over Captain-General Thomas Marik. After consulting with his senior advisors, Victor replaced the dying child with a substitute. Marik, however, had his suspicions, and took steps to confirm them. In September of 3057, assailants dressed as Capellan commandos attempted to kill Joshua's

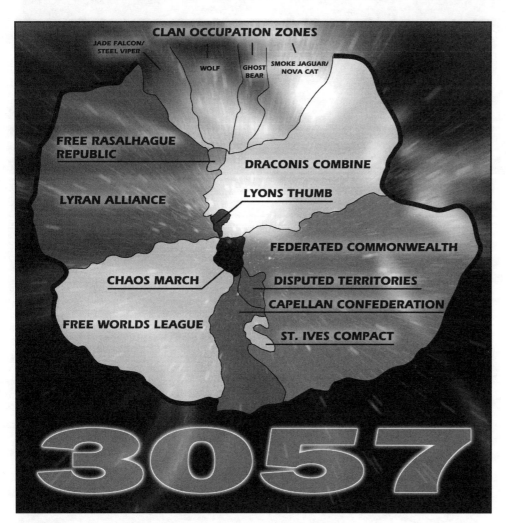

CLAN OCCUPATION ZONES

JADE FALCON/
STEEL VIPER

WOLF   GHOST   SMOKE JAGUAR/
         BEAR   NOVA CAT

FREE RASALHAGUE
REPUBLIC

DRACONIS COMBINE

LYRAN ALLIANCE

LYONS THUMB

FEDERATED COMMONWEALTH

CHAOS MARCH

DISPUTED TERRITORIES

CAPELLAN CONFEDERATION

FREE WORLDS LEAGUE

ST. IVES COMPACT

3057

intensified. The Clans had long been divided into two camps: the Crusaders, who sought to restore the Star League to the Inner Sphere through conquest, and the Wardens, who believed their responsibility lay in safeguarding the Inner Sphere until the Great Houses reestablished the Star League on their own. Many of the Clans, especially Clan Jade Falcon, chafed beneath the truce that ilKhan Kerensky had signed and willingly seized any excuse to break it. Opposition to the Truce of Tukayyid soon erupted into a Clan-style civil war between Clan Jade Falcon and Clan Wolf, known as the Refusal War. Led by Phelan Kell, who had risen among his Clan captors to become Khan Phelan Ward of Clan Wolf, a significant portion of Clan Wolf's warriors fled to the safe haven of the Kell Hounds' homeworld, Arc-Royal. The rest of Clan Wolf fought a losing battle against the Jade Falcons.

Both conflicts ended suddenly and swiftly, in a surprising series of twists. Having taken back from Victor Davion the worlds that had once belonged to the Free Worlds League, Thomas Marik concluded a peace treaty with the Archon Prince. Sun-Tzu Liao, unwilling to continue his own campaign in the absence of Marik's

double; two days later, Thomas Marik claimed he could prove that the Joshua Marik on New Avalon was not his son, but a duplicate. To retaliate for the death of his son, Marik sent troops into the Commonwealth's Sarna March.

A horrified Katherine publicly denounced Victor for his deception, recalled all Lyran troops to her half of the Federated Commonwealth, severed relations with her brother's realm and announced the formation of the Lyran Alliance. Katherine went so far as to change her name to Katrina, in honor of her famous Steiner grandmother, to symbolize the completeness of her break with the Davion half of the realm. She then declared her nation neutral, securing the Free Worlds League border and leaving that nation free to fight against the Federated Commonwealth. In conjunction with Marik's invasion, Sun-Tzu Liao sent Capellan troops into the Sarna March to reconquer worlds his grandfather had lost during the Fourth Succession War. Aided by Katherine's neutrality and united by their hatred for House Davion, Marik and Liao prosecuted their war against the Federated Commonwealth with surprising speed and success.

As the threat of a wider war between the nations of the Inner Sphere loomed, political infighting between the Clans

backing, grudgingly agreed to end hostilities. The Kell Hounds, having refused Katrina Steiner's demand for aid in defending the Lyran Alliance against Capellan aggression, established an anti-Clan defensive zone centered on Arc-Royal. By this act, the mercenary unit carved its own fiefdom out of Katrina's realm. In the oddest turn of events, the Wolves who had battled the Jade Falcons merged with that Clan and then won freedom from their Jade Falcon conquerors. This new Clan, led by the highly intelligent Khan Vladimir Ward, briefly called itself Clan Jade Wolf, until the death of Falcon Khan Elias Crichell at Khan Vlad Ward's hands gave Vlad the clout to revive his Clan as the "new" Clan Wolf. Intelligence indicates that Khan Vlad will stop at nothing to destroy Khan Phelan, leader of the Wolves in exile.

THE UNIVERSE
TURNED UPSIDE DOWN

The first five years after Tukayyid, tumultuous though they were, seemed tranquil compared to the explosive events of 3058–61. Those years saw many of the certainties by which Clan and Inner Sphere alike had lived violently overturned, giving way to a new order fraught with possibilities and perils.

In the wake of the Sarna March invasion, the Word of Blake seized its chance to capture Terra, cradle of humanity and ComStar's stronghold. Troop movements from the Free Worlds League into the so-called Chaos March provided cover for the Word of Blake Militia to move several divisions within striking distance of humanity's homeworld, and the high demand for mercenary troops in that same region of space did the rest. Brion's Legion, a mercenary unit that had constituted nearly half the strength of ComStar's Terran Defense Force since the Fourth Succession War, abruptly ended its ComStar contract in favor of a higher-paying Chaos March assignment. Unwilling to relocate Com Guard forces from the Clan border, ComStar's Precentor Martial chose to replace Brion's Legion with another mercenary unit—the Twenty-first Centauri Lancers. The Lancers, however, never arrived on Terra. Instead, the Word of Blake sent its own troops, which masqueraded as the Lancers for long enough to move the rest of their forces into position.

In late February of 3058, the Word of Blake struck, from the inside as well as on the battlefield. The Com Guards on Terra, taken by surprise and unable to use the planet's formidable defenses because of Blakist sabotage, fought a bloody but ultimately losing battle across every Terran continent. By early March of 3058, the Word of Blake held Terra in an iron grip from which it has yet to be dislodged. Precentor Martial Focht of ComStar declined to attempt the reconquest of Terra as long as the Clans remained a greater threat to the Inner Sphere.

During those same months, Clan Jade Falcon drove deep into the Lyran Alliance and captured several planets, until Inner Sphere forces stopped the Falcon advance on the world of Coventry. Conceived as a show of strength in the aftermath of the Refusal War, the Coventry campaign was to have far more ominous consequences for the Clans than the Falcon commanders could have anticipated. On Coventry, the Falcons were deprived of victory by two events: preliminary moves by Clan Wolf to strike at worlds in the Jade Falcon occupation zone, and the arrival of a coalition force from across the Inner Sphere, led by Prince Victor Steiner-Davion of the Federated Commonwealth. The Inner Sphere and Jade Falcon armies were evenly matched; neither side could win Coventry without a protracted and bloody battle, and both commanders realized it. Prince Victor invoked the Clan rite of safcon to ensure a safe landing for his troops, and then offered Falcon Khan Marthe Pryde the only honorable way out—*hegira*, the traditional right of a defeated enemy to leave the field with his forces and honor intact. Under other circumstances, Pryde might have refused; but with the Wolf Khan making clear his intent to attack her Clan's holdings, she could not afford to leave those worlds defended by mere garrison troops. She accepted hegira, and the Jade Falcons left Coventry without another shot being fired.

The success of the coalition force on Coventry taught the Inner Sphere that old enemies could bury their differences and fight together in the face of a common enemy. Before the year was out, Prince Victor and other Inner Sphere leaders would act on that lesson, launching the campaign that obliterated a once-mighty Clan and ended the invasion of the Inner Sphere.

THE STAR LEAGUE REBORN

In October of 3058, the leaders of the various Inner Sphere powers gathered on the Lyran capital of Tharkad to accomplish peacefully what they had failed to achieve during centuries of war—the rebirth of the Star League. Despite the deep divisions that remained among them, fueled by the legions of dead soldiers and civilians from all sides, the rulers of the Inner Sphere agreed to join together for a single purpose—to end the Clan threat, once and for all. To prove themselves a force to be reckoned with, the new Star League chose to destroy a single Clan: the Smoke Jaguars. Initially, the Star League intended only to drive the Jaguars out of their occupation zone. However, information from a Clan traitor enabled them to strike at Clan Smoke Jaguar's homeworld as well.

In 3059 and 3060, Clan Smoke Jaguar died at the hands of the combined armies of the Inner Sphere. Their occupation zone overrun, their homeworld in ruins and their warrior caste decimated, the Jaguars essentially ceased to exist. The Inner Sphere force then turned its attention toward the rest of the Clans. Lacking the might to defeat the entire Clan military, Prince Victor Steiner-Davion led his forces to Strana Mechty, the heart of Clan space and Clan culture. There, they defeated the Crusader Clans in a hard-fought Trial of Refusal. The Crusaders' defeat ended the invasion, in a way none of its proponents could have envisioned. Far from taking Terra and rebuilding the Star League in the Clans' image, the Crusader Clans found themselves locked into their Inner Sphere occupation zones or driven from the Inner Sphere entirely.

Clan Nova Cat, which had sided with the Inner Sphere in obedience to the mystic visions of its leaders, was given its own fiefdom in the Draconis Combine. For what their fellow Clans termed treason, the Nova Cats were Abjured and their holdings in Clan space found forfeit. Clan Ghost Bear, which chose not to fight in the Trial for a cause it no longer believed in, has also become a permanent presence in the Inner Sphere. They now occupy part of what was once the Free Rasalhague Republic, from which they will guard the Inner Sphere against incursions by other Clans unwilling to accept the invasion's end. What other plans they may have for using their military might remain anyone's guess.

Clan Steel Viper suffered the most humiliating fate of all the Invading Clans, next to the shattered Smoke Jaguars. Thinking to take advantage of Jade Falcon weakness in the aftermath of the Refusal War, the Vipers challenged Falcon dominance of the two Clans' shared occupation zone. They failed, and left the Inner Sphere rather than be destroyed by their Falcon antagonists.

As the man who ended the most fearsome threat the Inner Sphere had ever known, Victor Steiner-Davion should have been the hero of the hour. In the eyes of many, he was—but his own people were not among them. The Prince had left his youngest sister, Yvonne Steiner-Davion, as regent on New Avalon in his absence. He returned to the Inner Sphere to find Yvonne deposed and the Federated Commonwealth in the hands of Katrina Steiner-Davion. Apparently, Katrina had secretly been plotting just such a takeover for years, as a prelude to becoming the next First Lord of the Star League. Even without a realm, however, Prince Victor remained a political force to be reckoned with. At the Second Whitting Conference, Precentor Martial Anastasius Focht of ComStar announced his retirement and named Victor as his successor. The new Precentor Martial used his position to vote Coordinator Theodore Kurita into the post of First Lord.

The newborn Star League remains calm on the surface, but tensions are simmering beneath. The former Prince of the Federated Commonwealth has so far made no attempt to regain his lost throne, unwilling to inflict a civil war on his people. The

fact remains, however, that Precentor Martial Steiner-Davion has a crack military force at his disposal, and increasing numbers in the Federated Commonwealth see him as a hero for his defeat of the Clans. In the face of these two potential threats, the Archon Princess sits uneasily on the throne of New Avalon, and may yet be provoked into rash action. Meanwhile, Clans Jade Falcon and Wolf remain committed to renewing the invasion. Clan Wolf formally repudiated the results of the Strana Mechty Trial, and Clan Jade Falcon is unlikely to abide by an outcome so offensive to its pride. Neither Clan has the strength to move in force yet, but each is rebuilding at a swift pace. The Capellan Confederation has begun military action against the St. Ives Compact, intent on recapturing it. And in the Draconis Combine, the presence of the Nova Cats and the stresses of reabsorbing Jaguar-held worlds have breathed new life into moribund reactionary movements opposed to the Coordinator and his liberalization of Combine society. For the moment, his position remains strong; but for how long, no one can truly say.

Once again, the Inner Sphere is poised precariously between peace and war. At any moment the balance of power may shift, setting BattleMechs on the march and worlds ablaze.

TWILIGHT OF THE CLANS

The year 3058 will go down in Inner Sphere history as the year the Clan threat died and the Star League was reborn. At the Whitting Conference on Tharkad in October of that year, the lords of all the Great Houses met at the instigation of Prince Victor Steiner-Davion. The conference saw the Star League formed anew and the decision made to do the seemingly impossible—to destroy a Clan.

Prince Victor and other military planners chose Clan Smoke Jaguar as the target, for several reasons. Of the most prominent Crusader Clans that had invaded, the Wolves and the Jade Falcons were still recovering from their recent war and could therefore be dismissed by their fellow Clans as weak targets. Clan Nova Cat, though originally Crusader, was making overtures to the Draconis Combine, which eliminated them from consideration. The Smoke Jaguars were the most powerful and vicious of the Crusader Clans; destroying them would be fitting punishment for the brutalities they had committed, as well as substantially weakening the Crusader cause.

Talks between the Draconis Combine and the Nova Cats, traditional enemies of the Smoke Jaguars, had made it clear that the Cats would give up many of their worlds after token fights intended to satisfy Clan honor. Armed with this knowledge, the Inner Sphere's military leaders planned assaults in waves on Smoke Jaguar-occupied worlds from bases in the Draconis Combine. When a Smoke Jaguar MechWarrior defected to ComStar and brought with him the so-called Exodus Road—the path to the Jaguar homeworld of Huntress—the military leaders expanded their plans to include a long-range strike at that planet. They assembled an assault group including forces from every Star League member-state, code-named Task Force Serpent, and placed it under the overall command of Marshal of the Armies Morgan Hasek-Davion of the Federated Commonwealth. His reputation for battlefield brilliance and his personal integrity made him the ideal choice to command this motley force of soldiers.

TASK FORCE SERPENT

The Federated Commonwealth had already placed many of its crack units at the disposal of Operation Bulldog, the assault on the Jaguar occupation zone. The FedCom sent two units to Task Force Serpent: the First Kathil Uhlans, Marshal Hasek-Davion's old command, and two Teams of MI6 commandos known as the Rabid Foxes. Prince Victor also assigned two *Fox*-class corvettes to the task force, adding considerably to its naval might. ComStar, the St. Ives Compact, Free Rasalhague, the Free Worlds League and the Lyran Alliance also sent veter-

an and elite troops. With its 'Mech units tied up in Operation Bulldog, the Draconis Combine sent three Draconis Elite Strike Teams equipped with the latest battle armor, and a formidable *Kyushu*-class frigate. By contrast, the Capellan Confederation provided Kingston's Legionnaires, a regular regiment known for questionable tactics.

The task force also included prominent mercenary forces, all under the banner of the Star League. Representing the Northwind Highlanders were McLeod's Regiment, the First Gurkhas and the Royal Black Watch. The Eridani Light Horse, descendants of an SLDF unit that had refused to go on Aleksandr Kerensky's long-ago Exodus, found their devotion to Star League traditions richly rewarded when the unit's overall commander, General Ariana Winston, was named second-in-command of Task Force Serpent.

BEYOND THE PERIPHERY

The task force went first to the Federated Commonwealth world of Defiance, where they trained against each other and against ComStar's Invader Galaxy, a force built to mimic Clan unit structure and tactics and used mainly as an opponent for training Com Guard troops. On 1 May 3059, Task Force Serpent left for Clan space under a cloak of secrecy.

In mid-December, Task Force Serpent unexpectedly encountered a Ghost Bear flotilla. After a fierce naval battle, dubbed "Trafalgar," the SLDF defeated the Ghost Bears and claimed an intact *Whirlwind*-class WarShip. The victory left them with three hundred warriors and more than a thousand civilians as prisoners. Those who gave their bond-oath were accepted as bondsmen. The others were marooned, as the task force lacked sufficient food and water to keep them all prisoner and could not risk setting them free.

As the task force drew closer to Huntress, disaster struck. On 3 January 3060, Marshal Morgan Hasek-Davion was found dead in his room. When a routine autopsy discovered poison in his system, General Ariana Winston launched an intensive investigation. A lucky find in the task force records revealed five people who appeared to have no past before joining ComStar—among them one Lucas Penrose. When brought in for questioning, Penrose killed his guards and then held the ship hostage, claiming he had planted a bomb in an ammunition bay. Penrose demanded a face-to-face talk with General Winston and a JumpShip to take him back to the Inner Sphere. Upon discovering that the bomb was a ruse, the general shot Penrose with his own pistol.

THE CONQUEST BEGINS

When the task force reached Huntress, the DEST troopers successfully disarmed the planet's space-defense system. On 5 March, Task Force Serpent jumped into Huntress space.

They found three Smoke Jaguar WarShips waiting for them. The ensuing naval battle damaged several SLDF WarShips and destroyed one. The SLDF won the fight, however, and the task force swiftly sent its DropShips burning toward Huntress.

The initial assault hit several major targets. All task force units captured their objectives, though some suffered more casualties than others. The Northwind Highlanders took heavy losses when they unexpectedly encountered ProtoMechs—smaller versions of BattleMechs that fought like super-Elementals. In the face of fierce opposition, Marshal Sharon Bryan of the Lyran Guards called for supporting fire from an orbiting task force WarShip. The bombardment disintegrated several Jaguar 'Mechs and broke the morale of the survivors. With that terrible display of raw destructive power, the invasion of Huntress ended in victory.

Task Force Serpent then began the second part its mission: destroying the Jaguars' capacity to make war, targeting all facilities that could be used for making or storing war materiel. Meanwhile, ilKhan Lincoln Osis of Clan Smoke Jaguar pleaded for help from his fellow Khans. His plea fell on deaf ears, however. The Khans of Clans Wolf and Jade Falcon convinced the Council that the assault was a Smoke Jaguar internal matter, and the other Clans voted unanimously against getting involved. An enraged Khan Osis left for Huntress with his personal force of elite troops.

THE WAR BACK HOME

Back in the Inner Sphere, Operation Bulldog had enjoyed phenomenal success. Far sooner than expected, the Inner Sphere coalition force led by Prince Victor Steiner-Davion had pushed the Smoke Jaguars off world after world. The entire operation was concluded in roughly four months—less time than computer simulations had predicted for the first wave. The remaining Smoke Jaguars fled toward Huntress, unaware that it was also a target. Prince Victor led a small part of his army in pursuit, arriving on Huntress just in time to prevent a Smoke Jaguar counterattack from destroying the task force.

JAGUAR COUNTERATTACK

On 19 March, the Jaguar transports fleeing the Inner Sphere arrived in the Huntress system. The Clan reinforcements immediately burned toward Huntress, while their WarShips took on the SLDF navy. The Star League flotilla eventually won a Pyrrhic victory that cost it much of its power.

Warned by the fleet commander that the Clan forces were on their way, General Winston split her forces into three large groups to force the Clans to do the same. Star Colonel Paul Moon, the leading Smoke Jaguar officer, challenged General Winston to meet him on the plains west of Lootera. In the name of the Star League, the general accepted. The battle opened with artillery salvos from the SLDF's northern army. Then the Jaguars slammed into the SLDF lines, possessed by a berserk fury that characterized all the fighting by the Jaguars thrown out of the Inner Sphere. When the Jaguar Khan revealed his presence in Lootera, joining the troops there with the Jaguar's Den Command Trinary, it gave the Jaguar forces a morale boost.

THE CAVALRY ARRIVES

The Jaguars continued to attack and harass General Winston's forces; though each assault brought the Jaguar troops nearly equal casualties, the Clan was slowly gaining the advantage, primarily because the Inner Sphere forces were stranded in a hostile land with no hope of reinforcements. Determined to carry out her directives, General Winston was killed in fierce fighting just minutes before Task Force Serpent received word of Prince Victor's arrival in the Huntess system.

Ten days later, the conquest of Huntress was over. Of Task Force Serpent, little remained. Few of its units could boast less than 80 percent losses. The soldiers had sacrificed themselves in the crucible of war so that the rest of the Inner Sphere could rest easy in the hard-won peace. Now it was up to Prince Victor Steiner-Davion and his fresh forces to end the Clan war for good.

ON TO STRANA MECHTY

The defeat of the Smoke Jaguars got the Clans' attention. In a bold move, Prince Victor traveled to the Clan homeworld of Strana Mechty and challenged all the Clans to a Trial of Refusal against the invasion of the Inner Sphere. If the Inner Sphere won, the invasion would cease. If the Clans won, the Truce of Tukayyid would be dissolved and the invasion would continue.

One company from each Inner Sphere realm fought the bodyguard Binary and Khan of each Crusader Clan. Painting the invasion as a Crusader Clan matter, the Warden Clans chose not to participate. However, in a surprising turn of events, Clan Nova Cat fought on the side of the Star League. After brutal fighting, in which Prince Victor was forced to kill ilKhan Lincoln Osis in hand-to-hand combat, the SLDF won the Trial. Prince Victor and the SLDF had achieved the impossible; they had brought peace back to the Inner Sphere.

THE RETURN HOME

Prince Victor's achievement came at great personal cost. In his absence, Archon Katherine Steiner-Davion of the Lyran Alliance assumed the reins of government in the Federated Commonwealth, where she remains in power. For the good of his subjects, Prince Victor gracefully accepted the situation, and has since become Precentor Martial of ComStar in the wake of Anastasius Focht's retirement. In that position, the prince will continue to safeguard the welfare of the Federated Commonwealth and its sister Star League nations.

[Victor: I know the last bit is laying it on a bit thick, but your people should know something to counteract the misinformation Katherine is doubtless spreading about your role in all this. I'd be more than happy to leak this document in a few of the right places to brush up your image, should it become necessary to take Katherine on. —JC]

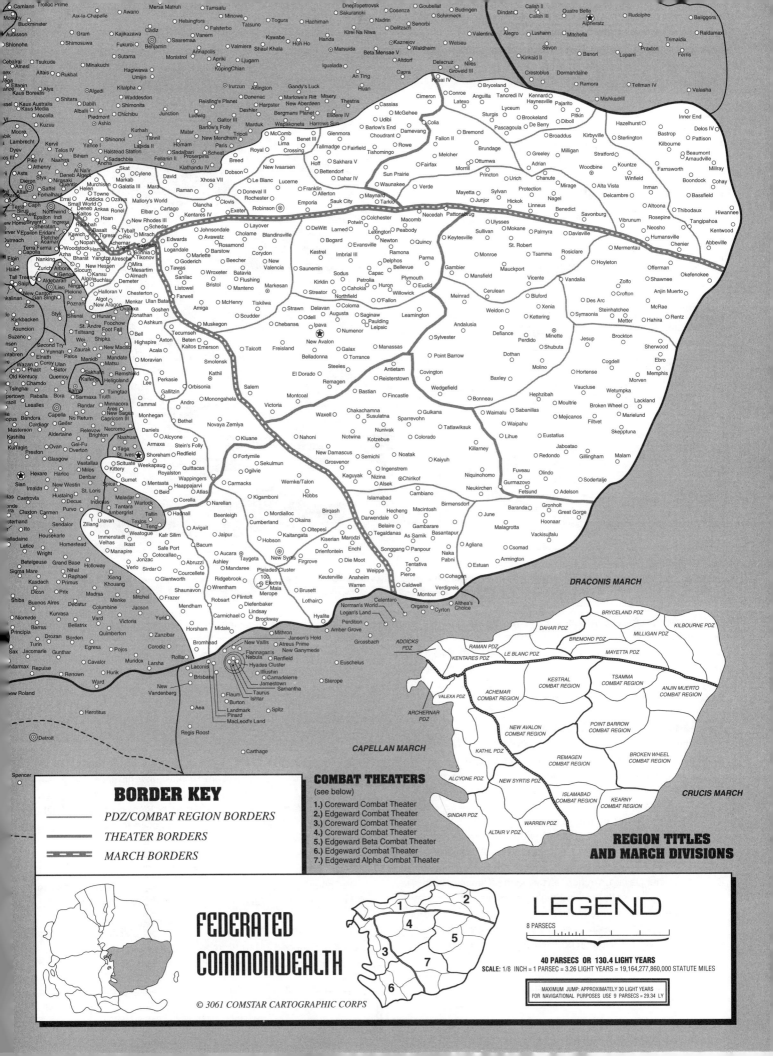

THE FEDERATED COMMONWEALTH

[The following book excerpt should give you an idea of the party line being spouted in the Federated Commonwealth these days by Katherine's supporters. I'm told it's on the bestseller list on New Avalon, though largely because a few people are placing a lot of bulk orders. The head of Lightbringer Press has ties to Alicia Savinson, head of Lyran Intelligence. —JC]

CURRENT EVENTS

—From *Manifest Destiny: The Steiner Renaissance*, by Richard Keller; Lightbringer Press, New Avalon Division, 3061

... In these troubled times, where old certainties have fallen away and new ones have not yet replaced them, the duty of a ruler has never been more clear. She must provide stability and continuity for her people; she must put their needs before her own desires for personal glory; and she must be prepared to take on the responsibilities of others who fall short of these ideals. All these accomplishments and more are the hallmark of Katrina Steiner-Davion, Archon of the Lyran Alliance. With the Archon having recently assumed the helm of the Federated Commonwealth, we can only hope our perennially uneasy realm will finally enjoy the peace and prosperity of its Lyran sister-state—a prosperity based on peaceful commerce rather than on the engines of war.

War, however, may yet loom on our horizon. The former leader of this nation, Victor Steiner-Davion, is rightly hailed for his part in ending the Clan invasion of the Inner Sphere. But with the greatest military threat to our region of space defanged, what is a consummate warrior like Victor to do with himself? Where will he focus his energies next, this leader of men into the bloody crucible of battle? The invitation of our former regent, Yvonne Steiner-Davion, to the Archon to take control of a Federated Commonwealth that Yvonne proved incapable of leading has left Victor without a throne. Though Victor has tried hard in recent years to downplay his increasing jealousy of the Archon's popularity, persistent rumors of his bitter feelings toward her must be taken as at least partly true. Might he not act on those feelings and attempt to forcibly retake the throne on New Avalon? Let us examine the evidence.

THE MILITARY THREAT

Though he has disbanded the gallant army from across the Inner Sphere that defeated the Clans, Victor does not lack for military resources. Quite the contrary. Just months ago, at the Second Whitting Conference, Precentor Martial Anastasius Focht announced his retirement and appointed Victor Steiner-Davion in his place. The new Precentor Martial can call on the military might and expertise of the Com Guards, which remains formidable despite reported losses in the Smoke Jaguar occupation zone and on the Clan world of Huntress. And with the Clan threat essentially removed, the Com Guards units currently stationed in the remnant of the Free Rasalhague Republic are no longer needed. Precentor Martial Steiner-Davion may redeploy them where he pleases.

The Rasalhague-based troops show no signs of leaving as yet, and sources familiar with the Com Guards indicate that they intend to stay as a counterbalance to the hefty military presence of Clan Ghost Bear. Misinformation, however, is a tactic historically beloved of many powers, ComStar among them. And with a deposed princeling in such an important position within that organization, the whole of ComStar may be at least somewhat biased in favor of their Precentor Martial's personal agenda. Who is to say, therefore, how long the Com Guards will be staying in Free Rasalhague?

POLITICAL CONNECTIONS

Victor Steiner-Davion's closeness to the Kuritas of the Draconis Combine is another cause for worry. The Combine has traditionally considered the Federated Commonwealth, and before that the Federated Suns and the Lyran Commonwealth, as its greatest enemies. Only the common threat of the Clans induced the Combine's leaders to mollify their hostility toward us. With that threat essentially gone, might not Coordinator Theodore Kurita of the Combine accede to his good friend Victor's request for units to join an invasion force? Surely more than a few commanders in the Draconis Combine Mustered Soldiery would welcome a renewal of war with "the Davion enemy," especially if they had hopes of being rewarded with a Federated Commonwealth world or two.

There is as yet no clear evidence that Precentor Martial Davion has made any such request of the Coordinator. Certain signs, however, must be taken as deeply troubling. Early in the Clan war, Victor Davion risked the lives of the men under his command to rescue the Coordinator's heir, Hohiro Kurita, from behind enemy lines on Teniente. By all indications, the two have been friends ever since. Still closer to Victor is the Coordinator's daughter, Omi Kurita. In a public broadcast made throughout the Combine just before the onset of the recent anti-Clan operations, Omi confessed to a profound personal attachment between Victor and herself. Worse, the broadcast was clearly intended to make this relationship acceptable in the eyes of her nation. Omi's denial that the two had been lovers strains credibility, especially given the fact that Victor saved her from a pack of assassins on a night when the two of them had been left alone in a private sanctuary. Victor has gone far beyond the non-aggression pact agreed to ten years ago by his father, Prince Hanse Davion; he has practically become a member of the Kurita family. Can such a man truly have the interests of the Federated Commonwealth's citizens at heart?

As yet, the prospect of invasion fortunately remains purely theoretical. Theodore Kurita's investiture as the new First Lord of the Star League, ironically enough, makes armed incursion into the Commonwealth less rather than more likely. As First Lord, Theodore must take into account the opinions and votes of all of the Star League's member-states, which will hamstring any inclination on his part to approve the use of SLDF troops for Victor Davion's personal ends. Therefore, Victor's command of the SLDF does not necessarily enhance his military capability. Furthermore, Archon Princess Katrina will not allow blood to be shed in any corner of her realm in order to feed a warrior's dreams of conquest. She can likely count on the backing of Houses Liao and Marik, who have their own reasons for thwarting any adventurism that Victor Steiner-Davion might attempt.

ENEMIES WITHIN?

Meanwhile, the Federated Commonwealth faces problems closer to home. The tragic murder of Marshal Morgan Hasek-Davion has elevated his son George to the Hasek dukedom in the Capellan March, placing one of the former prince's most devoted supporters in a powerful position to interfere with the Archon's rule. For the moment, Duke Hasek appears to be preoccupied with settling affairs in his own backyard; however, that could change at any time. He shares his late father's closeness to ex-Prince Victor, and might easily become the figurehead for other March leaders unable to appreciate the benefits of the late change in the Federated Commonwealth's rulership. Rumor has it that more than one duke would prefer to have an inexperienced regent on the throne, if not outright independence from this realm. The persistence of these stories raises enough smoke to suggest fire somewhere. The Capellan March? Possibly. Or perhaps the Skye Province, which encompasses part of the Lyran Isle of Skye region that has historically harbored would-be secessionists. Only time will tell where the threat lies, and whether the Archon Princess can act in time to save us all from it … .

RECENT HISTORY

—From *And Nothing But the Truth*, an "underground alternative" political newsletter popular throughout the FedCom; November 3061 issue

GRIM HARVEST

Three Killings and Their Consequences

19 June 3055: Archon Melissa Steiner. 20 April 3056: Clan war hero Galen Cox. 24 April 3056: Duke Ryan Steiner of the Isle of Skye. These three assassinations, within the space of ten months, would forever reshape the Federated Commonwealth's political landscape and destabilize the entire Inner Sphere. Some say Victor Steiner-Davion ordered the killings; others, though far fewer, whisper that the culprit was Katrina Steiner-Davion of the Lyran Alliance. Both camps have overlooked the true masterminds behind these terrible events.

The death of Archon Melissa Steiner-Davion left the Federated Commonwealth bereft of the one leader beloved enough to hold this huge realm together. Since her death, her son Prince Victor has failed to keep the Federated

Commonwealth intact. If the fracturing of the FedCom was the point of Archon Melissa's assassination, then the immediate question is, who benefitted? Who stood to gain the most from a divided FedCom—a FedCom whose former halves had become actively hostile to one another, as in the days before the famous marriage that led to the merger of these two Successor States?

Everyone knows the "party line" about Archon Melissa's death—the one most often heard over dinner in secluded restaurant booths, or over cocktails in the private apartments of minor nobility and rich business execs. Those allegedly in the know claim that Prince Victor Steiner-Davion killed his mother because he didn't want to wait any longer for his throne. Their evidence? Prince Victor's failure to make it to Archon Melissa's funeral. His alleged propensity for violence because of his combat record. The simple fact that, as heir to the throne, he seemed to have the most to gain. But did he really? Victor got nothing that wouldn't have come to him anyway, and to get it through murder would have guaranteed him a deeply divided realm even without the secession of the Lyran half. To make himself the ruler of a nation whose citizens suspected him of murder seems a high price to pay for impatience—especially since Archon Melissa might well have abdicated in his favor in just a few more years.

But wait, say the believers in Victor's guilt. What about the assassinations of Duke Ryan Steiner and Galen Cox? Duke Ryan had openly accused the Prince of Melissa's death, and Galen Cox was fast becoming a focus for anti-Davion separatists in the Isle of Skye region. Killing Duke Ryan was clearly in Victor's interests—he silenced one of his most prominent accusers while cutting the legs from under Ryan's Skye secessionist movement. Meanwhile, Galen Cox was developing an image as a Skye native-son-turned-war-hero, enhanced in the popular imagination by his rumored romantic liaison with Katherine Steiner-Davion. Cox's own military achievements and Skye background, plus Katherine's reflected popularity, made him the secessionist movement's heart. And surely any man who would murder his own mother could kill a former comrade-in-arms without flinching.

A plausible enough scenario—but the entire case rests on the outcome of the killings, which are not as beneficial to Prince Victor as it might appear. Killing Ryan Steiner so soon after the duke's accusations about Melissa would only confirm their "truth" in the public mind. And to assassinate a close personal friend with whom he had served against the Clans would have proved Victor a monster, totally devoid of normal human feeling—not an image that would aid him in governing the realm he allegedly wanted badly enough to kill for it. The case against Victor is hogwash, as is readily apparent to anyone who examines it. So if not Prince Victor, who?

Those who paint Katherine Steiner-Davion as the villain claim she intended Victor to take the blame for all three deaths, thereby creating an untenable political situation that only she, with her image as a peacemaker, could salvage. Katherine supposedly intended to force Victor to abdicate in her favor—or, fail-

ing that, to elevate her to co-rulership of the Federated Commonwealth in hopes that her popularity would help him. He actually did the latter in 3056; a little more than a year later, Katherine Steiner-Davion formally took the Lyran half of the Commonwealth out of the union.

So Katherine Steiner-Davion apparently gained as much as Victor did from the deaths of Melissa and Ryan Steiner: a realm of her own, untroubled by a strong Skye secessionist movement. There is also the rumor that she and Duke Ryan worked in concert to kill Archon Melissa, and that Katherine then silenced her former co-conspirator. Why she should have arranged Galen Cox's death in a bombing four days before Duke Ryan was shot dead is never explained. Her motive for killing Cox is similarly left in the dark; to all appearances, she cared greatly for the man and was devastated at his death. Her accusers maintain that she was playing a part, trying to win Cox over and thereby drive a wedge between him and Victor; but in that case, killing him when it failed to work was surely an extreme reaction to a minor flaw in her alleged master plan. And it doesn't explain why he was important enough to warrant killing in the first place. Victor has several personal friends and advisors; why choose Galen Cox, a simple soldier?

The end result of the assassinations was a sundered state whose two parts were led by a brother and sister grown deeply suspicious of each other. Duke Ryan and Galen Cox both became martyrs to the Skye secessionist cause; their deaths weakened the movement for the moment, but also assured its long-term survival by giving the people of Skye a fresh grievance. Furthermore, the death of Ryan Steiner weakened the Federated Commonwealth by reinforcing Prince Victor's image as a cold-hearted killer. As for Cox's death, there is some evidence that Katherine was the actual target. When that attempt at assassination failed, the real power behind the killings set Plan B in motion; they swiftly arranged the death of Ryan Steiner in order to force Victor and Katherine into actions they would not otherwise have taken. These actions served the agenda of an Inner Sphere power whose members had already proven adept at long-range plotting, and who wanted to make sure they were the only stabilizing force: the reactionary ComStar splinter group that calls itself the Word of Blake.

Under the leadership of the megalomaniac Primus Myndo Waterly, the old ComStar had already attempted to shatter the Inner Sphere in order to save it. Thanks to the timely intervention of Precentor Martial Anastasius Focht, Waterly's plot did not succeed. The late Primus's spiritual heirs broke away from ComStar and formed the Word of Blake, and they remain passionately devoted to their self-image as the sole saviors of humankind. If anything, they've gotten worse in the decade since Waterly's downfall. They intended to succeed where she failed—but in order to "save" the Inner Sphere, they first need to take out every other power with the potential to stabilize it. The Federated Commonwealth was one such power; by fracturing it through assassinations and pinning the the blame on innocent parties, the Blakists have eliminated a major obstacle to their plan. Even Archon Katherine's recent takeover won't slow the Blakists down for long; the FedCom and the Lyran Alliance remain separate realms on paper, and Victor still has support among the nobles of the old Federated Suns. The situation remains highly unstable, and the Word of Blake will surely exploit that fact to its advantage ... .

THE LIAO-MARIK INVASION

[This next excerpt is from A Recent History of the Federated Commonwealth, a textbook published early last year by Lightbringer Press. According to my agents, it just became standard reading for military history classes in Federated Commonwealth military academies. The slant on recent events is ... interesting. —JC]

... The year 3057 saw warfare renewed between the nations of the Inner Sphere, a scant five years after the victory over the Clans at Tukayyid. In that year, the Free Worlds League and the Capellan Confederation invaded the Federated Commonwealth's Sarna March.

The spark that touched off the invasion was an act of unprecedented and cruel duplicity by then-Prince Victor Steiner-Davion. Some years back, when the Clan threat was at its height, the leaders of the Great Houses met on Outreach to formulate a combined defense. As surety for delivery of badly needed war materiel from the Free Worlds League, Prince Hanse Davion of the Federated Commonwealth agreed to give Joshua Marik, the League's heir, advanced treatment for his leukemia on the Commonwealth capital of New Avalon. When Victor Steiner-Davion succeeded his father in mid-3052, he inherited this obligation along with the throne. He also inherited a problem. The treatments were failing; despite their best efforts, the top doctors at the New Avalon Institute of Sciences could not keep Joshua Marik alive for long. And with Joshua gone, Victor had no lever over the Captain-General of the Free Worlds League. Victor therefore went ahead with a risky and ultimately doomed plan to kill Joshua and replace him with a double. [That canard never dies. You and I know Joshua died of natural causes, but we'll likely never prove it to the satisfaction of conspiracy theorists. —JC] When agents of the Free Worlds League discovered the truth, Captain-General Thomas Marik responded by declaring war against Prince Victor's realm.

Because Marik intended his military strike to penalize Victor personally, he chose his target with care. Together with forces from the Capellan Confederation, Free Worlds League troops invaded the Sarna March, location of League and Capellan worlds lost to Federated Commonwealth forces a quarter of a century earlier. As Marik himself put it in his public declaration of hostilities, " ... no one who wishes to be liberated from the Davion yoke need endure [Victor Steiner-Davion's] oppression any longer. Toward this end I have begun the re-occupation of former Free Worlds League planets ... In addition, I will support self-determination movements in the similarly occupied Capellan systems of the Sarna March ... I will back those who wish to determine for themselves who will rule them and what their future will be." [Those "self-determination move-

ments" were almost all plants by Sun-Tzu Liao. He'd spent years seeding former Capellan worlds with agents and terrorists, just waiting for the chance to activate them. —JC]

Just two days after Thomas Marik's declaration of war, Archon Katrina Steiner-Davion formally announced the formation of the Lyran Alliance. She further declared the Alliance's neutrality in the Marik-Liao conflict, and invited Lyran military units serving anywhere in the Federated Commonwealth to return to Alliance space. Several units took their new Archon up on her offer, leaving Victor short of troops and extremely short of JumpShips with which to transport his loyalist units to trouble spots. As a result, the first wave of the invasion went spectacularly badly for FedCom forces.

Meanwhile, Marik forces hit six worlds and mercenary forces in Marik employ dropped onto several more to aid Capellan-inspired revolutions. With no way of predicting where the enemy would strike next and insufficient ships with which to redeploy his own units, Victor had no hope of stopping the invasion. The Prince received a momentary respite courtesy of the Draconis Combine, which moved "peacekeeping" troops into the Lyran-controlled Lyons Thumb in response to the alleged militarization of Thumb worlds. The Combine deployments moved troops from the Federated Commonwealth border, which freed up Davion border units to move to the Sarna March. [Katherine was building up the Lyran military presence; that, plus her claim to Northwind, made the Combine understandably worried that she might try a drive toward Dieron. The Thumb situation remains a thorn in her side that we can exploit. —JC] The JumpShip shortage remained a problem, however, until Archon Katrina proposed selling the JumpShips to Victor—an offer he grudgingly accepted. [Of course, the offer came only after Capellan-sponsored revolts broke out on Sarna March worlds that Katherine claimed for the Lyran Alliance. Plus, she only sold you back a few.—JC]

The second wave of the invasion went less well for the attackers, but brought Prince Victor no advantage. Most worlds not taken by Marik or Liao forces in this wave declared themselves independent; many banded together with nearby worlds in mutual-defense associations to preserve their newfound liberty. By the time Thomas Marik sued for peace, the Sarna March had dissolved into anarchy. Dubbed the "Chaos March," it has become a no-man's land of conflicting allegiances between the FedCom, the Lyran Alliance, the Capellan Confederation and the strongest local warlord.

CONFLICT WITH THE CLANS

In 3058, Clan Jade Falcon launched a lightning strike into the Lyran Alliance and took four worlds before Victor Steiner-Davion finally answered the Archon's request for military aid. Instead of defending the realm he still considered part of the Federated Commonwealth, the Prince had been spending his time on Tukayyid, engaging in anti-Clan war exercises sponsored by ComStar. [In fact, Katherine didn't call on you until weeks after the initial Clan assault on Coventry. And before that, Tormano Liao and General Nondi Steiner had imposed a news blackout across the Alliance specifically to keep you from getting wind of the Falcon assaults. —JC] Victor formed up a motley force composed of units involved in those exercises, and set out for the embattled world of Coventry.

Victor's coalition force could have taken on the invading Clan troops, but Victor chose otherwise—a strange decision, considering his obsession with the Clan threat. Rather than fight the Falcon force, whose strength nearly matched his own, Victor Steiner-Davion allowed the Clanners to retreat intact from Coventry. This action left the Alliance in possession of the planet but also left the invading forces unscathed.

Over the next three years, Prince Victor's failure to engage the Jade Falcons on Coventry only deepened his obsession with the Clan threat. He had backed down in the face of it once; he was determined not to do so again. *[A wordy accusation of cowardice, which carefully avoids any mention of the real situation. Katherine's propagandists are working overtime. —JC]* Coventry had so warped his judgment that he put his own realm's interests at risk, allying himself ever more closely with the Kuritas of the Draconis Combine. Like Victor, Coordinator Theodore Kurita wanted to take the war to the Clans; in Victor's mind, this one fact was sufficient to wipe out every past conflict between the Combine and his own nation.

The Killing of a Clan

Encouraged by Theodore Kurita, Victor formulated a plan to drive an entire Clan from the Inner Sphere. The Whitting Conference, held on Tharkad later that year, gave him the chance to put his idea into action. Setting himself at its head, Victor Davion created a multi-unit task force dedicated to destroying Clan Smoke Jaguar. He spent much of the next year reclaiming the Jaguar occupation zone for the Draconis Combine, while his own realm wavered under the inexperienced hand of Regent Yvonne Steiner-Davion. When the assault on the occupation zone ended in an early victory, instead of tending to his domestic responsibilities, Victor Davion departed for the next battlefield—the Jaguar homeworld of Huntress, a thousand light-years away in Clan space. *[The implication is that you went because you felt like it. No mention of the real reason—that the premature rout of the Smoke Jaguars would likely have resulted in the slaughter of Morgan Hasek-Davion's task force once the fleeing Jaguar OZ forces caught up with it. —JC]*

The Huntress assault ended in another victory, but at a high price. Among the losses to the Federated Commonwealth were Morgan Hasek-Davion, Marshal of the Armies, who was cut down by an unknown assassin before his task force reached its destination; and the First Kathil Uhlans, who were decimated in fierce fighting against stiff Smoke Jaguar resistance. The united Clan threat to the Inner Sphere is mercifully receding, but danger from the Clans remains as long as any of them retain a military presence in Inner Sphere space. Other dangers to the Federated Commonwealth exist as well, especially now that the Clans have been so greatly diminished. Now more than ever, the Federated Commonwealth needs patriotic, dedicated soldiers to defend her—against any threat, no matter what its source.

[The following news broadcasts should give you an idea of how the bulk of the FedCom sees the big events of the past three years—the rebirth of the Star League, the recent victory over the Clans and the death of Morgan Hasek-Davion. The final transcript merits particular attention, as a gauge of current public opinion in the FedCom and Katherine's response to it. —JC]

THE STAR LEAGUE REBORN

—Transcript of holovid broadcast from New Avalon, 21 November 3058

ANCHOR: The historic Whitting Conference ended today, having achieved two goals that many would have believed impossible: the re-creation of the Star League and the forging of a unified military force to fight the Clans. Just a few hours ago, conference delegates signed the Star League Constitution, ushering in a new era of cooperation between the Successor States. On the military front, a spokesman for Precentor Martial Anastasius Focht confirmed the creation of a joint task force that will take on the Clans in their occupation zones. The task force will be led by the Precentor Martial himself with Prince Victor Steiner-Davion as his deputy, and backed by a reserve force under the command of Marshal of the Armies Morgan Hasek-Davion. The exact target of the task force remains the subject of excited speculation—experts believe that the assault will be confined to a single Clan, though some are expecting a broad-based assault on all the Clan militaries in the Inner Sphere. The conference's military planners have so far declined to provide specifics, citing "operational security." Whatever the truth, it is an undeniable fact that the Inner Sphere—by means of a resurrected Star League Defense Force, proudly headed by two noble scions of House Davion—will no longer sit back and wait for the Clans to attack. The Inner Sphere is going to fight back for the first time since the victory on Tukayyid—and this time, our forces may win more than a fifteen-year breathing space.

INTERESTING TIMES

—Transcript from *Real News*, a holovid news magazine based on New Syrtis, 31 December 3058

ANCHOR: ... There may be no better symbol of our changing times than the visit of Prince Victor Steiner-Davion to the capital of the Draconis Combine. Long known to the people of the FedCom as "Black Luthien," the world earned that name as much for the dark deeds of its rulers as for any geographical features it possesses. Throughout history, our two nations have fought countless wars that left thousands dead—the most recent less than twenty years ago. And yet, within those two decades, the universe has changed to the point where the ruler of the Federated Commonwealth can receive an apparently genuine welcome from the leaders and people of the Combine ... as Prince Victor did just two days ago, when he set foot on Luthien for the very first time. <ROLL FOOTAGE: VICTOR'S ARRIVAL IN RECEPTION AREA, TAKASHI KURITA MEMORIAL SPACEPORT. CLOSE ON VICTOR, THEODORE KURITA EXCHANGING BOWS.>

In the days since, Prince Victor has enjoyed Combine hospitality to its fullest. He has made every effort to accommodate himself to the customs and expectations of his hosts, playing the unaccustomed role of diplomat with more skill than many might have expected of this soldier-prince. <ROLL FOOTAGE: VICTOR ACCEPTING KATANA PRESENTED BY THEODORE KURITA, VICTOR SAMPLING SUSHI AT RESTAURANT IN IMPERIAL CITY, VICTOR ENJOYING KOTO CONCERT WITH OMI KURITA.> So well has he subsumed the Davion lord within a tourist persona

that the question cannot help but arise: why? Does he believe the Combine's aid against the Clans to be so necessary that he will not risk offending his hosts by showing himself as a Davion—even down to the clothes he wears and the food he eats? We believe that our Prince has the interests of our realm at heart, and we applaud the bold step he has taken to ensure our protection against the Clans. But what kind of a partnership is it when the Prince of the Federated Commonwealth feels he cannot even wear his native garb in the capital city of the nation that was, until recently, his own nation's greatest enemy? And what might that enemy do once the common Clan threat recedes?

We can only hope that the leaders of the Combine will not revert to type, should the new SLDF succeed in its mission. Hopefully, the Prince's determined effort to show himself "one of them" will pay off in bonds of trust that will hold even when the Clans are no longer threatening Combine worlds. Certainly Prince Victor appears to believe so. We can only pray that he is right … .

[On this same theme, one particularly explosive rumor that has recently surfaced alleges that for years, you had been secretly funneling FedCom cash to the Combine's WarShip program—supposedly because of your obsession with the Clans and your attraction to Omi. That one is particularly popular in the Draconis March. —JC]

TASK FORCE SERPENT

—Transcript of holovid broadcast, WNSY of New Syrtis, Capellan March; 15 June 3061

<VOICEOVER accompanies footage of Morgan Hasek-Davion at various stages of his life: graduating from the military academy, accepting a battlefield honor from Prince Hanse Davion, marching at the head of his unit in a parade through the streets of New Avalon, attending a court function with his wife and their then-young son George, in the receiving line at George Hasek's wedding (standing next to Prince Victor), accepting an honor from Prince Victor Steiner-Davion at the Royal Court, arriving on Tharkad for the Whitting Conference.>

VOICEOVER: If the measure of a man lies in his actions, then Grand Duke Morgan Hasek-Davion was among the giants of his generation. A brilliant tactician and gifted leader of men who never wavered in his loyalty to his royal cousin, Prince Hanse Davion, and later to Hanse's son Victor, Morgan Hasek-Davion epitomized the best of the Federated Commonwealth. From his early days as a simple lance commander to command of the crack First Kathil Uhlans to his most recent post as Marshal of the Armies, Morgan consistently displayed courage, foresight and a deep personal commitment to the welfare of his troops as well as that of his nation. These qualities made him the best possible choice for the last command of his life—leading the task force sent to destroy Clan Smoke Jaguar on its homeworld.

The story of Morgan Hasek-Davion's final command begins at the Whitting Conference in late 3058. There, the military leaders of the Inner Sphere were engaged in planning a massive assault on the Clan Smoke Jaguar occupation zone when an unexpected event caused them to broaden their target. A Clan defector to ComStar presented that organization with the road to the Clan homeworlds. This pathway through deep space enabled the Inner Sphere to take the war to the Clans with a vengeance. Following it would lead them to the world of Huntress, where they could utterly destroy the Smoke Jaguar war machine.

Secrecy was of the essence. The Clans had developed their own intelligence operation, known as the Watch; if they learned

of the proposed assault on Huntress, the Jaguars would likely reinforce the planet and slaughter the task force upon arrival. Only the advantage of surprise would allow the task force to succeed. So Morgan Hasek-Davion agreed to be officially relegated to command of a mere "reserve" force, allegedly intended to reinforce the troops fighting in the occupation zone. The true importance of his command was not revealed.

The reserve force, dubbed Task Force Serpent, included units from every Inner Sphere realm, as well as mercenary units known for their integrity and skill in battle. Soon after the Whitting Conference ended, Morgan Hasek-Davion led his "reserve force" to the FedCom world of Defiance, where the troops underwent rigorous training exercises. Designed in part to enable the disparate units to fight as a cohesive whole, the exercises went a long way toward forging Task Force Serpent into a potent weapon. Marshal Hasek-Davion's personal charisma and integrity did the rest, keeping the leadership together whenever disagreements or old suspicions threatened the task force's hard-won unity.

On the first of May, 3059, Task Force Serpent left Defiance—allegedly for the Draconis Combine, where it would remain in readiness for attacks on the occupation zone. In reality, the task force had begun the first leg of its long journey to Clan space. But Marshal Hasek-Davion would not see Task Force Serpent's bloody and hard-won victory. On 30 January 3060, he was found dead of an apparent heart attack. A subsequent autopsy uncovered the presence of fugu poison in his system, apparently ingested along with a whisky nightcap. The fugu—better known as the Japanese puffer fish—and other details of the crime seemed to point to Combine involvement; but the Combine leadership had no reason to want the Marshal dead or the task force compromised. Indeed, the Combine had everything to gain from Task Force Serpent's success. General Ariana Winston, who assumed command upon Morgan's death, rejected the too-obvious conclusion and ordered a full investigation.

The investigation turned up Lucas Penrose, apparently an agent of Loki and without a doubt the one who had poisoned the Marshal. Penrose provoked a violent incident and was killed before he could be interrogated, however, and so the exact identity of his employers remains unknown. Who ordered Marshal Hasek-Davion's death? Was it Loki? Or was Penrose acting on someone else's behalf?

Theories are legion, hard facts few. One school of thought blames reactionary anti-Davion elements in the Draconis Combine, who preferred to see their nation enslaved by the Clans rather than accept the help of their historical enemies, and who also wanted vengeance for Marshal Hasek-Davion's part in the War of 3039. Another theory points to the Capellan Confederation, whose Chancellor allegedly wanted the Marshal dead for his actions against Capellan worlds in the Fourth Succession War. Chancellor Sun-Tzu Liao comes from a family well-known for instability, and might well have been willing to risk Task Force Serpent's survival to rid himself of a personal enemy. Even stranger scenarios paint Lyran Archon Katrina Steiner-Davion or the fanatical Word of Blake as the culprits.

Some claim that the Archon killed the Marshal to rob Prince Victor of a valued advisor and friend, and also to sabotage the task force. Her motive for the latter: a secret alliance with Clan Smoke Jaguar, in which she agreed to help them in return for their aid against incursions by Clan Jade Falcon. Proponents of the Word-of-Blake theory claim that the Blakists intended to cripple Task Force Serpent and thereby ensure a savage Clan assault that would shatter the Inner Sphere; the Blakists could then step in as its saviors, assuring their dominance for the forseeable future.

We may never know the truth. But we do know that Duke Morgan Hasek-Davion was one of a rare breed, and will be sorely missed. In the words of the famous playwright William Shakespeare, "We shall not look upon his like again."

STORM WARNINGS

[The following never made it out over the airwaves; it was confiscated by Katherine's people. According to several sources, rallies like this one are becoming increasingly common throughout the Federated Commonwealth. —JC]

—Transcript of local news broadcast from the city of New Hope, Kathil, Capellan March; 12 December 3061

REPORTER: ... The crowd has been gathering for several hours now in Hope Park, waiting for word that local authorities have rescinded their ban on this peaceful rally. Many are carrying signs expressing their gratitude to Victor Steiner-Davion, lately the ruler of the Federated Commonwealth, for saving it and the entire Inner Sphere from the Clans. <CUT TO SIGN THAT READS "LONG LIVE THE PRINCE; ALLIANCE OUT"> Others show more controversial sentiments—one possible reason why the mayor and city council have forbidden the crowd to march.

<CLOSE SHOT OF WOMAN, AGE 45, PREMATURELY GREY HAIR, BLUE KNIT DRESS>

WOMAN: We have nothing against the Archon ... well, most of us don't, anyway. She's a perfectly fine ruler, and things have been all right here since she took over. But we've always looked to the Davions, and we don't see any reason why the Archon won't let Prince Victor take his throne back now that he's done fighting the Clans. It would be the right thing to do.

REPORTER: You don't regard Archon Katrina as a Davion, then, even though she's Hanse Davion's daughter?

WOMAN: *She* doesn't see herself as a Davion. Her own actions have proved that—taking the Lyran worlds out of the Commonwealth that her parents worked so hard to create, wearing Steiner blue in so many of her public appearances, even changing her name. I don't see what's wrong with plain old Katherine. My mother's name was Katherine.

REPORTER: But you're not actively protesting the Archon's right to rule?

WOMAN: I don't know about right. I suppose she's got as much right as any Steiner-Davion to sit on the throne. But now that Prince Victor is back, she should busy herself with her own worlds, and let him see to his. Just like things were before. That's all.

<A YOUNG MAN IN A RED SWEATER, HIS HAIR CUT SHORT MILITARY-STYLE, MOUNTS AN IMPROVISED PLATFORM IN THE MIDDLE OF THE PARK. HE BEGINS TO ADDRESS THE CROWD.>

MAN: It's been five hours now, and no word has come from the mayor's office. We are being denied our God-given right to free speech; denied the freedom of assembly; denied the right to walk where we want to walk in our own hometown; and for what? Because the mayor and the city council are afraid. Afraid that if they let us walk the streets of New Hope, proclaiming our support for our Prince, someone might get angry. Someone with a lot of power, who can make their lives miserable from the throne on New Avalon. Someone who usurped that throne from its rightful occupant. The Lyran Archon, who calls herself Katrina and has rejected her Davion heritage, has no place ruling over Davion worlds. She has deprived Prince Victor of his realm and even of the hero's welcome he so richly deserved after delivering us from the Clans. She forced him into temporary exile on Luthien, capital of the Draconis Combine, while she lorded it over the nation that will always be Prince Victor's home. The state we once called enemy has shown more gratitude to our Prince than his own sister! This is a disgrace, and we his loyal subjects won't stand for it. We *will* protest; we *will* march through our own city and bear witness to this wrong—

<SOUND OF SIRENS APPROACHING.>

REPORTER: What's going on now ... Bill, point the camera over that way, will you?

<FLASHING LIGHTS AND LOUD SIRENS AS SEVERAL RIOT-CONTROL VEHICLES PULL UP TO THE PARK OUTSKIRTS. POLICE IN FULL RIOT GEAR POUR OUT OF THEM AND HEAD FOR THE CROWD. MELEE ENSUES.>

REPORTER: Oh, my God ... I don't believe it! The police are clubbing down protesters right and left ... God, there's so many of them! A few people are fighting back, using their signs as weapons ... Bill, over there! The policeman who just went down ... Reporting live from Hope Park—it's chaos out here, bodies falling every which way. This violent response by authorities, seemingly unprovoked, is absolutely unprecedented ... uh-oh, they're heading this way ... ! Turn the camera off, Bill. Don't let them get the footage—don't let—

THE FEDCOM MILITARY— STATUS REPORT

—Prepared by Dr. Michael Pondsmith, military analyst and instructor at Sakhara Military Academy; 30 December 3061

Despite defections after the Lyran secession and the losses taken during the Chaos March invasion, the Armed Forces of the Federated Commonwealth remain formidable. Even the recent offensives against the Clans have done less damage to the FedCom military than might have been expected. The Coventry victory was a largely bloodless one, and the First Kathil Uhlans were the only significant FedCom force involved in the assault on Huntress. However, not only did the Uhlans take heavy casualties, but the surviving warriors—almost to a man—followed the unit's leader, Andrew Redburn, into service with the new Star League Defence Force.

The assault on the Smoke Jaguar occupation zone resulted in higher casualties simply because of the larger number of FedCom units involved. During Operation Bulldog, the Third Davion Guards RCT took substantial casualties on Luzerne. No other FedCom unit took significant damage. The single company of FedCom troops involved in the Trial of Refusal on Strana Mechty took only a single casualty: Danai Centrella, eldest daughter of the Magestrix of Canopus.

The Lyran secession and the invasion of the Chaos March cost the FedCom some of its units through defection to the Lyran Alliance or battlefield losses. Most of the latter have since rebuilt, however. The Third Donegal Guards and the Fifth Lyran Regulars abandoned their posts on Styk and on Saiph and Tall Trees, respectively. The First Kestrel Grenadiers fought McCarron's Armored Cavalry to a stalemate on New Canton, but ultimately withdrew in the face of terrorist attacks and growing hostility among the local population. Gustafson's Grenadiers remain mired in guerrilla warfare on Caph; similarly, the Thirtieth Lyran Guards continue to fight for the independence of New Home. The Second FedCom RCT took the heaviest casualties of any loyalist unit in the Chaos March; successive battles with Liao and Marik forces on Hsien destroyed the regiment.

In the St. Ives Compact matter, Katherine has continued FedCom support, moving the Fifth Davion Guards to replace the Fourteenth Donegal Guards and re-deploying the Illician Lancers. Those two units, along with the Seventh F-C RCT, are actively opposing Capellan forces on St. Ives worlds, but Katherine has officially moved their base of operation to Spica; a signal, perhaps, whether intentional or not, of Katherine's idea of the final Capellan solution.

Most dismaying is the effective loss of the Northwind Highlanders, a skilled and powerful mercenary unit contracted to House Davion after Prince Hanse Davion returned the unit's homeworld to them in the Fourth Succession War. The Third Royal RCT commander unfortunately chose to attack the Highlanders, who were furiously debating whether or not to fulifll their contract and fight for House Davion. After heavy fighting, the Third was driven off Northwind by MacLeod's Regiment and Stirling's Fusiliers. Since that incident, the Northwind Highlanders have remained cool toward House Davion; though they bear you no personal ill will, they are likely to remain neutral in any conflict between you and Katherine.

As you will recall, to directly counteract the loss of the Northwind Highlander regiments, you ordered the rebuilding of three famous, traditionally Davion units that were all destroyed within the last fifty years. I know this effort was to work hand in hand with your new BattleMech program—which has already resulted in the *JagerMech* III and *Enforcer* III designs—in boosting the spirits of the Federated Commonwealth, while repairing your tarnished image. In mid-3060, all three regiments—the Fifth Davion Guards RCT, the Forty-first Avalon Hussars and the Second New Ivaarsen Chasseurs—entered service. Steeped in Davion tradition, they have helped turn the hearts of many a citizen as well as warrior back to you and their proud Davion heritage.

Of course, as soon as Katherine assumed the throne of New Avalon, she could not miss the opportunity to return the favor and created the Third Robinson Rangers, in the hopes of purchasing the loyalty of the Robinson family as well as the common citizen of the Draconis March. Alarmingly, this ploy seems to have worked well for her.

The rebuilding of the AFFC's JumpShip fleet is near completion, though it has unfortunately absorbed a large portion of the military budget. Additionally, the FedCom footed the lion's share of the astronomical cost of Operation Bulldog; consequently, the AFFC is facing a funding shortfall. This may be good news in a way, as Duchess Katherine will have to cope with the problem. However, an underfunded army does the FedCom no good in the long run. The cash crunch may also become leverage for Katherine; she can selectively fund units loyal to her while starving those she considers insufficiently supportive; most likely the precise rationale behind the creation of the Third Robinson Rangers.

[We've recently discovered another reason for the money trouble. Katherine's government recently uncovered fraudulent dealings by a FedCom noble; apparently he was fudging the numbers on military equipment needed to fight the Clans. He managed to skim a fair amount of money and materiel before getting caught, and it looks like this case may be just the tip of the iceberg. We might want to consider helping some of these people—that hurts Katrina while putting the nobles in your debt. The latter could be especially useful. —JC]

Katherine's recent takeover of the FedCom has left many pro-Davion military units restive. Several of them retain their loyalty to you personally as well as to House Davion, and they resent being led by a woman who has made her preference for her Steiner heritage so strikingly clear. Despite the best efforts of Katherine's spin doctors, a good portion of the FedCom military is not buying her party line of the whole Commonwealth's eventual re-integration under her enlightened leadership. Should you decide to take action against her at some future point, this report will help you determine whose loyalties you can and cannot count on, as well as who you might be able to persuade to follow your cause.

No mercenary units were included, as they will fight for the hand that feeds them.

[As a final note concerning loyalties, I have concrete information proving that General Motors of Kathil and Johnston Industries of New Syrtis have both hired significant mercenary elements and employed them in securing those planets that have had their trade disastrously disrupted by the chaos of the last half-decade. The fact that these two important FedCom conglomerates would undertake such a bold, independent military action, shows a grave lack of respect and confidence in the current Federated Commonwealth government. Further proof that the waters are not as calm as Katherine would have everyone believe. —JC]

ARMED FORCES OF THE FEDERATED COMMONWEALTH

(Deployment as of 30 December 3061)
Commander: Archon Princess Katherine Steiner-Davion
Aide: Marshal of the Armies Jackson Davion
BattleMech Strength: 87 Regiments

THE DRACONIS MARCH
Commander: Field Marshal James Sandoval
Aide: Marshal Aileen Lugo
BattleMech Strength: 29 Regiments, 1 Battalion

COREWARD COMBAT THEATER (ROBINSON OPERATIONS AREA)
Theater Commander: Field Marshal Vanessa Bisla
Aide: Marshal Kingsley Phillips
BattleMech Strength: 19 Regiments, 2 Battalions

Addicks PDZ (Addicks Command)
Commander: Marshal Andrew Terlecki
Aide: Hauptmann General Douglas Garett
BattleMech Strength: 3 Regiments

Unit Name	Experience	Loyalty	Faction	Homeworld
Addicks DMM	Regular	Reliable	Neutral	Addicks
(CO: Leftenant General Nancy Bannson)				
6th F-C RCT	Regular	Reliable	Katherine	Addicks
(CO: Hauptmann General James McConnel)				
12th Deneb Light Cavalry	Regular	Reliable	Neutral	Tybalt
(CO: Leftenant General Jeffrey Neece)				

Kentares PDZ (Kentares Command)
Commander: Marshal Anton Jacowitz
Aide: Marshal Charles Swaine
BattleMech Strength: 4 Regiments

Unit Name	Experience	Loyalty	Faction	Homeworld
Clovis DMM	Green	Reliable	Neutral	Kentares IV
(CO: Leftenant General Brian Bruning)				
1st NAIS Cadet Cadre	Green	Fanatical	Victor	Schedar
(CO: Leftenant General Jonathan Sanchez)				
8th Crucis Lancers RCT	Regular	Reliable	Neutral	Mara
(CO: Hauptmann General Frank Jeffson)				
5th Lyran Guards RCT	Green	Reliable	Katherine	Markab
(CO: Hauptmann General Louise Kopper)				

Raman PDZ (Raman Command)
Commander: Marshal Melford Dennis
Aide: Hauptmann General Lee Chou
BattleMech Strength: 4 Regiments

Unit Name	Experience	Loyalty	Faction	Homeworld
Raman DMM	Green	Reliable	Katherine	Raman
(CO: Leftenant General Renee Mazner)				
1st Chisholm's Raiders RCT	Green	Questionable	Katherine	Breed
(CO: Hauptmann General Arisota Neece)				
5th Donegal Guards RCT	Regular	Reliable	Katherine	Benet III
(CO: Hauptmann General Ursa Potroy)				
41st Avalon Hussars	Regular	Reliable	Victor	Benet III
(CO: Hauptmann General Laura Hamilton)				

Le Blanc PDZ (Le Blanc Command)

Commander: Marshal Mason Vanderkellos
Aide: Hauptmann General Vivian Colgate
BattleMech Strength: 5 Regiments, 1 Battalion

Unit Name	Experience	Loyalty	Faction	Homeworld
Robinson DMM	Green	Reliable	Neutral	Le Blanc
(CO: Leftenant General Jennifer Durret)				
Robinson Academy Training Battalion	Green	Reliable	Neutral	Robinson
(CO: Kommandant Samuel O'Day)				
1st Robinson Rangers	Veteran	Fanatical	Neutral	Robinson
(CO: Haumptmann General Mai Fortuna)				
10th Lyran Guards RCT	Veteran	Fanatical	Victor	Robinson
(CO: Marshal James McFarland)				
1st New Ivaarsen Chasseurs	Elite	Fanatical	Victor	New Ivaarsen
(CO: Leftenant General Sal Cole)				
2nd New Ivaarsen Chasseurs	Regular	Fanatical	Victor	New Ivaarsen
(CO: Hauptmann General Krisi Johnson)				

Dahar PDZ (Dahar Command)

Commander: Marshal Nasha Tiljurga
Aide: Hauptmann General Salvatore Herrmann
BattleMech Strength: 3 Regiments, 1 Battalion

Unit Name	Experience	Loyalty	Faction	Homeworld
Dahar DMM	Regular	Reliable	Katherine	Dahar IV
(CO: Leftenant General Brian DeWaters)				
3rd Crucis Lancers RCT	Elite	Reliable	Victor	Cassias
(CO: Hauptmann General Acabee Zardetto)				
17th Avalon Hussars RCT	Regular	Reliable	Neutral	Cassias
(CO: Hauptmann General Kev Evans)				
Sakhara Academy Training Battalion	Green	Reliable	Katherine	Sakhara V
(CO: Kommandant Elkin Odds)				

EDGEWARD COMBAT THEATER (WOODBINE OPERATIONS AREA)

Theater Commander: Field Marshal George Powell
Aide: Hauptmann General Edward Vishlo
BattleMech Strength: 9 Regiments, 2 Battalions

Bremond PDZ (Bremond Command)

Commander: Marshal Mary Tallman
Aide: Hauptmann General Brian Gruber
BattleMech Strength: 1 Regiment

Unit Name	Experience	Loyalty	Faction	Homeworld
Bremond DMM	Regular	Reliable	Katherine	Bremond
(CO: Leftenant General Syraman Simpreeni)				

Bryceland PDZ (Bryceland Command)
Commander: Marshal Petra Nichols
Aide: Hauptmann General Bannion Gessern
BattleMech Strength: 4 Regiments, 1 Battalion

Unit Name	Experience	Loyalty	Faction	Homeworld
Bryceland DMM	Regular	Reliable	Katherine	Bryceland
(CO: Leftenant General Oci Begurnson)				
1st Conroe Training Battalion	Green	Reliable	Katherine	Tancredi IV
(CO: Kommandant Leona Peterson)				
3rd Davion Guards RCT	Veteran	Fanatical	Victor	Kesai IV
(CO: Marshal Jim Seymour)				
1st Ceti Hussars RCT	Regular	Fanatical	Victor	Pajarito
(CO: Marshal Vance Lamont)				
3rd Lyran Regulars	Regular	Reliable	Katherine	Pitkin
(CO: Leftenant General Jessica Carson)				

Mayetta PDZ (Mayetta Command)
Commander: Marshal Vonda DeGreer
Aide: Hauptmann General Mary Ann Heinrich
BattleMech Strength: 1 Regiment

Unit Name	Experience	Loyalty	Faction	Homeworld
Mayetta DMM	Green	Reliable	Katherine	Mayetta
(CO: Leftenant General Jason Yalos)				

Milligan PDZ (Milligan Command)
Commander: Marshal Lynn Merrow
Aide: Hauptmann General Juan Nishioka
BattleMech Strength: 1 Regiment

Unit Name	Experience	Loyalty	Faction	Homeworld
Milligan DMM	Green	Reliable	Katherine	Milligan
(CO: Leftenant General Jill Farlon)				

Kilbourne PDZ (Kilbourne Command)
Commander: Marshal Lisa Talrude
Aide: Marshal Frannie Assure
BattleMech Strength: 2 Regiments, 1 Battalion

Unit Name	Experience	Loyalty	Faction	Homeworld
Kilbourne DMM	Green	Reliable	Katherine	Kilbourne
(CO: Leftenant General Mariva Kelly)				
Kilbourne Academy Training Battalion	Green	Reliable	Katherine	Kilbourne
(CO: Kommandant Sam Collin)				
1st Crucis Lancers RCT	Regular	Fanatical	Victor	Bastrop
(CO: Marshal Ivor Wasjinji)				

THE CAPELLAN MARCH
Commander: Field Marshal George Hasek
Aide: Marshal Roman Steiner
BattleMech Strength: 42 Regiments, 1 Battalion

COREWARD COMBAT THEATER (KATHIL OPERATIONS AREA)
Theater Commander: Field Marshal Suzanne Zellner
Aide: Hauptmann General Vivian Chou
BattleMech Strength: 25 Regiments, 1 Battalion

Achernar PDZ (Achernar Command)
Commander: Marshal Richard Kleindienst
Aide: Leftenant General Jay Pfeifer
BattleMech Strength: 9 Regiments

Unit Name	Experience	Loyalty	Faction	Homeworld
Achernar SMM	Green	Questionable	Katherine	Achernar
(CO: Haumptmann General Walter Flostet)				
Tikonov Martial Academy Training Group	Green	Questionable	Katherine	Tikonov
(CO: Leftenant General Greg Murray)				
Nanking SMM	Green	Questionable	Katherine	Nanking
(CO: Leftenant General Fritz Tull)				
Davion Assault Guards RCT	Veteran	Reliable	Victor	Tigress
(CO: Marshal Stephan Cooper)				
3rd Republican	Veteran	Questionable	Katherine	Yangtze
(CO: Leftenant General Karl Lopiz)				
1st F-C RCT	Veteran	Reliable	Neutral	Nanking
(CO: Marshal Ally Swanson)				
1st Kestral Grenadiers	Elite	Fanatical	Victor	Zurich
(CO: Marshal Agatha Stromp)				
1st Republican	Veteran	Questionable	Katherine	Kansu
(CO: Leftenant General John Joseph Atherton)				
2nd Republican	Regular	Questionable	Katherine	Algol
(CO: Leftenant General Suzie Foster)				

Valexa PDZ (Valexa Command)
Commander: Marshal Piper Burullo
Aide: Hauptmann General Quentin Drathers
BattleMech Strength: 5 Regiments, 1 Battalion

Unit Name	Experience	Loyalty	Faction	Homeworld
Valexa CMM	Regular	Reliable	Victor	Valexa
(CO: Leftenant General Sarah Delittle)				
1st Bell Training Battalion	Green	Reliable	Neutral	Axton
(CO: Kommandant Paula Quarnry)				
3rd F-C RCT	Regular	Reliable	Katherine	New Aragon
(CO: Hauptmann General Charles Finnigan)				
5th Crucis Lancers RCT	Veteran	Fanatical	Victor	Demeter
(CO: Hauptmann General Olaf Richardson)				
5th F-C RCT	Green	Reliable	Katherine	Chesterton
(CO: Hauptmann General James White)				
1st Aragon Borderers	Veteran	Reliable	Victor	New Aragon
(CO: Leftenant General Jimmy Kirston)				

Kathil PDZ (Monongahela Command)
Commander: Marshal Ashton Cumberland
Aide: Hauptmann General Lana Knothe
BattleMech Strength: 3 Regiments

Unit Name	Experience	Loyalty	Faction	Homeworld
2nd NAIS Cadet Cadre	Green	Fanatical	Victor	Kathil
(CO: Leftenant General Helen Sanderson)				
8th F-C RCT	Regular	Reliable	Katherine	Kathil
(CO: Hauptmann General Mitchell Weintraub)				
6th Syrtis Fusiliers RCT	Elite	Reliable	Neutral	Novaya Zemlya
(CO: Hauptmann General Richard Silver)				

Alcyone PDZ (Alcyone Command)
Commander: Marshal Kinsely Crossburns
Aide: Hauptmann General Galen Meinecke
BattleMech Strength: 8 Regiments

Unit Name	Experience	Loyalty	Faction	Homeworld
Alcyone CMM	Regular	Reliable	Katherine	Alcyone
(CO: Leftenant General Dan Kendall)				
20th Avalon Hussars RCT	Veteran	Fanatical	Victor	Alcyone
(CO: Hauptmann General Jack Roberts)				
5th Syrtis Fusiliers RCT	Green	Reliable	Neutral	Lee
(CO: Hauptmann General Nathaniel Hasek)				
3rd NAIS Cade Cadre	Green	Fanatical	Victor	Lee
(CO: Leftenant General Carlos Post)				
8th Donegal Guards RCT	Veteran	Reliable	Katherine	Monhegan
(CO: Hauptmann General Tadeusz Pasnik)				
1st Kittery Borderers	Regular	Reliable	Neutral	Kittery
(CO: Leftenant General Deedee Faulkner)				
1st Kittery Training Battalion	Green	Reliable	Neutral	Kittery
(CO: Kommandant Raul Bethune)				
5th Davion Guards RCT	Regular	Fanatical	Victor	Spica
(CO: Marshal Linda Archer)				
7th F-C RCT (2 battalions)	Regular	Fanatical	Victor	Spica
(CO: Hauptmann General Timothy Seiser)				

EDGEWARD COMBAT THEATER (TAYGETA OPERATIONS AREA)
Theater Commander: Field Marshal Jennifer Lawson
Aide: Hauptmann General Clifford Scott
BattleMech Strength: 17 Regiments

New Syrtis PDZ (New Syrtis Command)
Commander: Marshal Hugh Teitjan
Aide: Leftenant General Peter Zaro
BattleMech Strength: 1 Regiment

Unit Name	Experience	Loyalty	Faction	Homeworld
New Syrtis CMM	Green	Questionable	Neutral	New Syrtis
(CO: Leftenant General Tia Caruthers)				

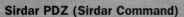
Sirdar PDZ (Sirdar Command)
Commander: Marshal Adam Korsant
Aide: Marshal Lyle Cerny
BattleMech Strength: 11 Regiments

Unit Name	Experience	Loyalty	Faction	Homeworld
Sirdar CMM	Regular	Reliable	Katherine	Sirdar
(CO: Leftenant General Russel Ito)				
4th Donegal Guards RCT	Veteran	Reliable	Katherine	Velhas
(CO: Hauptmann Generall Victor Amelio)				
3rd Ceti Hussars RCT	Regular	Reliable	Neutral	Manapire
(CO: Hauptmann General Kellie Lee-Merrow)				
15th Deneb Light Cavalry RCT	Regular	Reliable	Katherine	Demeter
(CO: Marshal Michael Lipstein)				
1st Federated Suns Armored Cavalry	Elite	Fanatical	Victor	Ziliang
(CO: Hauptmann General Rudolph Chapman)				
1st Capellan Dragoons	Regular	Questionable	Neutral	Verlo
(CO: Leftenant General Ulso Dripe)				
2nd Ceti Hussars RCT	Veteran	Reliable	Neutral	Frazer
(CO: Hauptmann General Oscar Carlson)				
2nd Chisholm's Raiders RCT	Veteran	Reliable	Katherine	Verlo
(CO: Hauptmann General Helen Eisner)				
22nd Avalon Hussars RCT	Veteran	Reliable	Katherine	Bromhead
(CO: Marshal Donna Iona)				
2nd Davion Guards RCT	Veteran	Fanatical	Victor	Bromhead
(CO: Hauptmann General William Kossacks)				
Davion Light Guards RCT	Veteran	Reliable	Neutral	Mendham
(CO: Hauptmann General Jon Buckvold)				

Altair PDZ (Ridgebrook Command)
Commander: Marshal Gil Carlson
Aide: Hauptmann General Salvatore Watselburg
BattleMech Strength: 2 Regiments

Unit Name	Experience	Loyalty	Faction	Homeworld
Ridgebrook CMM	Green	Reliable	Katherine	Ridgebrook
(CO: Leftenant General Seth Miller)				
11th Avalon Hussars RCT	Regular	Reliable	Katherine	Brockway
(CO: Hauptmann General Justin Leabo)				

Warren PDZ (Warren Command)
Commander: Hauptmann General Coaler Merrick
Aide: Leftenant General Joey Zibler
BattleMech Strength: 3 Regiments

Unit Name	Experience	Loyalty	Faction	Homeworld
Warren CMM	Green	Reliable	Katherine	Warren
(CO: Leftenant General Martin Masar)				
2nd Albion Training Cadre	Green	Fanatical	Victor	Enchi
(CO: Leftenant General Vincent Rasmussen)				
8th Syrtis Fusiliers RCT	Regular	Reliable	Neutral	Lothair
(CO: Hauptmann General Deborah Palu)				

THE CRUCIS MARCH
Commander: Field Marshal Simon Gallagher
Aide: Marshal Bertrom Winn
BattleMech Strength: 15 Regiments, 1 Battalion

COREWARD COMBAT THEATER (MARKESAN OPERATIONS AREA)
Theater Commander: Marshal Sharon Zardetto
Aide: Hauptmann General Ruby Ellis
BattleMech Strength: 8 Regiments, 1 Battalion

Archemar Combat Region (Marlette Command)
Commander: Marshal Peter Chesterton
Aide: Hauptmann General Mary Lyman
BattleMech Strength: 1 Regiment, 1 Battalion

Unit Name	Experience	Loyalty	Faction	Homeworld
Marlette CMM	Regular	Reliable	Katherine	Marlette
(CO: Leftenant General Dennis Waxon)				
Goshen War College Training Battalion	Green	Reliable	Neutral	Goshen
(CO: Kommandant Archibald Enoch)				

Kestral Combat Region (Kestrel Command)
Commander: Marshal Phillip Abrams
Aide: Leftenant General Christopher Espinosa
BattleMech Strength: 1 Regiment

Unit Name	Experience	Loyalty	Faction	Homeworld
Kestrel CMM	Regular	Reliable	Neutral	Kestrel
(CO: Leftenant General Vivian Petty)				

New Avalon Combat Region (New Avalon Command)
Commander: Marshal Gilliam Davis
Aide: Hauptmann General Jadwiga Poole
BattleMech Strength: 6 Regiments

Unit Name	Experience	Loyalty	Faction	Homeworld
New Avalon CMM	Regular	Reliable	Katherine	New Avalon
(CO: Leftenant General Russel Payne)				
1st Davion Guards RCT	Elite	Fanatical	Victor	New Avalon
(CO: Marshal Bishop Sortek)				
Davion Heavy Guards RCT	Elite	Fanatical	Victor	New Avalon
(CO: Marshal Ann Adelmana)				
10th Deneb Light Cavalry RCT	Veteran	Reliable	Katherine	New Avalon
(CO: Hauptmann General Jameson Gaston)				
3rd Robinson Rangers	Veteran	Reliable	Katherine	New Avalon
(CO: Leftenant General Jason McBride)				
19th Arcturan Guards	Green	Questionable	Katherine	Salem
(CO: Leftenant General Gloria Bishop)				

EDGEWARD ALPHA COMBAT THEATER (CHIRIKOF OPERATIONS AREA)
Theater Commander: Marshal James Flinn
Aide: Hauptmann General Victoria Seymour
BattleMech Strength: 3 Regiments

Nunivak Combat Region (Nunivak Command)
Commander: Hauptmann General Brenda Mast
Aide: Leftenant General Rudolph Bratge
BattleMech Strength: 1 Regiment

Unit Name	Experience	Loyalty	Faction	Homeworld
Remagan CMM	Regular	Reliable	Katherine	Nunivak
(CO: Leftenant General Hans Scheller)				

Islamabad Combat Region (Islamabad Command)
Commander: Hauptmann General Lucille Carton
Aide: Leftenant General Zeller Shuftan
BattleMech Strength: 1 Regiment

Unit Name	Experience	Loyalty	Faction	Homeworld
Islamabad CMM	Green	Reliable	Katherine	Islamabad
(CO: Leftenant General Carrie Zetso)				

Malagrotta Combat Region (Malagrotta Command)
Commander: Hauptmann General David Paulson
Aide: Leftenant General Eda Shrake
BattleMech Strength: 1 Regiment

Unit Name	Experience	Loyalty	Faction	Homeworld
Malagrotta CMM	Green	Questionable	Katherine	Malagrotta
(CO: Leftenant General Andrew Grundy)				

EDGEWARD BETA COMBAT THEATER (MINETTE OPERATIONS AREA)
Theater Commander: Marshal Jonathan Steiner-Sortek
Aide: Hauptmann General Harold Halbrig
BattleMech Strength: 4 Regiments

Point Barrow Combat Region (Point Barrow Command)
Commander: Hauptmann General Sheridan Miley
Aide: Leftenant General Ross Irsud
BattleMech Strength: 1 Battalion

Unit Name	Experience	Loyalty	Faction	Homeworld
Point Barrow Academy Training Battalion	Green	Reliable	Katherine	Point Barrow
(CO: Kommandant Laurie Empen)				

Tsamma Combat Region (Tsamma Command)
Commander: Hauptmann General Jeremy Swaine
Aide: Leftenant General Jocasta Zibler
BattleMech Strength: 1 Regiment

Unit Name	Experience	Loyalty	Faction	Homeworld
Tsamma CMM	Regular	Reliable	Katherine	Tsamma
(CO: Leftenant General Michael Buckley)				

Anjin Muerto Combat Region (Anjin Muerto Command)
Commander: Hauptmann General Suzane Lipstein
Aide: Leftenant General George Kubas
BattleMech Strength: 1 Regiment

Unit Name	Experience	Loyalty	Faction	Homeworld
Anjin Muerto CMM	Regular	Reliable	Katherine	Anjin Muerto
(CO: Leftenant General Earl Renquin)				

Broken Wheel Combat Region (Broken Wheel Command)
Commander: Hauptmann General Albert Carson
Aide: Leftenant General Robin Maynard
BattleMech Strength: 1 Regiment, 2 Battalions

Unit Name	Experience	Loyalty	Faction	Homeworld
1st Albion Training Cadre	Green	Fanatical	Victor	Broken Wheel
(CO: Leftenant General Derrick Gray)				
Filtvet Academy Training Battalion	Green	Reliable	Katherine	Filtvet
(CO: Kommandant Asumi Tomisawa)				
1st Brockton Training Battalion	Green	Reliable	Katherine	Brockton
(CO: Kommandant Leslie Stokoi)				

NOTABLE PERSONALITIES

[The first two of the following come from Katherine's own people, via one of my own agents inside Loki. (The profile on me makes especially amusing reading from where I sit ... .) The profiles on Arthur, Yvonne and Peter are my own estimations of them as people to watch over the next few years, especially if you do decide to boot Katherine off the throne at New Avalon. Because other people may need access to these profiles in the future, I have used the third person when referring to you in them. —JC]

LIEUTENANT GENERAL JERRARD CRANSTON

Rank/Position: Lieutenant General, SLDF Intelligence Command
Year of Birth: 3020 (age 41)

Profile:

Officially serving as an ill-defined "aide" to Victor Steiner-Davion since mid-3056, the individual known as Jerrard Cranston has actually been acting as Victor's primary intelligence advisor—his true function kept secret in order to facilitate his ability to spy. That point became moot with his appointment as head of the SLDF Intelligence Command in 3061. According to official records, Jerrard Cranston hails from the world of Callison in the Isle of Skye. After a brief stint with the Eleventh Lyran Guards, he requested and received a transfer to the First Lyran Guards RCT, with whom he saw combat against the Clans on Maestu in 3051. His career is not easily traceable over the next six years; soon after the ComStar victory on Tukayyid in 3052, he apparently retired from military life, only to reappear four years later as an aide to then-Prince Victor of the Federated Commonwealth.

Recently obtained information points to a possible explanation for this gap in Jerrard Cranston's official records. Though we have not yet confirmed it, the evidence indicates that Jerrard Cranston may be Galen Cox, hero of the Clan War, believed killed in a terrorist bombing on Solaris VII in April of 3056. Cranston first appeared in Victor's entourage not long after that, and has been conspicuously at his side during several major public events since. On the other hand, the source of this allegation is notorious for bending the truth if it suits his cause, and may not be entirely reliable.

Physically, Cranston resembles Galen Cox, though not sufficiently to arouse suspicion. Both men are of average height and fair coloring, but with nondescript features that make easy identification impossible. Jerrard Cranston wears a beard, while Cox habitually went clean-shaven. The beard may be an attempt at disguise, or may simply reflect an innocent man's personal preference. Both men are also veterans of the Clan war. Our agents will endeavor to get closer to Cranston in the coming weeks and months, to attempt independent verification of his true identity. *[Nice of them to warn me ... .—JC]*

BARON TANCRED SANDOVAL

Rank/Position: Baron of Robinson
Year of Birth: 3019 (age 42)

Profile:

Tall and graceful, with striking good looks and exceptional skill in the ancient art of fencing, the Baron of Robinson is among the Federated Commonwealth's most eligible bachelors. It is no surprise that he caught the eye of Yvonne Steiner-Davion, lately regent of the Commonwealth. However, he is considerably more than a handsome face. Tancred Sandoval is also politically astute and unfortunately loyal to the former prince of this realm. Departing from his family's traditional hatred of the Draconis Combine, Tancred has remained loyal to Victor in spite of Victor's clearly pro-Combine stance and even his rumored romantic liaison with Omi Kurita.

Until recently, Baron Sandoval was attached to the FedCom Interior Secretariat, and taught fencing on the side at the NAIS. During Yvonne Steiner-Davion's brief regency, Sandoval acted informally as her political adviser, until increasing anti-Combine unrest in the Draconis March prompted Yvonne to send him to that troubled region as her personal envoy. He remains in the Draconis March, fortunately too preoccupied with events there to make trouble on Victor's behalf. Should that change, he will have to contend with his own family's opposition to Victor's return. The rest of the Sandovals have never trusted the nonaggression pact with the Combine, and Victor's clear favor toward that realm has cost him their political and military support. Baron Sandoval's father still commands the Draconis March defenses, and can be expected to back Archon Katrina's leadership in preference to a pro-Combine prince.

DUCHESS YVONNE STEINER-DAVION

Rank/Position: Duchess of New Avalon
Year of Birth: 3039 (age 22)

Profile:

At twenty-two, Yvonne Steiner-Davion has been through more of a political baptism by fire than many scions of noble houses undergo in a lifetime. The youngest of Hanse Davion and Melissa Steiner's five children, she was thrust by circumstances from the relative obscurity of life as a pre-law student at the NAIS to the regency of the Federated Commonwealth, only to see the throne snatched out from under her. When Prince Victor Steiner-Davion went off to fight the Clans, he chose Yvonne as his regent in lieu of her older brothers (Peter was unavailable, Arthur unsuited to such a heavy responsibility). Though capable and intelligent, Yvonne ultimately fell victim to her own inexperience. Manipulated into believing that civil unrest was rising across the Commonwealth, Yvonne committed the understandable but grave error of inviting her sister Katherine to come to New Avalon and stop the FedCom's apparent slide into chaos. Katherine has since become the FedCom's sole ruler, though she has not yet been bold enough to declare its two halves officially reunited. Yvonne fled to Luthien, where she knew the returning Prince Victor would be arriving to a hero's welcome. She has since returned to Tharkad, but has kept a low profile, apparently firmly convinced of her own incompetence.

Despite her current low spirits, Yvonne remains an intelligent young woman with more ability than she gives herself credit for. If her self-confidence could be restored, her recent learning experience at Katherine's hands should make her even more of an asset. In addition to her father's reddish hair and grey eyes, Yvonne has also inherited his patience and his ability to focus on details; all she lacks is the confidence in her own judgment that led "The Fox" Hanse Davion to execute the bold moves that earned him his nickname. During Yvonne's brief tenure on the FedCom throne, she formed close ties with Tancred Sandoval, whose political savvy compensated to an extent for her inexperience. The connection between them might also be of use, should it become necessary to remove Katherine from the throne.

CADET ARTHUR STEINER-DAVION

Rank/Position: Cadet
Year of Birth: 3037 (age 24)

Profile:

The youngest of the three Steiner-Davion sons, Duke Arthur has an unfortunately deserved reputation as "all heart and no brain." He is prone to act on impulse, often prompted by emotion rather than reason, and also bows to the prevailing winds. Upon graduation from the Battle Academy on Robinson in late 3062, he will likely join a unit stationed in the Draconis March.

With regard to support for an attempt to dethrone Katherine, Arthur is a chancy prospect. Prince Victor's close ties to the Draconis Combine may make him suspect in the eyes of a brother who has spent the past several years steeped in the Draconis March's anti-Combine atmosphere. Furthermore, Arthur has become a rallying point for those who believe Victor abandoned them to their old enemies by going off to fight the Clans. Those feelings were muted while the Clans posed the bigger threat, but now old fears of the Combine are increasingly coming to the fore. While at the Battle Academy, Arthur has grown close to the Sandoval family, who almost universally regard the Combine as the only enemy worth guarding against. This may make him a problem should anti-Combine sentiment rise to the point where it threatens the newfound unity of the Star League. Anti-Combine elements in the Draconis March may attempt to use Arthur as a figurehead—and frankly, Arthur is emotional enough to be vulnerable to that kind of manipulation. If at all possible, he should be assigned to a unit stationed far away from the Draconis March—preferably one that will give him daily contact with Combine citizens, so he can learn a little broad-mindedness.

LEFTENANT PETER STEINER-DAVION

Rank/Position: Leftenant/Duke of Tharkad
Year of Birth: 3035 (age 26)

Profile:

Known as a gifted MechWarrior and something of a hothead, Peter Steiner-Davion has undergone several traumatic experiences in the past six years that have hopefully changed him for the better. While stationed on Lyons in the Isle of Skye in 3056, Peter was the target of a bombing attempt by the Free Skye Militia (FSM). Little more than a week later, Peter fell victim to a trap laid by Duke Ryan Steiner, then the major power behind the Skye secessionist movement. Duke Ryan planted rumors that FSM terrorists had taken refuge in Bellerive, a small religious community on Lyons. Knowing that Peter would lead his militia lance to liberate the town, Ryan booby-trapped its most prominent building: the church. Responding to missile fire from the church steeple, Peter fired his autocannon at it in an attempt to disable the launcher without harming the building. The moment he fired, pre-set explosives decapitated the church and set off an inferno that consumed the entire hamlet. Ryan's agents captured the entire incident on film, intending to publicize it as a "Davion massacre" of innocents and discredit Peter—and through him, his brother Victor. The plot would have succeeded, had ComStar not intercepted the footage and repackaged it as a trailer for a holovid entertainment.

In an effort at damage control, Prince Victor pulled Peter's lance off Lyons and reassigned him as Tormano Liao's FedCom liaison. Peter found himself a pawn once again, manipulated by Liao into leading a suicidal assault against a Capellan-connected mercenary unit on the planet Shiloh. Had Kai Allard-Liao not intervened to stop the attack, Victor would have been forced to declare war on the Capellan Confederation to avenge Peter's death.

The shocks of two escapes from death, his own involvement in the Bellerive slaughter and the humiliating knowledge of how easily he could be used led Peter to enter Saint Marinus House on the world of Zaniah—a retreat made famous by the mercenary Morgan Kell, who spent some years there before coming out of retirement to lead the Kell Hounds. Peter remains on Zaniah, but by all accounts is a changed man. His MechWarrior skills are undoubted; if a few years of serious contemplation have given him equivalent skill at handling people and controlling his temper, he might make Prince Victor a valuable ally.

THE BATTLE OF COVENTRY

—From the personal records of General Caradoc "Doc" Trevena, head of the advisory staff of the commanding general of the SLDF (a hauptmann with the Tenth Skye Rangers during the Falcon attack)

Historians speak of the battle of Coventry as "the bloodless victory." In a way, they're right; a combination of smart political maneuvering and luck helped us avoid a final confrontation with the Jade Falcons that could only have been a bloodbath. But for myself and others who were on Coventry when the Clan force landed, the conflict was anything but bloodless.

Coventry was partly a result of the Truce of Tukayyid, which halted the Clan invasion and deprived a new generation of Clan warriors of the chance to prove themselves in battle. The other major factor was the Refusal War, a bitter clash between the Crusader Clan Jade Falcon and the Warden Clan Wolf that savaged both sides, leaving them potential targets for their fellow Clans. The Falcons' drive toward Coventry was Khan Marthe Pryde's way of blooding her fledgling warriors and proving the Falcons' viability to the other Clans.

In response to the Clan incursion, Archon Katrina Steiner-Davion of the Lyran Alliance authorized the Coventry Expeditionary Force (CEF) to oppose them, though she kept a majority of the most experienced units on Tharkad in anticipation of a Falcon drive toward the Lyran capital. After the Falcons defeated the CEF, Katrina deployed the Coventry Relief Force (CRF), the troops initially assembled to defend Tharkad, as reinforcements. The relief force was joined by a multi-House and mercenary army, led by Prince Victor Steiner-Davion of the Federated Commonwealth. Together, the two armies successfully kept control of Coventry.

Katrina had hoped Victor's force would win a token victory or even succumb to the Falcons, discrediting him and leaving the real glory to be reaped by the CRF. Instead, Coventry solidified Victor's position as a skilled leader and encouraged him to pursue his plan for an Inner Sphere attack against the Clans.

INVASION

On 30 January 3058, Clan Jade Falcon forces crossed into the Lyran Alliance and struck four worlds. Though the Lyran defenders stood little chance against the technologically superior Clan machines, they forced the attackers into bloody battles for each planet.

Meanwhile, Archon Katrina dropped from sight, leaving the Alliance's defense in the hands of advisor Tormano Liao and General Nondi Steiner, head of the LAAF. General Steiner and Mandrinn Liao placed House units on alert along the Falcons' line of advance and hired mercenary units to man strategic defensive positions. Extrapolating from the direction of the Falcon attacks to that point, the mandrinn and the general accurately predicted the Falcons' next target: Coventry.

COVENTRY

In early March, the Falcons arrived in the Coventry system. They first landed at Port St. William Spaceport, Coventry's main port facility. The Second Falcon Jaegers' DropShips dropped OmniMechs and Elementals north of the city. An artillery barrage by the defending Third Battalion of the Tenth Skye Rangers hurt, but failed to slow, the Falcon column. The Falcons eventually pushed the Third Battalion out of the spaceport, whereupon Kommandant Oheler's troops withdrew and regrouped northeast of the city.

Meanwhile, the Jade Falcon Eyrie Cluster was dropping onto the Coventry Military Academy. The fighting on the academy grounds was spirited and savage, but in the end, Clan technology and training prevailed, and the cadet cadre withdrew to a rally point five kilometers east.

The third arm of the invasion force went after Coventry's most valuable prize: the Coventry Metal Works main processing plant. Heavy initial losses to aerospace interception prompted the Falcon commander to land at an alternate LZ more than two kilometers west of the plant, allowing Kommandant Claudia Peyman to use the time to move her troops into blocking position between the Metal Works and the Clan landing zone. Peyman's militia command, made up of green reservists and retired veterans piloting vintage 'Mechs, acquitted itself better than expected, inflicting 65 percent casualties on the Falcon unit before being forced to withdraw.

GUERRILLA WARFARE

After the initial attack, the fighting tapered off sharply. The surviving Inner Sphere defenders were too badly shot up to mount an effective counterattack, and the Jade Falcons were busy ferrying in new troops to replace their substantial losses. The defending forces not engaged during the first few days of fighting began waging guerrilla war against the invaders. Among these 'Mech-equipped guerrilla units was my own command, the Second Company of the Tenth Skye Rangers' First Battalion.

When word of the Clan invasion reached the First's command post at the McKenzy Molecular Smelter, Kommandant Horst Sarz got roaring drunk, at which point I assumed command of the unit. Badly equipped as we were, we had no hope of taking on a Falcon regiment, so I led the First into the caves, mine tunnels and deep canyons that lace Coventry's Cross-Divide Mountains. From this warren, we launched several successful raids against the Clan invaders.

The guerrilla campaign culminated in a two-pronged attack against a Falcon supply base near Collivette. Led by Leftenant

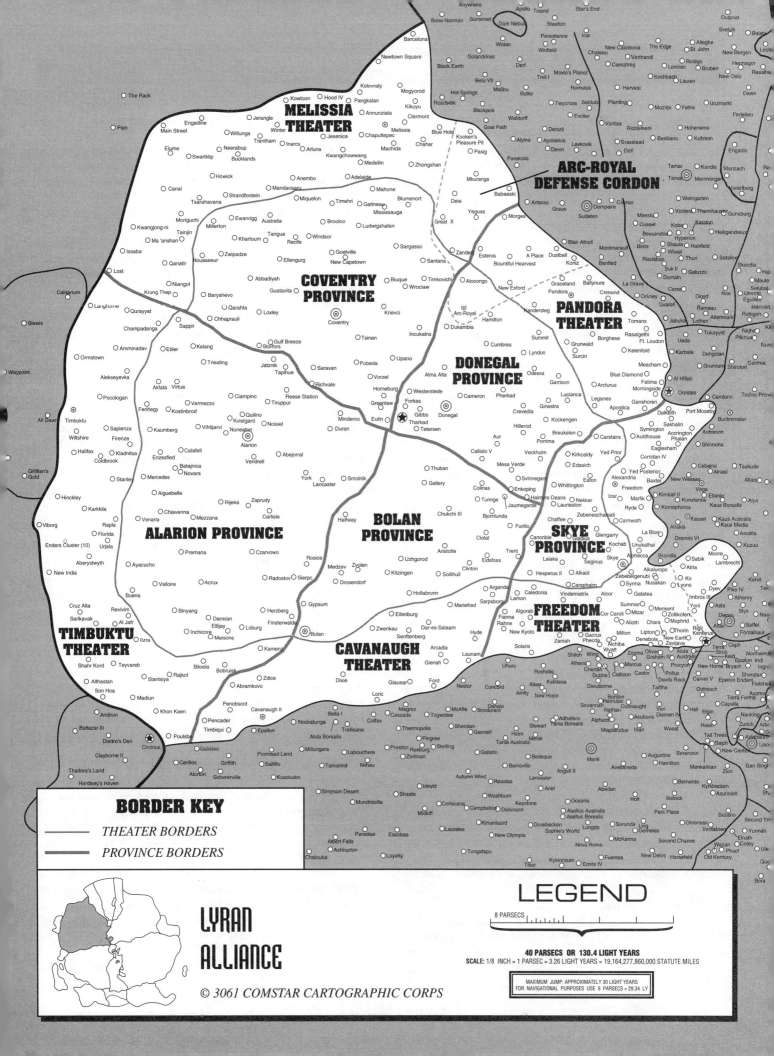

Isobel Murdoch, the first raiding party smashed aside the tiny Clan force of light 'Mechs and Elementals. They gathered up several truckloads of supplies and fled before Clan reinforcements could arrive. Meanwhile, two 'Mech lances under my command lured several Falcon 'Mechs into a narrow pass with false sensor readings and destroyed them.

COVENTRY EXPEDITIONARY FORCE

In the meantime, a relief force was assembling on the Lyran capital of Tharkad. Made up of the Eridani Light Horse, Wolf's Dragoons, Waco's Rangers and the Crazy Eights, this force was originally intended to defend Tharkad should the Falcons advance that far. The Archon, however, sent it to Coventry. On 10 April 3058, the newly christened CEF launched its first effort to drive the Falcons from the planet.

Shelly Brubaker of Wolf's Dragoons Delta Regiment broadcast a *batchall* to the Falcon forces, announcing her intention to destroy the Port St. William spaceport using only one of her three battalions. On the Flatlands east of the city, Brubaker's First Battalion met and smashed through two Trinaries of the Twelfth Falcon Regulars. The Dragoon force then ran rampant through the port until the rest of the Falcons arrived, wrecking everything within reach. The battle that followed was among the campaign's most brutal, and ended in a Dragoon withdrawal. The mercenaries had achieved their objective, however, which was to render the spaceport unusable by the Jade Falcons.

Probing the Defenses

During the ensuing week, the CEF and the Falcons engaged in several small skirmishes, testing each other's strength. On 21 April, the CEF launched a three-pronged attack against the Falcons at Port St. William. While the Dragoons and the Eridani Light Horse attacked the city directly, the remnants of the Coventry Militia, the Academy cadets and the Tenth Skye Rangers swung westward to screen the mercenary column from a possible flanking attack. In the third arm of the operation, Waco's Rangers and the Crazy Eights moved through the wild, hilly region known as the Dales to make a surprise attack behind enemy lines. My recon company was assigned to guide the mercs through the Dales' rough terrain.

Unfortunately, Star Colonel Arimas Malthus of the Falcons guessed our strategy and laid an ambush near the Dales. As the last Ranger 'Mech entered a large, grassy field between the Dales and Port St. William, the Falcon heavies and assaults unleashed a barrage of missile fire from behind the aspens that ringed the field. While the Falcon forces battered the Ranger 'Mechs, the Tenth Skye recon lance fought a delaying action and simultaneously sent word of the attack to the rest of the CEF. Only the timely arrival of the Dragoons' Delta Regiment prevented the destruction of the other merc units.

The Siege of Lietnerton

The failure of the Port St. William assault prompted a CEF pullback to Lietnerton. Short on supplies and combat-capable troops, the CEF could do little but wait and hope for more reinforcements. On 8 May, the Falcons launched an all-out attempt to drive the CEF from Coventry. Elements of the Jade Falcon Eyrie Cluster made a night march through a thunderstorm and attacked the Coventry Militia and Tenth Skye Rangers shortly after dawn. A combination of Skye Rangers artillery and Light Horse aerospace attacks eventually drove the Falcons back.

The Falcons attacked again on 9 May, striking at the Eridani Light Horse along the southern edge of town. The Light Horse gunners responded with an artillery barrage that took out several OmniMechs and the Falcons' artillery positions. The ensuing close-quarters battle ended in a Falcon withdrawal, leaving Lietnerton in CEF hands.

THE CAVALRY ARRIVES

As the battle for Coventry ground down to a stalemate, the Archon requested aid from the Free Worlds League and the Capellan Confederation, which sent the Knights of the Inner Sphere and the mercenary unit Harloc's Raiders to the defense of Tharkad. These units arrived on Coventry along with the Eleventh Lyran Guards and three more Wolf's Dragoons regiments. At the same time, Archon Katherine finally choose to ask her brother, Prince Victor Steiner-Davion, for help. Conveniently, Victor was attending war exercises on Tukayyid when war broke out on Coventry. The units on Tukayyid, including the First Genyosha, the First St. Ives Lancers and ComStar's Invader Galaxy, joined the Davion Heavy Guards and two Kell Hounds regiments—more than enough to challenge the Falcon Galaxies.

ENDGAME

On 5 June, the coalition task force arrived. Prince Victor invoked safcon for the Inner Sphere force—a request the tradition-bound Clan leaders had little choice but to accept. The Prince and the Falcon Khan agreed to meet four days later in the village of Whitting to conduct a formal batchall.

When Victor learned that his force and the Clans were evenly matched, he realized that wresting the planet away from the enemy would mean a long and bloody battle, with no guarantee of victory. And even if the coalition force won, its weakened state would leave the Inner Sphere vulnerable to other Clan incursions. Unknown to anyone else at the time, Khan Marthe Pryde of the Jade Falcons faced a similar dilemma. Shortly after the coalition force's arrival, she had received a message from Khan Vlad Ward of the Wolf Clan, in which he informed her that he was moving troops to strike at worlds in the Falcon occupation zone. If Khan Pryde kept her forces on Coventry, she stood to lose worlds in the Falcon OZ. Transferring her forces from Coventry without a fight, however, risked disgracing her Clan.

Prince Victor solved the dilemma and won the famous "bloodless victory" by offering the Falcons *hegira*—the right of a defeated enemy to withdraw from the battlefield with his forces and honor intact. Khan Pryde accepted, and the campaign for Coventry came to an end.

THE LYRAN ALLIANCE

Alpha Level Clearance/Eyes Only
TO: Katrina Steiner-Davion, Archon of the Lyran Alliance and Princess of the Federated Commonwealth
FROM: General Alicia Savinson, Commander in Chief of the Lyran Intelligence Corps
RE: Current State of the Lyran Alliance—Comprehensive Intelligence Briefing

Your Highness,

As you requested, the following report covers the current state of affairs in the Lyran Alliance and identifies potential trouble spots, paying particular attention to possible military action by the former Prince Victor Steiner-Davion. In the interests of clarity, I have included a brief summation of significant events in the Alliance since the Inner Sphere victory at Tukayyid, as I feel it is impossible to fully understand the present situation without some reference to the immediate past. (As the historical portion of this report may also be used by others within the LIC, I refer to Your Highness throughout that part in the third person.)

General Sharon Bryan, originally of the Eleventh Lyran Guards, whose recent exploits against the Clans have won her and her unfortunately destroyed unit richly deserved praise and promotion, has provided a military briefing and troop deployments. Following these are brief profiles of various individuals that the LIC will be keeping an eye on over the next several months.

I have every confidence that, upon completing the transfer of power in the Federated Commonwealth, you will settle the potential problems outlined in this report with your habitual skill and dispatch. This briefing should prove useful in that endeavor.

RECENT HISTORY

The tumultous sequence of events that led to the renewal of an independent Lyran state began in June of 3055, with the tragic assassination of Archon Melissa Steiner. Without her guiding hand at the helm, the unwieldy political construct known as the Federated Commonwealth could not hold together. The throne of the two combined realms passed to Archon Melissa's oldest son, Victor Steiner-Davion. Unfortunately for the realm—and particularly for its Lyran subjects—the first Archon Prince proved unequal to the challenges of rulership. Accustomed to leading men in battle, he had little notion of how to govern in peacetime, and his near-pathological desire to emulate his famous father Hanse Davion in all things had for years led him to slight his Steiner heritage. These flaws, combined with a desperate ambition to prove himself, made him precisely the wrong leader to shepherd his vast nation through the troubles that followed Archon Melissa's death. Indeed, so obvious was his desire to rule that many believe he ordered his mother killed to inherit her throne (though the accusation has yet to be proved).

THE SKYE REBELLION

Within less than a year of Archon Melissa's assassination, perennial secessionist agitation came to a head in the Isle of Skye region. Led by Duke Ryan Steiner, a thorn in the side of the legitimate ruling Steiner line for decades, the Skye separatists swelled the ranks of their supporters by painting their incipient rebellion as a strike for freedom from the Davion prince of the FedCom. With little gift for or understanding of politics, Victor Davion turned for help to his oldest sister Katherine, Duchess of Tharkad. A consummate politician in the service of peace, Katherine did everything she could to temper rising anti-Davion feeling throughout Lyran worlds. She defended Victor staunchly against accusations of murder by many, including Duke Ryan. Less than a year later, Katherine again defended Victor against charges that he had ordered Ryan killed to silence him—despite the fact that the clearly professional sniper attack on Ryan was beyond the scope of the troubled "lone gunman" allegedly guilty of the murder. She spoke out strongly and often for her brother, setting aside her grief for the victim of yet another assassination just days before Ryan's death—that of Galen Cox, an Isle of Skye native son and hero of the Clan war, to whom she had grown close. She persisted in her loyalty to Victor even after Cox's death was also laid at his feet, downplaying evidence of a serious rift between the two men shortly before Cox's demise.

After Duke Ryan's death, the Skye separatist movement floundered. In what would become the first move toward Lyran independence from the FedCom, Duchess Katherine acceded to her brother's request that she act as his regent on Tharkad while he moved the FedCom government back to New Avalon. As regent, Katherine made peace in Skye her first priority. Then, as always, she focused on the well-being of her people rather than the abstract needs of interstellar politics. Over the next few years, the duchess oversaw the revitalization of Skye, including the building of hospitals, schools and other such vital humanitarian institutions. These actions went a long way toward damping secessionist fires among the local population.

THE ALLIANCE IS BORN

While the Isle of Skye was enjoying its newfound peace, the rest of the FedCom was heading for its next crisis with the speed of a running BattleMech. Joshua Marik, the young heir to the Free Worlds League, was dying of leukemia at the New Avalon Institute of Science. Focused on the Clan threat to the exclusion of all else, Prince Victor declined to tell Captain-General Thomas Marik the truth about his son's condition. He feared that, without Joshua as a hostage, the Captain-General would no longer honor his promise to provide the FedCom with war materiel needed to fight the Clans. Instead, Victor replaced

the dying boy with a double. When the substitution came to light—along with suggestions that Victor had arranged the child's death rather than waiting for the disease to run its course—a horrified Duchess Katherine responded in the only way she could. She disassociated herself and her portion of the FedCom from her brother, renaming her realm the Lyran Alliance and declaring it an independent state. At the same time, she issued a moving appeal for all Lyran units serving in the FedCom and all expatriate Lyran citizens to return home. Finally, she emphasized the totality of the break by fully embracing her Steiner heritage, changing her name to Katrina and reclaiming the title of Archon.

Fires of War

Prince Victor refused to recognize the Alliance, but was in no position to do anything about the secession. Just days earlier, Thomas Marik had declared war on the Federated Commonwealth. In concert with troops from the Capellan Confederation, Marik forces struck the Sarna March.

Recognizing the rightness of Marik's cause, Archon Katrina kept the Alliance neutral. This action, along with Katrina's reputation as a peacemaker, led Thomas Marik to avoid striking Sarna March worlds claimed by the Lyran Alliance. Unfortunately, Sun-Tzu Liao did not show the same restraint. Liaoist agents sparked rebellions on three Lyran-claimed worlds, two of which have yet to return to Lyran control. All in all, however, Archon Katrina's timely actions spared the Lyran Alliance a war it could ill afford. The Alliance treasury even profited somewhat from the conflict. On the advice of Mandrinn Tormano Liao, the former leader of the Free Capella movement, Katrina sold back to Victor Davion a portion of the military JumpShips that had been serving near the Clan border when the war broke out. The money has since been earmarked for charitable causes, many of them on the disputed worlds of the Chaos March. [I doubt that last assertion. My people are still trying to find out where the money actually went. —JC]

In the wake of the Marik–Liao invasion, Victor Davion claimed sovereignty over many of the Chaos March worlds also claimed by the Alliance. The war had not gone well for Davion forces, however, and Victor remained too preoccupied with the Clans to make military overtures against Alliance worlds. Unfortunately, the need to consolidate her own government prevented Archon Katrina from doing much more in the Chaos March than providing supplies and occasional funding to Lyran units bogged down in the widespread factional fighting. Though the Archon has not forgotten the Chaos March, she wisely chose to put the welfare of the rest of her realm above military adventurism.

THE FALCON STRIKES

After the Chaos March invasion ended in late December of 3057, the Lyran Alliance enjoyed a year of peace. It was not to last, however. In late January of 3058, Clan Jade Falcon forces struck at the Alliance worlds of Engadine, Wilunga, Neerabup and Bucklands. Ongoing unit reorganization in the Lyran Alliance

Armed Forces, intended to ensure a strong and cohesive army committed to the preservation of the Alliance, had left those worlds either lightly defended by reshuffled units or lacking any defense at all. The Falcons crushed the scant opposition on all four worlds, and by February had struck at three more. They seemed poised to continue, and in early March landed on Coventry.

Archon Katrina, who had remained uncharacteristically out of the public eye in order to draft important political reforms, swiftly organized an expeditionary force to relieve the defenders of the beleaguered planet. The force's elite mercenary units made some initial gains, but soon found themselves on the defensive. At that point, Archon Katrina organized a second force to relieve Coventry. To assure victory against the Clan marauders, Katrina took one final and courageous step. She requested military aid from Victor Steiner-Davion, despite the risk that Victor might use it as a pretext to re-annex the Lyran Alliance. With her accustomed political astuteness, she reasoned that Victor's overwhelming obsession with fighting the Clans would keep him from using a victory on Coventry as a springboard for further military action. To attempt forcible annexation of the Lyran Alliance would cost Victor troops, weakening his forces to the point where they could no longer hope to defeat the Clans in battle.

The Archon's instincts proved correct, in every particular save one. Rather than fighting the Jade Falcons on Coventry, Victor made the extraordinary move of allowing them to withdraw from the battlefield intact. For this bloodless victory, many hailed him as a hero, though others rightly criticized him for allowing the enemy to walk away unscathed.

The battle for Coventry set an important precedent: namely, that the former enemies of the Inner Sphere could fight side by side effectively against a common foe. The Archon's second relief force and the small army that Victor led both incorporated units from across the Inner Sphere. Within three months of the Coventry victory, Archon Katrina took steps to turn the idea of a unified Inner Sphere into reality. She called for a conference of the Inner Sphere's political and military leaders, to be held on Tharkad, at which the lords of the Great Houses would finally achieve peacefully what they had failed to accomplish through centuries of war: the rebirth of the Star League.

THE WHITTING CONFERENCE

The historic Whitting Conference, named for the village on Coventry at which the Inner Sphere had defeated the Falcon invaders, began on 1 October 3058. For the next several weeks, political negotiators hashed out a new Star League Constitution, while military leaders planned a no-holds-barred assault on the Clans. The objective of the assault was to make the Clans sit up and take notice of the "barbarian" Inner Sphere, and to teach them the true horror of war. Knowing that the SLDF lacked the strength to take on all the Clan militaries at once, the planners chose to make an example of a single Clan: the Smoke Jaguars. The Jaguars had started the invasion and were among its staunchest Crusader backers. Their fall at the hands of the

"inferiors" they despised would seriously damage the Crusader faction among the Clans and enable the anti-invasion Warden faction to call off hostilities.

Initially, the assault was intended to drive the Smoke Jaguars from their occupation zone. In the midst of the planning sessions, however, Precentor Martial Anastasius Focht received an unexpected but vital piece of information: the route from the Inner Sphere to the Clan homeworlds. The military leaders swiftly reworked their attack plans to include the Smoke Jaguar homeworld of Huntress. They created two separate task forces, one of which would liberate the Jaguar occupation zone. The other would make the long trek to Clan space. Dubbed Task Force Serpent, this second army would attack Huntress and destroy Clan Smoke Jaguar's capability to make war.

While the military experts planned the death of a Clan, Archon Katrina and the other political leaders labored to create the new Star League Constitution. By mid-November, they had accomplished their goal: a constitution in the spirit of the old Star League that also took into account the circumstances that had led to the rise of the new. In the most significant change from the original document, the post of First Lord of the Star League would rotate between the members of the First Council, each of whom would serve a three-year term.

Though the succession was to be determined by lot, Archon Katrina pointed out that it behooved the Inner Sphere to choose its first leader with due deliberation—especially if they meant to impress the Clans with the seriousness of what they had achieved. The Archon received the necessary two-thirds council vote to void the lot choice, and proceeded to nominate Sun-Tzu Liao as First Lord. The nomination was narrowly confirmed, with the unexpected backing of Victor Davion.

The signing of the Star League Constitution took place on 21 November 3058. Archon Katrina, whose tireless efforts had contributed most to this historic event, called it "the pinnacle of my career. The rebirth of the Star League will stand as a monument to those here who sign their names in ratification, and to those for whom it was signed. This day there is once again a united Inner Sphere, and that should strike fear into the hearts of our enemies everywhere."

CURRENT EVENTS

The renewal of the Star League is a monumental achievement, but its peace is fragile at best, even here in the Lyran Alliance. Preserving that peace will require careful monitoring of—and possibly swift action against—several potential threats.

The most worrying of these is the possibility of an armed incursion by Victor Davion, who recently succeeded Anastasius Focht as Precentor Martial of ComStar. Now that you have assumed control over the Federated Commonwealth, you are in a position to once again unify it with the Lyran Alliance—an action that, if taken, would increase the likelihood of invasion by the FedCom's former prince. Victor never formally relinquished his claim to Alliance worlds, and though any military action on his part would likely begin in the FedCom, there is no guarantee that it would stop there—especially if Victor believes that you intend to formally reunify the two states under your leadership. Doing so would make you the most powerful political and military leader in the Inner Sphere, a situation that Victor's perennial jealousy would not permit him to tolerate.

In the wake of Victor's return from Clan space, various individuals and groups on several worlds have publicly called him a hero; some have gone on to agitate for his return to the FedCom throne. That such pro-Victor loyalists are active in the FedCom is not surprising; however, pockets of pro-Victor and generally pro-Davion sentiment have begun to crop up within the Alliance as well. One of the most prominent is Coventry, which owes Victor its freedom from the Jade Falcons. Though many elsewhere in the Alliance have questioned Victor's decision to allow the Clan enemy to escape, the people of Coventry almost universally see him as their savior. This view, and accompanying pro-Davion sentiments, go beyond the grassroots to Coventry's ruler, Duke Frederick Bradford. Never a supporter of yours, he has actively encouraged pro-Victor feelings and demonstrations among his subjects. Unless action is taken, it may only be a matter of time before the duke's subversive attitudes lead to open rebellion.

Other pockets of pro-Davion sentiment exist on the worlds of New Exford and Kikuyu (both of which border the Jade Falcon occupation zone); the four worlds taken by the Falcons during their 3058 incursion but given up after Coventry; the game world of Solaris; and, surprisingly enough, in the Isle of Skye region. The border worlds fear attack by the Falcons, and so prefer the leadership of a warlord like Victor Steiner-Davion. Engadine, Neerabup, Wilunga and Bucklands harbor grassroots movements loyal to Victor personally, because his actions on Coventry liberated their worlds. The presence of the Sixth Donegal Guards RCT on Kikuyu, who took over from the Eridani Light Horse when that unit accompanied Task Force Serpent to Huntress, has kept subversive elements under control so far. On New Exford and the captured planets, however, pro-Davion feeling appears to be rising.

As for Solaris, subversive feeling is currently confined to Davionist fighters in its various 'Mech stables, who have recently begun dedicating their matches to "Victor Steiner-Davion, once and future Prince of the Federated Commonwealth." Cenotaph Stables, owned by Victor's close friend Kai Allard-Liao of the St. Ives Compact, has taken the lead with this type of effrontery. There is no indication, however, of mass support for Victor—or for anyone else—on the game world. The faint pro-Davion leanings in the Isle of Skye, inexplicable on the surface, stem from that region's perennial secessionist bent. Certain secessionist leaders appear to be using admiration for "the hero who ended the Clan war" as a wedge to agitate for independence from Tharkad.

Thus far, security forces have successfully suppressed all rallies, marches and other outward signs of support for the former ruler of the FedCom, thereby keeping him from claiming "the will of the people" as a pretext for invasion. There is always a chance, however, that word of these activities may reach

Victor through ComStar ROM, whose considerable intelligence resources are now at his command. Should he become aware of the depth of our measures to restore order, he may take them as an excuse to launch the very assault we have been attempting to avert. Another possibility, even more disquieting, is that Victor or his supporters outside the Alliance are behind the recent upsurge in pro-Victor demonstrations. Davion agents may well be the creators of this supposed "grassroots" support, intended to provide moral cover for an attack. Victor may also be backing those rulers of Clan border worlds whom we recently caught defrauding the Alliance military of cash and arms. We have yet to determine how deeply that corruption goes.

The situation is highly unstable and will bear further watching. Highlighting your own part in the rebirth of the Star League, thereby reinforcing your longstanding image as a peacemaker, should help to blunt any genuine opposition. Dissatisfied citizens may need reminding that peace, not war, brings lasting prosperity. The promise of economic opportunity, brought by the visionary leader who re-created the Star League and made possible a renewed golden age, should go a long way toward assuring your political dominance over the FedCom as well as reinforcing your power in the Alliance.

ARC-ROYAL DEFENSE CORDON

The Arc-Royal Defense Cordon, formed on the last day of December, 3057, remains a dagger poised at the heart of the Lyran Alliance ... if Grand Duke Morgan Kell and his son Phelan, self-styled Khan of the exiled Wolf Clan, choose to make it one. Thus far, the presence of Clan Jade Falcon on the other side of the Alliance border has kept the leaders of the Kell Hounds mercenary unit in line. However, the virtual collapse of the Clan threat may have changed the situation. Considering the military power at the Kells' disposal, we should be prepared for a worst-case scenario: a strike downward toward Tharkad in support of Victor Davion, should the Precentor Martial lead troops into Alliance territory.

The Kell Hounds' historical loyalty to House Steiner has unaccountably eroded in recent years, to the point where they avidly support Victor Davion above their own Archon. I can only assume that Morgan Kell believes the scurrilous rumor—fortunately not widespread—that you ordered the assassination of Melissa Steiner-Davion six years ago. His son Phelan, who went over to the Clans, may also have played a role, convincing the elder Kell to take the first step toward independence so that Phelan's people could claim a safe haven. Whatever his reasons, Morgan Kell's change of heart remains an unpleasant fact. His Arc-Royal Defense Cordon has turned a large portion of the Alliance into a virtual sovereign state, covering most of the Lyran border along the Jade Falcon occupation zone. The arrival of Clan Wolf (in exile), a splinter branch of the formidable Wolf Clan led by the traitorous Phelan Kell, has bolstered the ARDC's military power to the point where the Kells might hope to defend its de facto independence by force of arms.

Until recently, as publicly stated by Morgan Kell, the ARDC was intended as a buffer against a hypothetical Jade Falcon invasion force. Fortunately for the Alliance, the Jade Falcons remain a threat, though a much-diminished one. Reliable reports indicate that the Falcons refused to accept the end of the invasion. However, the so-called Refusal War that split the Wolf Clan also left the Falcon military a shadow of its former self. The Falcons are in the process of rebuilding, and the bitter hatred between them and the Wolves (in exile) should make it difficult for the Kells to order the Wolves into action against any other enemy. Hopefully, the Falcons will remain enough of a danger to keep the ARDC's forces preoccupied, without becoming strong enough to overwhelm them and threaten the Alliance directly. If not, the Kells' devotion to Victor Davion may make the ARDC a problem on several fronts. Even if the Wolves (in exile) do not support Victor militarily, the ARDC could still become a sanctuary for pro-Davion agitators and a base of operations for Davion partisans attempting to destabilize the Alliance.

ISLE OF SKYE

This region, so recently pacified by Your Highness in the wake of Duke Ryan Steiner's assassination, is poised to become a flashpoint once again. Now that the people of Skye no longer have Victor Davion as a lightning rod for their grievances, their minds are turning toward independence from your own government. Your recent assumption of rulership in the Federated Commonwealth has temporarily diverted your attention from Skye, a situation that secession-minded local dukes show signs of exploiting.

Principal among these is Duke Robert Ryan Kelswa-Steiner, son of Duke Ryan Steiner. A chip off the paternal block, Robert exceeds even his late sire in his driving ambition to rule over an independent Skye—and perhaps even to claim the Steiner throne. Duke Ryan appears to have deliberately kept his son out of the limelight during the last outburst of secessionist fever six years ago. Since Ryan's assassination, however, Duke Robert has begun to assert himself. Thus far, his relative inexperience as a ruler and the pacifist influence of his mother, Duchess Morasha Kelswa of Tamar, have kept him from becoming a major menace to Lyran stability. The duchess cannot be expected to control him indefinitely, however, and he is gaining political experience every day. His most recent undertaking was to form the Tamar Cavaliers using his own family's wealth. With his new Lyran Alliance 'Mech regiment having dubious loyalty to the current throne on Tharkad but being fanatically loyal to House Steiner, Duke Robert apparently intends to use them to solidify his position in what remains of the old Tamar Pact. The LAAF High Command could not censure the duke for his actions, because he transferred command of the unit to the the LAAF immediately upon the Cavaliers' deployment. From someone as young as Robert, this is a particularly astute political maneuver. The LIC is keeping him under surveillance, and will inform you of his activities.

Richard Steiner, AFFC Marshal in charge of the Skye March until the creation of the Lyran Alliance, also bears close watching. During the abortive Skye rebellion in 3056, he was in com-

munication with the Tenth Skye Rangers before they attacked the world of Glengarry in an allegedly unauthorized operation. The Marshal disclaimed all prior knowledge of the assault, but pointedly did nothing to stop it once it was underway. He was also hand-in-glove with Duke Ryan Steiner, and spent several months shifting units native to Skye into the Skye March under the guise of routine troop movements. Since that time, Richard Steiner has done nothing to attract excessive attention; his past actions, however, show an instinct for cautious subversion that is not reassuring. His new assignment to the command of the Cavanagh II Theater is an artful move that should keep him busy enough to keep him away from Duke Robert Steiner—and I believe keeping those two apart is imperative for the stability of the Lyran Alliance.

THE LYONS THUMB
AND THE CHAOS MARCH

These two adjacent regions of space pose problems as well, particularly the Lyons Thumb. The decision to reinforce Thumb worlds against potential attack by Liao or Marik forces during the Chaos March invasion prompted an in-kind response from Coordinator Theodore Kurita of the Draconis Combine; citing the "militarization" of the Thumb, he persuaded ComStar to allow him to station nearly nine full regiments of Combine troops in the region. Those troops remain in place, and with them the potential for formal annexation of the entire Thumb by the Draconis Combine. Precentor Martial Davion's partiality toward the Combine, combined with his appointment as commander of the SLDF and Theodore's position as First Lord, make it extremely likely that Theodore Kurita will move to annex the Thumb in the next three years, before his term as First Lord expires. Heavy lobbying in the First Council may net us the necessary votes to prevent him from doing so openly; however, the close ties between Theodore and Victor make it extremely likely that they will find some way of achieving this objective covertly.

The specific nature of those ties is a particular cause for concern. It is an open secret that Victor Davion and Omi Kurita have a personal "understanding," and many people believe that the two have been lovers. Evidence for the latter is not conclusive, though the unusual circumstances surrounding the failed attempt against Victor's life on Luthien are certainly suggestive. Whatever the full extent of their relationship, Theodore Kurita clearly regards Victor Davion as a friend. Should Theodore, as First Lord, attempt to use SLDF troops to annex the Lyons Thumb, there is no guarantee that Victor Davion will abide by any First Council vote mandating otherwise—or by any vote to replace the Combine regiments currently in the Thumb with SLDF forces.

The Chaos March remains a seething cauldron of factionalism and nominally independent worlds. Our own efforts to advance Lyran claims in that region have made little progress, even as Chancellor Sun-Tzu Liao has claimed several worlds for the Capellan Confederation. Should he continue to make gains, he may become bold enough to cross the line into Alliance territory. An opening move in that direction is likely to come on

LYRAN ALLIANCE ARMED FORCES RANKING CONVENTIONS

New Rank	Old Rank
Commissioned Officers	
Archon	Archon-Prince
General of the Armies	Marshal of the Armies
Senior Officers	
General (Head of Theater Command)	Field Marshal
Kommandant-General (Aide of Theater Commander)	*
Hauptmann-General (Head of a Province Command)	Marshal
Leutnant-General (Regimental Combat Team Commander)	Hauptmann General
Colonel (Regimental Commander)	Leftenant General
Leutnant-Colonel (Second-in-Command)	*
Junior Officers	
Hauptmann-Kommandant (Senior Battalion Commander)	*
Kommandant (Battalion Commander)	Kommandant
Hauptmann (Company Commander)	Hauptmann
First Leutnant (Lance Commander)	Leftenant
Leutnant (MechWarrior/Pilot/Driver)	*
Warrant Officers	
Chief Warrant Officer	*
Senior Warrant Officer	*
Warrant Officer, First Class	*
Warrant Officer	*
Enlisted Ranks	
Senior Sergeant Major	*
Staff Sergeant Major	*
Sergeant Major	Sergeant Major
Staff Sergeant	*
Sergeant	Sergeant
Senior Corporal	*
Corporal	Corporal
Private, First Class	*
Private	Private

* No equivalent of the new rank exists in the Armed Forces of the Federated Commonwealth.

ets more eager to deal with us. By increasing trade and perhaps even offering military aid, we can turn the Supremacy into a virtual client state, able to use its strategic position to frustrate Capellan designs.

The LIC's continuing efforts to destabilize the Styk Commonality are also beginning to bear fruit. Marcus Ahearn, the opposition candidate for mayor in Styk's capital city, has proved most receptive to suggestions that alignment with the Lyran Alliance will bring lucrative trade agreements that the Capellans cannot match. He has recently become a focus for pro-Alliance and even pro-FedCom feeling throughout Styk and Gan Singh; given time and sufficient backing, he stands an excellent chance of replacing the Commonality's current leadership.

MILITARY ASSETS

—Prepared by General Sharon Bryan, Commander of the Melissia Theater

Though generally strong and reliable, the Lyran Alliance Armed Forces faces several challenges that may temporarily blunt its military effectiveness. The LAAF is sufficiently prepared to counter military adventurism by parties such as Sun-Tzu Liao or Theodore Kurita, because there is no question of divided loyalties involved. Against an invasion attempt by Victor Davion, however, the picture is less clear.

Ongoing reassignments intended to reinforce unit loyalty to the Archon are proceeding as quickly as possible. Using the Fourth, Tenth and rebuilt Seventeenth Skye Rangers as a dumping ground for Davion loyalists has proved very successful in concentrating known agitators for easier surveillance while diffusing the strength of the Isle of Skye's most fanatical regiments. However, there is no avoiding a certain level of confusion when reorganizing an entire military force. The return to the ranking conventions of the old Lyran Commonwealth for the

Keid, where Lyran agents foiled a pro-Capellan rebellion sparked by our counterparts in the Confederation's Maskirovka. Sun-Tzu still resents losing a world he believed was his, and is likely to try retaking it before violating Alliance borders.

Lorete Montog-Chandler, planetary governor of the world of Sarna turned leader of the Sarna Supremacy, is a potential counterbalance to Capellan adventurism in the Chaos March. Sarna occupies a strategic location in the region, and the Supremacy has depended heavily on trade with the FedCom in its four years of independence. The Capellans' capture of one Supremacy world, however has given them a strangle hold over the small state, but that should only make the remaining plan-

LAAF, though reinforcing Lyran pride, has only compounded the confusion. The Archon's assumption of the FedCom throne has expanded the need for such troop reshuffling in order to remove the threat posed by fanatically pro-Davion units unable to accept the new reality. Until the reassignment process has run its course, the LAAF will be burdened with a weakness that Victor Davion can exploit. To counter the threat, I respectfully recommend beefing up units of proven loyalty and temporarily freezing the support pipeline for FedCom units whose loyalties are in question. Moving new academy graduates into field commands as soon as possible should also help, particularly as the changes recently made to the curriculum take hold. Within the next few years, I believe we can rely on a steady stream of new recruits whose loyalty to the Archon is beyond question.

The Chaos March war left the LAAF with the bulk of the FedCom's JumpShip fleet, most of which were serving in Lyran space in 3057. I suggest using this JumpShip surplus to reward loyal units; they may prove particularly tempting to AFFC units whose Davion loyalties are tenuous.

The following list of troop deployments indicates the depth of each unit's support for the Archon or Victor Steiner-Davion. In the event of a civil war, units listed as questionable or neutral should be treated as potential hostiles, and steps should be taken to prevent them aiding Victor from the inside. Units listed as reliable can generally be counted on to support the Archon, but may include some officers or enlisted personnel whose loyalties are less sure. Some of these units, along with those listed as questionable, might sit out a civil war rather than actively aiding the enemy; in either case, however, they are of no use to the Alliance. To forestall this potential loss of military strength, these units should be the primary focus of our reshuffling efforts over the next several months.

Finally, note that some unit designations have changed with the formation of the Alliance and the reforming of military boundaries within the Alliance. All previous March Militias now contain the designation for their respective Theater or Province. Additionally, those F-C units that remained in Alliance space have been designated as Alliance Guards.

LYRAN ALLIANCE ARMED FORCES

(Deployment as of 30 December 3061)
Commander: Archon Princess Katrina Steiner-Davion
Aide: General of the Armies Nondi Steiner
BattleMech Strength: 78 Regiments, 2 Battalions

FREEDOM THEATER
Theater Commander: General James Ellis
Aide: Kommandant-General Sarah Joss
BattleMech Strength: 14 Regiments, 2 Battalions

Unit Name	Experience	Loyalty	Faction	Homeworld
15th Arcturan Guards (CO: Colonel Suzanne Wright)	Regular	Reliable	Katrina	New Earth
2nd Robinson Rangers (CO: Colonel Theodor Mikul)	Regular	Reliable	Neutral	Phecda
5th Lyran Regulars (2 battalions) (CO: Colonel Jeanine Castro)	Veteran	Fanatical	Katrina	Freedom
Accrington FTM (CO: Colonel Marc Hulley)	Green	Reliable	Katrina	Accrington
3rd Royal Guards RCT (CO: Leutnant-General Kathy Parks)	Veteran	Fanatical	Katrina	Port Moseby
26th Lyran Guards RCT (CO: Leutnant-General Joy Corelli)	Veteran	Reliable	Neutral	Port Moseby
Alexandria FTM (CO: Colonel Karl Timmerman)	Green	Reliable	Katrina	Alexandria
Lyons FTM (CO: Colonel Kinglsey Gardner)	Green	Reliable	Katrina	Lyons
17th Arcturan Guards RCT (CO: Leutnant-General Davis Lillie)	Regular	Reliable	Katrina	Wyatt

Unit Name	Experience	Loyalty	Faction	Homeworld
Gacrux FTM	Green	Questionable	Katrina	Gacrux
(CO: Colonel Affonso Hamsun)				
32nd Lyran Guards RCT	Green	Reliable	Neutral	New Kyoto
(CO: Leutnant-General Gustav Van Buren)				
4th Alliance Guards RCT	Regular	Reliable	Neutral	Lipton
(CO: Leutnant-General Carl Bert Gregg)				
15th Arcturan Guards	Regular	Reliable	Neutral	New Earth
(CO: Colonel Suzane Wright)				
4th Deneb Light Cavalry RCT	Regular	Reliable	Neutral	Dalkeith
(CO: Leutnant-General Fran Vidal)				
11th Lyran Regulars	Green	Reliable	Neutral	Alphecca
(CO: Colonel Jeremy Donner)				

SKYE PROVINCE

Theater Commander: Hauptmann-General Rainer Poulin
Aide: Hauptmann-General Daniel Bishop
BattleMech Strength: 4 Regiments

Unit Name	Experience	Loyalty	Faction	Homeworld
1st Skye Jaegers	Regular	Fanatical	Katrina	Skye
(CO: Colonel Steve Pitcher)				
36th Lyran Guards RCT	Regular	Reliable	Neutral	Hesperus II
(CO: Leutnant-General Peter Zambos)				
15th Lyran Guards RCT	Elite	Fanatical	Katrina	Hesperus II
(CO: Leutnant-General Gina Ciampa)				
Nekkar SPM	Green	Questionable	Neutral	Nekkar
(CO: Colonel Isabella Held)				

PANDORA THEATER

Theater Commander: General Walther Gothard
Aide: Kommandant-General Thanom Hammerskjold
BattleMech Strength: 16 Regiments, 1 Battalion

Unit Name	Experience	Loyalty	Faction	Homeworld
3rd Donegal Guards RCT	Elite	Reliable	Katrina	Pandora
(CO: Leutnant-General Wendell Power)				
4th Davion Guards RCT	Elite	Fanatical	Neutral	Ft. Loudon
(CO: Leutnant-General Alberta Orsina)				
Pandora College Traning Battalion	Green	Reliable	Neutral	Pandora
(CO: Kommandant Cyrus Hubbard)				
Tamar Cavaliers	Regular	Fanatical	Neutral	Tomans
(CO: Colonel Anthony G. Liddle)				
11th Donegal Guards	Regular	Questionable	Katrina	Graceland
(CO: Colonel Cyrus Andes)				
5th Alliance Guards RCT	Regular	Reliable	Katrina	Ft. Loudon
(CO: Leutnant-General James Ito)				
1st Argyle Lancers	Veteran	Reliable	Victor	Crimond
(CO: Colonel Walter Scully)				
13th Donegal Guards	Regular	Reliable	Katrina	Meacham
(CO: Leutnant-General John Stokoi)				
Kelenfold PTM	Green	Reliable	Katrina	Kelenfold
(CO: Colonel Endre Douglass)				

Unit Name	Experience	Loyalty	Faction	Homeworld
3rd Lyran Guards RCT (CO: Leutnant-General Paul Zardetto)	Veteran	Fanatical	Katrina	Graceland
6th Lyran Guards RCT (CO: Leutnant-General Seth Alpert)	Elite	Reliable	Katrina	Rasalgethi
17th Donegal Guards RCT (CO: Leutnant-General Quitman Brown)	Regular	Questionable	Neutral	Rasalgethi
4th Lyran Regulars (CO: Colonel Chas Mohring)	Regular	Reliable	Neutral	Blue Diamond
23rd Arcturan Guards RCT (CO: Leutnant-General Nodine Killson)	Veteran	Reliable	Victor	A Place
Koniz PTM (CO: Colonel Konrad Davis)	Regular	Reliable	Victor	Koniz
20th Arcturan Guards RCT (CO: Leutnant-General Alden Gray)	Regular	Reliable	Victor	Morges
4th Skye Rangers RCT (CO: Hauptmann-General William Harrison von Frisch)	Elite	Questionable	Neutral	Morges

DONEGAL PROVINCE

Theater Commander: Hauptmann-General Rebecca Simons
Aide: Leutnant-General Claudia Saunders
BattleMech Strength: 4 Regiments

Unit Name	Experience	Loyalty	Faction	Homeworld
1st Donegal Jaegers (CO: Colonel Amy Smith)	Regular	Fanatical	Katrina	Donegal
24th Lyran Guards RCT (CO: Leutnant-General Peter Riskind)	Regular	Fanatical	Katrina	Donegal
1st Royal Guards RCT (CO: Archon Katrina Steiner-Davion)	Regular	Fanatical	Katrina	Tharkad
2nd Royal Guards RCT (CO: Leutnant-General Richard Regis II)	Veteran	Fanatical	Katrina	Tharkad

MELISSIA THEATER

Theater Commander: General Sharon Bryan
Aide: Kommandant-General Seamus Kinnell
BattleMech Strength: 14 Regiments

Unit Name	Experience	Loyalty	Faction	Homeworld
3rd Alliance Guards RCT (CO: Leutnant-General Marlin Andor)	Regular	Reliable	Katrina	Blue Hole
Qanatir MTM (CO: Colonel Woody Lounsbury)	Green	Reliable	Katrina	Qanatir
Neerabup MTM (CO: Colonel Mary Polk)	Green	Reliable	Katrina	Neerabup
7th Crucis Lancers (CO: Leutnant-General Jasper Zibler)	Winter	Fanatical	Neutral	Winter
9th Lyran Regulars (CO: Leutnant-General Jeanette Scarlett)	Regular	Reliable	Katrina	Main Street
22nd Skye Rangers (CO: Colonel Francisco de Argall)	Regular	Questionable	Neutral	Engadine
Chahar MTM (CO: Colonel Alica Mason)	Regular	Reliable	Katrina	Chahar

Unit Name	Experience	Loyalty	Faction	Homeworld
15th Lyran Regulars (CO: Colonel Lisa Orsini)	Regular	Reliable	Neutral	Hood IV
6th Donegal Guards RCT (CO: Leutnant-General Paul Urbanick)	Regular	Reliable	Katrina	Kikuyu
8th Deneb Light Cavalry RCT (CO: Leutnant-General Lisa Aileen Bortman)	Veteran	Reliable	Neutral	Kikuyu
39th Avalon Hussars RCT (CO: Leutnant-General Bella Bragg)	Regular	Reliable	Victor	Newtown Square
14th Donegal Guards RCT (CO: Leutnant-General Adam Steiner)	Regular	Reliable	Katrina	Barcelona
25th Arcturan Guards RCT (CO: Leutnant-General Gilda Felra)	Regular	Reliable	Victor	Mkuranga
17th Sky Rangers (CO: Colonel Karl Prafol)	Regular	Questionable	Victor	Lost

COVENTRY PROVINCE

Theater Commander: Haumptmann-General Mark Kostic
Aide: Leutnant-General Kimberly Mueller
BattleMech Strength: 2 Regiments, 1 Battalion

Unit Name	Experience	Loyalty	Faction	Homeworld
1st Coventry Jaegers (CO: Colonel Jason Walker)	Regular	Fanatical	Katrina	Coventry
Coventry CPM (CO: Colonel Judith Niemeyer)	Green	Reliable	Neutral	Coventry
Royal New Capetown Training Battalion (CO: Kommandant Alfred Vaughn)	Green	Reliable	Neutral	New Capetown

TIMBUKTU THEATER

Theater Commander: General Mils Steiner-Davis
Aide: General Olaf Dinesen
BattleMech Strength: 7 Regiment

Unit Name	Experience	Loyalty	Faction	Homeworld
11th Arcturan Guards RCT (CO: Leutnant-General Maria Estaban)	Regular	Reliable	Katrina	Timbuktu
42nd Avalon Hussars RCT (CO: Leutnant-General Edwin May)	Regular	Reliable	Neutral	Poulsbo
Teyvareb TTM (CO: Colonel Ethan Kuhn)	Regular	Reliable	Katrina	Teyvareb
Florida TTM (CO: Colonel Henry Watkins)	Green	Reliable	Katrina	Florida
8th Lyran Regulars (CO: Leutnant-General Cynthia Nelson)	Regular	Reliable	Neutral	New India
Alekseyvka TTM (CO: Colonel Lydia Arentsen)	Green	Reliable	Katrina	Alekseyevka
6th Crucis Lancers RCT (CO: Colonel Patricia Vineman)	Veteran	Reliable	Neutral	Langhorne

ALARION PROVINCE

Theater Commander: Haumptmann-General Peter Zenger
Aide: Leutnant-General Fay Nichols
BattleMech Strength: 3 Regiments, 1 Battalion

Unit Name	Experience	Loyalty	Faction	Homeworld
1st Alarion Jaegers	Regular	Fanatical	Katrina	Alarion
(CO: Colonel Julie Hoffman)				
Alarion APM	Green	Reliable	Katrina	Alarion
(CO: Colonel Brad Engle)				
Buena War College Training Battalion	Green	Reliable	Neutral	Buena
(CO: Kommandant Florence Ellinwood Landers)				
Carlisle APM	Green	Reliable	Katrina	Carlisle
(CO: Colonel Otto McIntyre)				

CAVANAUGH II THEATER

Theater Commander: General Richard Steiner
Aide: Kommandant-General John Vlachos
BattleMech Strength: 10 Regiments

Unit Name	Experience	Loyalty	Faction	Homeworld
10th Lyran Regulars	Regular	Reliable	Neutral	Cavanaugh II
(CO: Colonel Darrel Ingles)				
2nd Crucis Lancers RCT	Regular	Reliable	Victor	Timbiqui
(CO: Leutnant-General Anne Sung)				
7th Donegal Guards	Regular	Reliable	Katrina	Launam
(CO: Leutnant-General Daniel Voss-Steiner)				
Dar-es-Salaam CTM	Green	Reliable	Katrina	Dar-es-Salaam
(CO: Colonel Shalom Hubble)				
14th Lyran Guards RCT	Veteran	Reliable	Neutral	Ford
(CO: Leutnant-General K. Porter)				
2nd Donegal Guards RCT	Veteran	Reliable	Katrina	Gienah
(CO: Leutnant-General Delmar Voss)				
4th Crucis Lancers RCT	Veteran	Reliable	Neutral	Giausar
(CO: Leutnant-General Andrew Giggins)				
Dixie CTM	Green	Reliable	Katrina	Dixie
(CO: Colonel Alexander Johns)				
7th Lyran Regulars	Green	Reliable	Neutral	Loric
(CO: Colonel Clair Hamilton)				
Penobscott CTM	Green	Reliable	Katrina	Penobscot
(CO: Colonel Gary Metzger)				

BOLAN PROVINCE

Theater Commander: Hauptmann-General Mitchell Henders
Aide: Leutnant-General Jean Andrews
BattleMech Strength: 2 Regiments

Unit Name	Experience	Loyalty	Faction	Homeworld
1st Bolan Jaegers	Regular	Fanatical	Katrina	Bolan
(CO: Colonel Suzanne Lamber)				
Furillo BPM	Green	Questionable	Katrina	Furillo
(CO: Colonel Thomas Hogarth)				

CHAOS MARCH

Unit Name	Experience	Loyalty	Faction	Homeworld
Denebola FTM	Regular	Fanatical	Katrina	Caph
(CO: Hauptmann Lisa Gould)				

NOTABLE PERSONALITIES

Most of the following individuals represent potential threats to the stability of the Alliance, and bear careful watching over the next several months to determine how best to deal with them. I include a brief biography of Your Highness, produced as part of the popular "Famous Lives" holovid series, as evidence of the high esteem in which most of the Alliance holds you.

ARCHON PRINCESS KATRINA STEINER-DAVION

Rank/Position: Archon of the Lyran Alliance/Princess of the Federated Commonwealth
Year of Birth: 3032 (age 29)

Profile:

—Excerpt of transcript from "Famous Lives," broadcast 14 February 3061

... Born Katherine Morgan Steiner-Davion, the Archon of the Lyran Alliance is heir to the Inner Sphere's two most powerful ruling Houses. Unlike her older brother, who was trained in the arts of war, Katherine was groomed to govern from an early age. She modeled herself on her mother, the late Archon Melissa Steiner, and like her, has devoted her life to the advancement of her people through peace.

Though she comes of House Davion as well as House Steiner, the Archon's upbringing on Tharkad and her penchant for peace led her to favor her Steiner heritage. The Steiners have always been merchants rather than warriors, and the young Katherine showed little of her other siblings' desire for MechWarrior training. Instead, she devoted herself to statecraft. She soon became a master of the well-timed gesture and the ringing turn of phrase, and developed unrivaled skill at turning the media spotlight toward causes she deemed worthy.

Katherine Steiner-Davion closely resembles her famous grandmother, the fiercely intelligent and charismatic Archon Katrina Steiner. Out of her immense respect for that earlier Katrina, she eventually adopted her grandmother's name and title. In 3057, Duchess Katherine became Archon Katrina, and she has since led the Lyran Alliance with all of her grandmother's intelligence, devotion and grace. Her leadership has served the rest of the Inner Sphere as well as her own realm—most recently with her sponsorship of the first Whitting Conference, at which she resurrected the Star League.

In the hothouse atmosphere of Inner Sphere politics, of course, no one in the public eye can avoid collecting baggage from the ever-present rumor mill, and Archon Katrina is no exception. Among the more scurrilous stories whispered about her in the past decade are insinuations that she had a hand in her mother's tragic death; that her alleged "secret mission" to Clan space during the Coventry crisis was an attempt to forge an alliance with the now-defunct Clan Smoke Jaguar; and that she has made a secret pact with the Khan of Clan Wolf to carve up the Inner Sphere between them. Some also claim that the Archon is simply a master manipulator, willing to do anything to advance her personal power and caring nothing for her people except as a means to that end. They say she intends to become First Lord of the Star League by any means necessary, and that her recent takeover of the Federated Commonwealth is just another step along that path. But her own people know better, and time will surely reveal the Archon's true colors.

GRAND DUKE MORGAN KELL

Rank/Position: Grand Duke of Arc-Royal/Retired commander of the Kell Hounds mercenary unit
Year of Birth: 2986 (age 75)

Profile:

A cousin of the first Katrina Steiner, Morgan Kell is best known as the co-founder of the Kell Hounds mercenary unit, along with his brother Patrick Kell. After defeating *Tai-sa* Yorinaga Kurita of the Second Sword of Light in a climactic 'Mech duel on Mallory's World, Morgan retired for some years to the Saint Marinus House, a contemplative monastery on the world of Zaniah. Upon receiving word of his brother's death, Morgan re-emerged to lead the Kell Hounds. Though he has since passed formal command of the Hounds to Lieutenant Colonel Daniel Allard, he remains an influential voice in the unit.

Until the death of Melissa Steiner in a bomb blast that also killed Morgan's wife Salome and cost him his right arm, the devotion of the Kell Hounds and of Morgan Kell personally to House Steiner was beyond question. Since then, however, Morgan Kell's loyalties appear to have shifted. A staunch supporter of Victor Davion, he has shown marked coldness toward Archon Katrina, despite her clear status as House Steiner's most prominent representative. Whether this change of heart extends to House Steiner as a whole remains to be seen.

The rest of the Kell Hounds have followed Morgan's lead, but the Alliance still benefits from the Hounds' military expertise. In early 3058, Morgan Kell announced the formation of the Arc-Royal Defense Cordon, a sphere of influence centering on his own fiefdom of Arc-Royal and spanning a large section of the Lyran border shared with Clan Jade Falcon. Its publicly stated purpose—to defend the Lyran Alliance against Clan depredations—may indicate that the Grand Duke of Arc-Royal remains loyal to House Steiner in general, if not to the Archon specifically. On the other hand, this may simply be the first step toward secession. With the Clan threat much diminished, Duke Morgan is in a position to turn his "defense cordon" into an independent state, using the military might of the exiled Wolves to back it up. Because of his high profile in the Inner Sphere, open action against him is unadvisable at this time; depending on his own actions, however, that may change in the near future.

KHAN PHELAN KELL

Rank/Position: Khan, Clan Wolf (in Exile)/Commander of the Fourth Wolf Assault Guards
Year of Birth: 3031 (age 30)

Profile:
Phelan Kell is a living testament to the adage that "the fruit never falls far from the tree." Just as his father turned traitor to his traditional loyalties, so Phelan turned traitor to the Inner Sphere after his capture by Clan Wolf in their 3050 assault on the Free Rasalhague Republic. Evidence suggests that Phelan's advice to Ulric Kerensky, Khan of the Wolves and later ilKhan of the entire invasion, allowed Clan Wolf to absorb the FRR.

During his decade as a Wolf, Phelan went from bondsman to Bloodnamed warrior all the way to saKhan, second-in-command of the entire Wolf Clan. He became a Khan after the Refusal War, which claimed the lives of Wolf Khan Natasha Kerensky and ilKhan Ulric Kerensky. Phelan led the so-called Warden faction of the Wolf Clan away from the battlefields of the Refusal War to a safe haven on Arc-Royal, soon to become the centerpiece of the ARDC. He was among the military experts at the First Whitting Conference, invited there by then-Prince Victor Davion to offer the dubious benefit of his insight into Clan thinking and tactics. To be strictly fair, his Wolves fought admirably on the side of the SLDF; given Phelan's history of treachery, however, we can only wonder at the real purpose behind that display.

Always a gifted MechWarrior, Phelan Kell appears to have developed some skill at politics during his time with the Wolf Clan. His plans for the exiled Wolves unfortunately remain a question. He and his Clan appear to be busy making a home for themselves in the ARDC, venturing out only rarely on military expeditions; the most recent of these was against Clan Ghost Bear rather than an Inner Sphere target. An armed force as large and well-equipped as the exiled Wolf Clan, however, cannot bode well for the Lyran Alliance, especially as Khan Phelan appears to have overcome his youthful dislike of his cousin Victor and become a pro-Victor partisan.

DUKE THOMAS FREDERICK BRADFORD

Rank/Position: Duke of Coventry
Year of Birth: 3008 (age 54)

Profile:
Frederick Bradford—he almost never uses his first name—Duke of Coventry, has always been unsettlingly inclined to go his own way. With the ascension of Katrina Steiner-Davion to the Archonship of the Lyran Alliance, the duke's loose loyalties to the government on Tharkad appear to have slipped even more. Though he has so far stopped short of outright subversion, he has been notoriously slow to send reports and tax revenues to Tharkad, and rarely bothers to send an accredited representative to court. Private HPG transcripts acquired by this office indicate that during the recent Coventry crisis, Duke Frederick independently requested aid against the Falcons from Victor Davion; only the information blackout of the invasion corridor kept the message from getting through. Since the return of Task Force Serpent from Clan space, the duke has shown remarkable tolerance for pro-Victor demonstrations. In a recent press conference, he remarked that "it seems a poor return for the man who delivered us all from the Clans to find his own realm snatched out from under him."

Duke Frederick is popular with his people, and any move against him—political or otherwise—could easily backfire. His weakest point is his family; he is excessively devoted to his wife and their two young sons, and will do nothing that might harm them.

DUKE ROBERT KELSWA-STEINER

Rank/Position: Duke of Porrima
Year of Birth: 3034 (age 27)

Profile:
Just a few months past his twenty-seventh birthday, Duke Robert is a threat-in-progress to the stability of the Lyran Alliance. The only son of Duke Ryan Steiner of the Isle of Skye, Robert shares his late father's ambitions. He makes a point of calling himself Duke Robert Steiner, to emphasize his connection to the ruling Steiner line. In the years since his father's death, he has begun to carry on the duke's legacy of secessionist troublemaking, and in recent months has gained credibility with the remaining "old guard" of the Free Skye movement. All but moribund after the demise of its principal patron, Free Skye is beginning to assume new life under Duke Robert's fledgling leadership.

In addition to his paternal legacy, Robert is also the next heir to the Tamar Pact, ancestral holding of the Kelswa family. His status as his mother's successor gives him an additional power base, and gives the Free Skye movement additional resources to draw upon.

THE DRAGON ROARS

—Post-battle analysis, prepared by Narimasa Asano, military advisor to the Coordinator

In 3059, the combined armed forces of the Inner Sphere launched the first phase of a two-pronged assault on Clan Smoke Jaguar. The purpose of the attack was to drive the Jaguars from their Inner Sphere occupation zone and then to obliterate their capacity to make war by assaulting their homeworld. The following report summarizes the astoundingly successful operations in the occupation zone, known as Operations Bird Dog and Bulldog.

The Smoke Jaguars were chosen as the target of the SLDF assault for several reasons, including the viciousness they had shown in the orbital bombardment of Edo on the Combine world of Turtle Bay. From a military perspective, the Jaguars made the best target because they had concentrated their conquests and forces in Draconis Combine space, meaning that the SLDF coalition force could use the Combine government's strict control of its news media to more easily prevent news of its plans from leaking to Clan intelligence. Finally, the historical and bitter enmity between the Jaguars and their assigned "junior partners," Clan Nova Cat, made the Nova Cats likely to help the Inner Sphere cause by denying aid to the Jaguars at crucial points.

The leaders of the SLDF force began the offensive with Operation Bird Dog, inserting small guerrilla units on Jaguar-held worlds prior to the main invasion of the occupation zone. The insertions were intended to distract the Jaguars from the main force's preparations and persuade the Clan to reassign front-line units to deal with the insurgents. With Bird Dog well under way, the SLDF would launch all five waves of the main offensive—Operation Bulldog—in a mere eight months in order to keep the Smoke Jaguars off-balance. Conservative estimates put the end of the second wave a year after the start of the invasion, and the entire operation at roughly four years. Not even the rosiest projections came close to the stunning reality—Operation Bulldog ended in a Smoke Jaguar rout just under four months after the launching of the first invasion wave.

THE ENEMY OF MY ENEMY

Despite doubt and open hostility from many of his fellow leaders, Coordinator Theodore Kurita went ahead with his plan to enlist the Nova Cats as the SLDF's allies. He correctly guessed that the Cats could be persuaded to aid the SLDF coalition by offering only token resistance against SLDF forces on Nova Cat-held worlds in the occupation zone. Nova Cat commanders voluntarily revealed the numbers and quality of their troops by issuing pre-emptive batchalls to DCMS forces, and in

several cases bargained down their defending units to the point where no fighting took place. This indirect aid enabled the SLDF to concentrate its resources against Jaguar targets.

OPERATION BIRD DOG

Operation Bird Dog commenced on 13 May 3059. Company-strength commands—mostly ad hoc provisional units formed around volunteers from Combine, Federated Commonwealth and Lyran Alliance regiments—jumped to pirate points at nine worlds behind the Jaguar front lines. Armed with Combine-designed and Clan OmniMechs, these units waged guerrilla campaigns against Jaguar troops until the main invasion force reached them. The advance troops successfully disrupted Clan operations on the targeted worlds, effectively crippling the Jaguars' ability to meet a large-scale attack. The Bird Dog units also provided accurate intelligence for the main assault force and prevented Smoke Jaguar garrison troops from reinforcing their comrades on worlds targeted in the first invasion wave.

OPERATION BULLDOG

Spearheaded by the tenacious regiments of the DCMS, the SLDF force advanced rapidly into the occupation zone (OZ), capturing world after world with amazing speed. The first invasion wave lasted just five days, rather than the five months originally predicted. Consequently, the coalition launched Waves Two, Three and Four months ahead of schedule and achieved its objectives within weeks. So successful were these assaults that the military planners deemed Wave Five unnecessary.

WAVE ONE

Launched on 20 May 3059, Wave One of the invasion targeted five Smoke Jaguar-occupied worlds along the OZ border: Hyner, Port Arthur, Tarazed, Kiamba and Asgard. The SLDF force also targeted nine Nova Cat worlds, most of which the Cats effectively surrendered to their DCMS "attackers" with only token resistance. The Second Sword of Light triumphed over the Third Jaguar Cavaliers within three days on Hyner, and three DCMS regiments arrived at Port Arthur in time to snatch an Inner Sphere victory from the jaws of defeat against the Jaguars' 168th Garrison Cluster. The SLDF won swift victories on the other three Jaguar worlds as well, moving up the entire assault timetable by months. Along with the surrendered Nova Cat worlds, the conquests created an unbroken line of SLDF-controlled planets through which Jaguar forces would have to pass in order to stage a counterattack on the Combine.

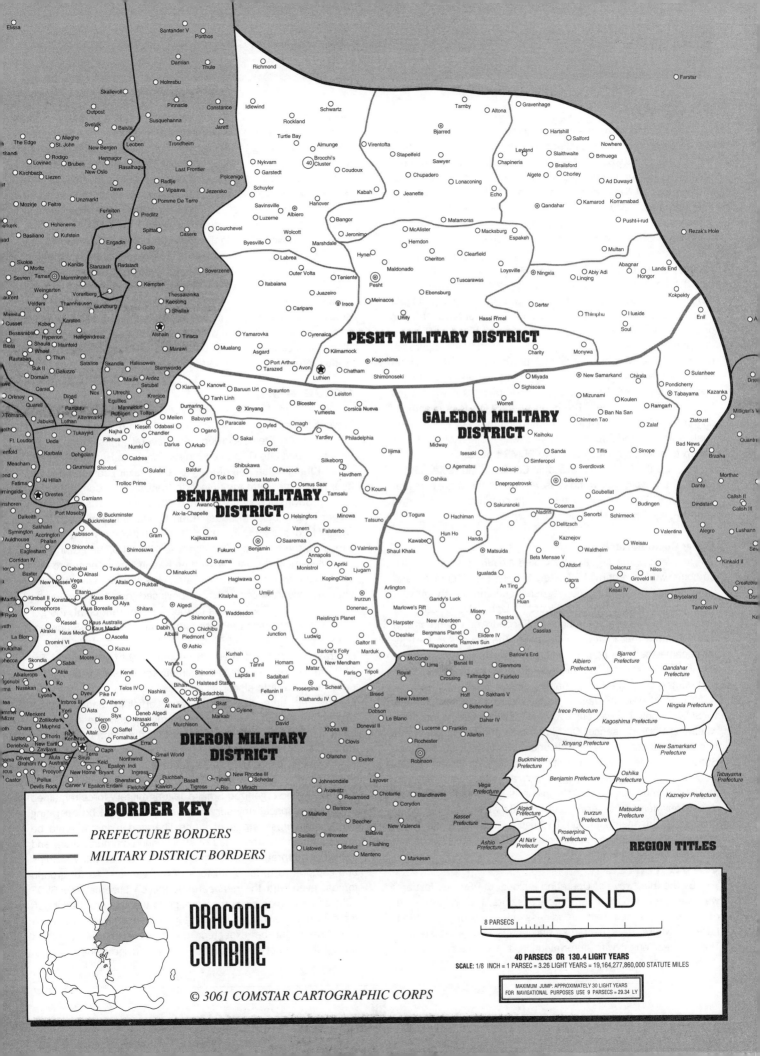

PESHT MILITARY DISTRICT

GALEDON MILITARY DISTRICT

BENJAMIN MILITARY DISTRICT

DIERON MILITARY DISTRICT

BORDER KEY

—————— PREFECTURE BORDERS

━━━━━━ MILITARY DISTRICT BORDERS

DRACONIS COMBINE

© 3061 COMSTAR CARTOGRAPHIC CORPS

REGION TITLES

Albiero Prefecture
Bjarred Prefecture
Qandahar Prefecture
Irece Prefecture
Ningxia Prefecture
Kagoshima Prefecture
Xinyang Prefecture
New Samarkand Prefecture
Buckminster Prefecture
Benjamin Prefecture
Oshika Prefecture
Tabayama Prefecture
Vega Prefecture
Algedi Prefecture
Irurzun Prefecture
Matsuida Prefecture
Kaznejov Prefecture
Kessel Prefecture
Ashio Prefecture
Al Na'ir Prefecture
Proserpina Prefecture

LEGEND

8 PARSECS

40 PARSECS OR 130.4 LIGHT YEARS
SCALE: 1/8 INCH = 1 PARSEC = 3.26 LIGHT YEARS = 19,164,277,860,000 STATUTE MILES

MAXIMUM JUMP: APPROXIMATELY 30 LIGHT YEARS
FOR NAVIGATIONAL PURPOSES USE 9 PARSECS = 29.34 LY

WAVE TWO

The second wave began on 26 June 3059. The success of Wave One prompted the coalition leaders to add three worlds to the list of second-wave targets, bringing the total to eleven planets. Turtle Bay and Almunge, both undefended, fell to the SLDF with no loss of lives or materiel. Three of the Legions of Vega liberated Turtle Bay, partly atoning for the loss of the planet years earlier. On Avon and Caripare, formerly under joint Nova Cat-Smoke Jaguar control, the SLDF forces and Nova Cat Clusters used the Nova Cat regions as staging bases for attacks on Jaguar territory. The Smoke Jaguars pulled back rather than fight to the death; they fell back on Byesville and Hanover as well, to nearby worlds not yet under attack. No Smoke Jaguar warriors escaped the worlds of Yamarovka, Virentofta, Nykvarn or Labrea, where the fighting was fierce and bloody. The only difficulties came on Luzerne, when a disastrous approach touched off a WarShip battle that prevented half the assault force from landing on the planet. Expecting to meet a single garrison Cluster, the SLDF force found itself facing a newly formed front-line Cluster as well. The beleagured SLDF units eventually dug in to defensible positions, from which they engaged in skirmishes against their opponents. Meanwhile, Clan Nova Cat continued to offer token resistance to DCMS troops.

By 7 July 3059, the Draconis Combine had reclaimed all the targeted Nova Cat worlds, as well as all the Smoke Jaguar worlds save Luzerne. Hostilities would continue on that world until the start of the invasion's third wave.

Jaguar Counterattack

In late July, the Jaguars attempted a counterassault on five Combine worlds: Pesht, McAlister, Matamoras, Meinacos and Lonaconing. On Pesht, the Jaguars' scorched-earth attacks were blunted by the Seventh Sword of Light, Ryuken-san, the Kell Hounds' First Battalion and the Second Wolf Legion after a running battle that lasted several days. The Hounds in particular became the anvil against which the Seventh Sword and the Ryuken-san smashed the Jaguars, and before long the SLDF had hunted down the last remaining Jaguar Stars.

On McAlister, the Jaguar troops did considerable damage to SLDF supply bases, but eventually succumbed to an overwhelming SLDF presence. On Matamoras and Meinacos, front-line Jaguar Clusters struck with enormous force, but the Inner Sphere defenders held on until reinforcements from nearby worlds arrived. On Lonaconing, a tactical miscalculation by the Jaguar commander enabled the planet's SLDF garrison troops to severely damage several Jaguar targets while avoiding costly large-scale engagements. On 13 August, the Jaguar commanders abandoned the counterattack and recalled their forces.

WAVE THREE

By the third wave of Operation Bulldog, the Smoke Jaguars were well prepared for Inner Sphere assaults. The first evidence of the enemy's new battle-readiness appeared on embattled Luzerne, where the Ryuken-roku encountered heavy resistance. The Jaguars fought with determination, but ultimately lost the planet on 8 August 3059. Jaguar forces made a smiliarly strong showing on Marshdale, decimating a company of the Ryuken-ni before succumbing to the rest of that unit along with the Ninth Com Guard Division. On Bangor, the Second Dieron, First Wolf Legion and Capellan House Daidachi swiftly overcame stiff Smoke Jaguar resistance; the Jaguars likewise fell to SLDF forces on the world of Schuyler. On Outer Volta, the Izanagi Warriors and the Eighth Sword of Light, supported by the Com Guard Thirty-Ninth Division, crushed the Clan opposition in just five days. Finally, on the worlds of Rockland, Coudoux, Garstedt and Schwartz, the Smoke Jaguars offered only token resistance.

On 13 August, Clan Smoke Jaguar's leaders ordered their forces to evacuate the occupation zone and return to Clan space. This decision enabled more than half of the Clan's forces stationed on third-wave target worlds to escape intact, along with complete commands from at least two garrisoned worlds left untouched by battle.

WAVE FOUR

Operation Bulldog's stunningly swift successes turned Wave Four of the invasion into a clean-up operation. While Prince Victor Steiner-Davion led several units through the Periphery and into Clan space to reinforce the Huntress assault force, Khan Phelan Kell of the Wolves (in exile) commanded the final few battles that took place in the Draconis Combine.

On Savinsville and Staplefield, the Jaguar garrison Clusters fought long enough to satisfy Clan honor, and then negotiated Trials of Possession with their SLDF counterparts in a manner similar to the token conflicts between the SLDF and Clan Nova Cat. The Smoke Jaguar garrison on Kabah initially hoped to hold out until ships returned from Matamoras to pull them off-world, until the Twenty-second Dieron convinced the Cluster commander that no such rescue was forthcoming. At that point, the garrison agreed to Trials of Possession against the DCMS unit and the supporting Nova Cat Cluster. On Jeronimo and Albieron, by contrast, the Jaguar forces left behind fought to the death. The SLDF forces on each planet claimed some salvage and a few prisoners, but little else.

By the time the fourth wave officially ended on 18 September 3059, the Draconis Combine and the SLDF had reclaimed every Smoke Jaguar world in the former occupation zone. Clan Nova Cat now occupies a distinct Prefecture within the Combine, and the Nova Cat Touman has formally joined the SLDF. As of 1 November 3059, Combine intelligence sources verified that no organized Smoke Jaguar military force remained in Combine space. Any surviving units that might be operating in the wilderness areas of some liberated planets would be small and cut off from lines of supply and communication, and therefore no threat to the Dragon. The DCMS lost four WarShips and captured two, for a net loss of two vessels. As for ground forces, even with the near-catastrophe on Luzerne, the SLDF inflicted more than twice the damage to the Jaguars than it suffered at their hands, while losing less than a quarter as many lives. As might be expected, Combine regiments averaged among the fewest losses and the most salvage gained.

THE DRACONIS COMBINE

Most noble Coordinator and First Lord:

The attached files are the report you requested on the state of the Draconis Combine in the wake of our recent victory over the Clans. I regret that the news is not better. As has been true all too often in the Inner Sphere's history, now that we have peace, we do not know what to do with it. Our nation remains strong and relatively stable for now, but the end of the Clan invasion has exposed several fault lines with the potential to shake the Combine to its foundations unless action is taken to repair them. Chief among these are our ties to the Federated Commonwealth, so recently transformed from enemy to ally and now possibly back again; and the integration of Clan Nova Cat into Draconis Combine society.

Parts of this report are my own work; other portions I have taken from reports given to me by *Tai-sa* Narimasa Asano, currently acting as your military advisor, and Omi Dashani of the ISF's Metsuke Division. The brief military analysis appended to this document comes from *Tai-sho* Tomoe Sakade, commander of the Kagoshima Prefecture. Per your orders, I have forwarded a copy to Jerrard Cranston, who currently serves as commander of the SLDF Intelligence Command and reports to Precentor Martial Victor Steiner-Davion. In the interests of clarity, I refer to Your Excellency throughout in the third person.

Most respected lord, may this report please and serve you.

—Ninyu Kerai-Indrahar, Director, ISF

ENEMIES WITHIN: THE BLACK DRAGONS

—Prepared by Omi Dashani, ISF Metsuke Division

In July of 3058, the secret society of reactionary malcontents known as the Black Dragons made an unsuccessful attempt to assassinate Coordinator Theodore Kurita during his public birthday celebration. Thwarted by a mercenary band in the employ of the Coordinator's cousin, Chandrasekar Kurita (familiarly known as "Uncle Chandy"), the attempt exposed treason at the highest levels of the ISF. Its mastermind was Hohiro Kiguri, head of the DEST and a member of Director Subhash Indrahar's trusted inner circle. The plot cost the lives of several loyal members of the Coordinator's personal guard, who fought Kiguri's minions as befits the noble warriors of the Otomo. It also claimed Subhash Indrahar, whose last act was to destroy Kiguri's fellow conspirators aboard their orbiting DropShip.

With Kiguri and his fellows dead and their supporters rooted out of the DEST in the resulting purge, the Black Dragons appeared to have finally suffered a mortal wound. They had already been weakened by the failure of an earlier plot to harm the Coordinator, an assault by the Black Dragon-affiliated Fifteenth Dieron Regulars on the Chaos March world of Towne in 3057. Had they succeeded in taking that former FedCom world, they might have forced the Coordinator into military action against the FedCom or against the Liao and Marik forces

then contesting for the planet. The botched assassination attempt, following on the heels of that earlier debacle, seemed to have rendered the Black Dragons harmless.

I regret to say, however, that this is not the case. My agents have seen recent signs of Black Dragon activity, beginning with Victor Davion's visit to Luthien in late 3058 and increasing since the end of the Clan war. The purge appears to have done less damage than we believed; the Dragons are not yet a major threat, but they are showing more life than is healthy for the Combine, and must be closely watched to prevent them from becoming a dagger pointed at the heart of House Kurita.

On 5 January 3059, a small band of assassins attempted to kill Prince Victor Davion and Omi Kurita at the Palace of Serene Sanctuary on Luthien. This heinous act was the Black Dragons' work; had they succeeded, the Clans would now be poised at our throats and the Combine would likely be at war with the Federated Commonwealth. In the three years since, the Dragons have attempted nothing so bold. Sources in the Combine underworld, however, indicate that the yakuza organization in the Benjamin District remains sympathetic to the Black Dragons' agenda. The late head of that organization was Benjamin Inagawa, a prominent Black Dragon sympathizer and the driving force behind the 3058 yakuza war that flared briefly in Imperial City.

Inagawa's death put a crimp in his organization's rise to power, but his successor is continuing to expand as much as he can. The new oyabun of Benjamin appears to have connections beyond the criminal, extending into the military command of the Dieron district. Though we have no conclusive evidence yet, there are hints of communications between *Chu-sa* Robert Jimmu of the Fifteenth Dieron and several "businessmen" with known ties to Inagawa's organization. One of these businessmen has also been seen in the company of Isokoru Kurita, Warlord of the Dieron District. Isokoru is known for his ambition and political skill, and the ISF continues to keep him under surveillance. Among his other contacts are at least two industrialists suspected of membership in the Black Dragons.

Meanwhile, other evidence indicates that the Black Dragons are gaining sympathizers in many areas of the Combine. Regrettably, the Coordinator's own actions have added fuel to this fire. A large part of the Black Dragons' rising strength comes from their appeal to those uneasy with the new order—specifically, with the acceptance of Clanners into the Combine and the increasingly close ties between House Kurita and Victor Davion. The latter received a hero's welcome on Luthien upon his return from Clan space in March of 3061, despite his being a scion of a Great House long considered our nation's deadly foe. This distinction, along with the Coordinator's clear approval of the attachment between Victor Davion and his own daughter Omi, sticks particularly deep in the Black Dragons' craw. In their view, honoring Victor Davion amounts to consorting with the enemy.

In late 3060, the Coordinator gave sanctuary to Yvonne Steiner-Davion after she abandoned her post as regent of the Federated Commonwealth. Reactionary elements have painted this act as a personal favor to a *gaijin* foe whose troubles the Combine ought to either disdain or exploit. The creation of a whole new prefecture for Clan Nova Cat just weeks ago is seen as similar "evidence" that the Coordinator has weakened the Combine by giving yet another enemy a haven within our borders.

THE FEDCOM AND ITS RULERS

Katrina Steiner-Davion's 3060 takeover of the FedCom may work in the Coordinator's favor, at least with regard to silencing the hard-liners. The Coordinator's personal friendship with Victor Steiner-Davion would seem to make Katrina an enemy, a characterization borne out by her provocative recent actions in the Lyons Thumb. Our nation's rapprochement with the FedCom is unlikely to continue as long as Katrina remains in charge—which means the Black Dragons and their ilk will no longer be able to use it as effectively against Coordinator Theodore. However, they are highly likely to exploit tensions in the Thumb, much as they attempted to do on Towne in the Chaos March.

Relations with the deposed FedCom prince, now Precentor Martial of ComStar, present more problems than advantages. In one of his first acts as First Lord of the Star League, Theodore Kurita appointed Precentor Martial Davion as general of the new SLDF—a step that reactionary elements may interpret as a signal that the Coordinator intends to help Victor retake his former realm via the Star League Defense Force. The idea that DCMS troops under the Star League banner may be ordered to fight and die so that one Davion can triumph over another is profoundly unsettling to many of our people. That the Black Dragons spreading such rumors have no evidence to back them hardly matters, as ordinary Combine citizens are used to knowing little of what their government does. Normally, they place unquestioning trust in the Coordinator's decisions. The unusual events of the past three years, however, have begun to give some people a sense that the universe is turning upside down, and they long for the old certainties. The Black Dragons are offering them those certainties, along with a caricature of our Coordinator on whom to blame their anxieties. Though as yet the people's loyalty remains strong, the Coordinator must understand and address their fears, before the reactionaries exploit them too far.

THE COST OF LIBERATION

—Prepared by Ninyu Kerai-Indrahar

The reclamation of Combine worlds from the former Smoke Jaguar occupation zone is proceeding as well as can be expected, though not without its difficulties. To have retaken what was ours is a momentous achievement; but as the first flush of victory dies away, the costs of re-integrating captured planets is becoming distressingly apparent. Clan Smoke Jaguar stripped many worlds of most of their usable resources, regarding its Inner Sphere conquests as storehouses to be raided without mercy or forethought for the benefit of their Clan's warrior caste. On other worlds, all citizens in occupations deemed "nonessential" by the Jaguars were pressed into making munitions to replace the Clan's diminishing supplies. These actions did grievous damage to planetary economies, plunging once-thriving worlds into poverty. The sheer brutality of the occupying forces added to the misery, and prompted the people to rebel against their conquerors.

The Coordinator's decision to arm these rebels via yakuza weapon-smuggling pipelines—a wise choice at the time—has unfortunately borne unanticipated fruit. Many resistance organizations are reluctant to lay down their weapons, having become accustomed to the freedom momentarily conferred by the possession of arms. Brutalized by the Smoke Jaguar regime, these people have become wary of any authority, including that of their Coordinator. It will take time and a great deal of patience to convince them to submit to their rightful ruler, who has their own best interests at heart. On other worlds, former rebel factions have welcomed the return of House Kurita to its rightful place over them, and surrendered their arsenals as evidence of their loyalty. These latter groups may represent our best chance of bringing their fellow resisters back into the fold without resorting to strong-arm tactics.

The worlds surrounding the former occupation zone have had their troubles as well. It has been just under a decade since the Smoke Jaguars took Kiamba, the last of the many Combine planets they conquered. In that time, the economies of nearby worlds and prefectures adapted to the loss of the occupied planets. The re-integration of those reclaimed worlds into Combine society and the amount of aid necessary to set them on the road to recovery have taken an economic toll on their neighbors, as well as on the Combine treasury. The economic dislocation has already sparked mild local unrest, and it provides fertile ground for reactionary forces to exploit. As the worlds of the former OZ regain their economic footing, we can expect these trouble spots to recede; until they do, however, we must remain braced for civil disturbances and watchful of those who would turn them into something more.

CLAN NOVA CAT AND THE COMBINE

The Combine worlds still held by Clan Nova Cat present a special problem. Even though the Cats fought for and have formally joined the Star League Defense Force, to many Combine citizens a Clanner is a Clanner, and therefore an enemy. They do not understand the Coordinator's decision to grant the Nova Cats their own prefecture in Combine space; as long as we are reclaiming planets from the Smoke Jaguars, they ask, why not reclaim all captured Combine territory from every Clan? Why grant one Clan—a Clan that dared attack Luthien in 3052 and that almost cost the Coordinator's eldest son his life—the right to govern the worlds it stole from us? Along those same lines of thought, some have questioned why we stopped Operation Bulldog with the conquest of the Jaguars. With such success, why did we not proceed to liberate the Alshain worlds that currently lie under Clan Ghost Bear control? Naturally, the Alshain Avengers are particularly ardent in their support of this idea.

Not every Combine citizen on every Nova Cat world feels this way, of course. Indeed, many are beginning to accept the Nova Cat Clansmen—however grudgingly—as the allies they wish to be. Enough suspicion remains, however, to make for a difficult situation. Less than three years ago, the Nova Cats were still conquerors; it will take some time before the people of the Combine can truly accept them, and some never will.

Since the creation of the Irece Prefecture, the tensions between members of Clan Nova Cat and the citizens of House Kurita have become especially acute, particularly on worlds in Nova Cat territory that are inhabited solely by Combine citizens. Lacking the day-to-day contact with Nova Cat civilians that their counterparts on shared worlds enjoy, the people of these worlds are more suspicious and resentful of their Clan overlords. The fact that the Nova Cats rule the prefecture under the aegis of the Coordinator is cold comfort, especially since the Combine government essentially gave these worlds to the Nova Cat Clan. While the populations of these planets in general remain loyal to the Coordinator, more than a few among them feel betrayed at being given over to "the Clan enemy" by a roomful of bureaucrats with maps.

The Irece Prefecture

The Nova Cats' Irece Prefecture arose out of several regrettable (but understandable) incidents between Nova Cat and DCMS military units throughout 3060 and 3061. The First Shin Legion lost badly to Nova Cat invaders on Cyrenacia during the Clan war, and many members of that unit still keenly feel their loss of face. They found it difficult to serve as garrison troops on Cyrenacia alongside Nova Cat forces after the end of Operation Bulldog. Tensions built for months, then finally erupted in a challenge to combat between a lance of the First Shin Legion and its Nova Cat counterpart. The battle resulted in a draw, with serious injuries on both sides. Rather than satisfying either side's sense of justice, this incident only heightened those tensions.

Similar trouble arose on the world of Avon, which was also split between Nova Cat and Draconis Combine garrison troops. In this case, the Nova Cats appear to have been the instigators, challenging the Fourth Pesht Regulars to a series of Clan "honor duels." It seems the Nova Cat unit in question lost face to the Third and Eleventh Regulars on Teniente in 3052; unable to win satisfaction from those units, the Cats made the Fourth Regulars their proxy. One of the duels involved the Fourth's executive officer, who lost the fight and was badly injured in the bargain. Less than a week later, the Eleventh Alshain Avengers—who shared garrison duties with the Fourth— engaged in a retaliatory strike against a Nova Cat lance while on training maneuvers.

This attack, unprovoked from the Nova Cats' point of view, was the most serious of the incidents. Given the history of the Eleventh Alshain, which had trained for years to fight the Clans, such an occurrence may have been inevitable. However, that did not make its consequences any more pleasant. Exemplary restraint on the part of senior DCMS officers, coupled with the

Nova Cats' extreme reverence for the Star League, fortunately kept the fallout in check. To truly defuse the situation, however, stronger measures were needed.

The planets occupied by Clan Nova Cat formed two distinct groups, with three additional worlds some distance away from either. One group consisted of the six worlds ceded to the Cats by Clan Smoke Jaguar; the other lay closer to the center of the Combine. Together with his military advisors, Coordinator Theodore persuaded the Nova Cats to trade some of their occupied worlds for planets nearer to other worlds they controlled. The world of Kanowit reverted to the Xinyang Prefecture; Courchevel was restored to the newly re-formed Albiero Prefecture; and the six former Jaguar worlds were also returned to the Combine. In exchange, the Cats received six worlds formerly unclaimed by any Clan. The resulting contiguous region of space was christened the Irece Prefecture for its capital of Irece, and is part of the Pesht military district.

The separation of Nova Cat and DCMS units caused by this redrawing of the Combine map has lowered tensions somewhat. We can only hope that time and trust in the Coordinator's wisdom will do the rest. The efforts of Theodore Kurita's youngest son, Minoru, should be of immense help in this regard. The divisions between our people and the Nova Cats remain deep, however, and it may only be a matter of time before an incident occurs between the Cats and local citizens that is too explosive to ignore.

THE COMBINE AND THE LYRAN ALLIANCE

—Prepared by Narimasa Asano, military advisor to the Coordinator

The usurpation of the FedCom throne by Katrina Steiner-Davion, Archon of the Lyran Alliance, has the potential to shift the balance of power between the Alliance and the Combine, principally by giving Archon Katrina a second realm from which to trouble us. Just a few years ago, the Alliance posed a realistic threat to Combine interests only in the Lyons Thumb; with the FedCom now under Lyran control as well, the self-styled Archon Princess is also beginning to cause us trouble in the FedCom border region known as the Draconis March.

THE LYONS THUMB

In 3058, the Archon of the Lyran Alliance engaged in a significant military build-up on worlds in the Lyons Thumb, a region of Lyran space that extends into the Combine. Though she justified her actions by claiming an increased risk of attack by Marik or Liao forces, which were then operating in the so-called Chaos March, DCMS military planners regarded the troop build-ups as a prelude to a drive into Combine space. To forestall Lyran military adventurism, Coordinator Theodore Kurita won ComStar's agreement to station nine DCMS regiments on Lyons worlds. The Archon grudgingly accepted their presence at the time, having little choice but to accept their aid in protecting her worlds from attack. She objected quite strongly "in principle," however, to the presence of "foreign troops" in her nation.

With the Chaos March invasion ended and the Clan threat much diminished, we might have expected some effort by Archon Katrina—military or political—to rid the Lyons Thumb of its "occupiers." Thus far, however, she has done nothing overt in the region, nor did she bring up the matter at the most recent Whitting Conference this past November. Given her driving ambition to control as much of the Inner Sphere as possible, coupled with her antagonism toward the Draconis Combine, I find it impossible to believe that she will simply let the matter lie. It is far more plausible that she intends to make some sort of move in the Lyons region before long, and is only waiting until all her pieces are in place to do it.

The Thumb is bordered by the Isle of Skye, now a part of the newly formed Skye Province and Freedom Theater, a region given to secessionist ambitions. Scattered reports of recent troop movements in Skye are being passed off as mere internal politicking, the understandable shifting of loyalist units to an area with a history of unrest, or the result of the organizational changes that have swept through the Lyran Alliance military in the last few years. However, such transfers of personnel also make excellent cover for a slow military build-up. No more Lyran units have yet been stationed on Thumb worlds, but their presence on nearby Skye planets enables Archon Katrina to swiftly call up reinforcements should she need them. Nine full DCMS regiments, however, present a formidable military obstacle. In order to use the Thumb worlds as a staging base from which to conquer Combine planets, the Archon must first reduce or remove those troops.

With the rebirth of the Star League, the ComStar-sponsored Combine regiments fall under the aegis of the SLDF—and the Coordinator's appointment of the new Precentor Martial as the SLDF's overall commander makes any military challenge to those units an act of war against the Star League. Archon Katrina still harbors ambitions of becoming the next First Lord, which open military adventurism would permanently quash; therefore, she must dislodge the troops in the Lyons Thumb by other means. I believe those means lie in the Federated Commonwealth—specifically, in the Draconis March.

THE DRACONIS MARCH

Reports from our agents indicate rising anti-Combine feeling in this border area of the FedCom. The people there have never entirely trusted the détente between our two nations that began in 3051, and Victor Davion's clear friendship toward the Combine has made them even more uneasy. Only our undeniable common enemy—the Clans—enabled many in the Draconis March to set aside their traditional enmity toward us (whom they habitually referred to as "Snakes"). Now, the folk of the Draconis March are remembering the enemy next door. Certain local leaders have even begun agitating for military action; believing us stretched thin by the reclamation of Smoke Jaguar-occupied worlds, they wish to take advantage of the distraction and carve out a "buffer zone" from Combine space.

The Duke of Robinson has been particularly vocal in this regard, along with Duke Arthur Steiner-Davion. Duke Arthur has fallen in with the rabidly anti-Combine Sandoval family, rulers of Robinson and of the Draconis March. Open-hearted and honest to a fault, Arthur is a favorite with the local population—especially since making repeated and highly emotional pledges over the past year not to abandon March worlds to conquest by the Combine. His high visibility as a scion of the FedCom's ruling family, coupled with his clear commitment to the safety of the Draconis March, has made him a rallying point for anti-Combine agitators and frightened locals. Arthur's support has emboldened both groups, and anti-Combine feeling continues to rise. I believe the Archon is deliberately fueling the unrest in the hope of forcing us to relocate DCMS troops from the relatively tranquil Lyons Thumb to the FedCom border. Such a move would deplete the Combine presence in the Thumb without any more direct—and risky—effort on Katrina's part, and would leave her with a much freer hand in that region. (Should we attempt to safeguard our interests in the Thumb, an assault launched by Marcher lords from all across the FedCom would give the Archon a plausibly deniable means of retaliation.)

THE COMBINE AND THE STAR LEAGUE
—Prepared by Ninyu Kerai-Indrahar

The Coordinator's recent election as First Lord of the Star League offers opportunities and dangers. Not since the days of our present ruler's noble ancestor, Minoru, has a scion of House Kurita claimed the First Lord's mantle. Theodore Kurita has accomplished by peaceful means what centuries of war could not: the legitimate, unquestioned title of First Lord, first among equals of a Star League that virtually everyone now living had believed lost forever. Driving home this momentous achievement to the people of the Combine will help unite them in the face of current difficulties, and will isolate reactionary elements such as the Black Dragons.

The Coordinator has already begun this process by publicizing the valiant feats of Combine units in Operation Bulldog and the Huntress campaign. He has also shown Victor Davion in his true colors—as a man who honors Combine traditions, who saved our realm from destruction at Clan hands, and who ensured the continuity of the Kurita line by rescuing heir-apparent Hohiro Kurita from the clutches of Clan Nova Cat. To acknowledge these actions by befriending such a man cannot possibly weaken or dishonor the Combine, as the Black Dragons and their ilk would have the people believe. Reminding the people of the honor that the First Lordship brings to this realm can only bolster the Coordinator's already considerable popularity, thereby depriving the reactionaries of recruits to their cause.

The dispatching of an SLDF force to the St. Ives Compact—one of the Coordinator's first acts as First Lord—is somewhat more problematic. Combine units make up only a small proportion of the forces involved, and their mission is limited to support and humanitarian aid—both of which will serve to mitigate any allegations that the Coordinator is dragging the Combine too deeply into gaijin affairs. Should matters escalate much further, however, First Lord Kurita faces a possible backlash at home. Our people are tired of war, and our realm cannot afford another drain on its resources while we are reabsorbing so many worlds. Further, to involve Combine military units in a far-away war between foreign powers when the Draconis March is becoming more belligerent would give weight to false accusations that the Coordinator cares more for gaijin than for his own nation. The Coordinator must therefore weigh his obligations as First Lord against the needs of his own people, and steer a middle course between them.

MILITARY ANALYSIS
—Prepared by *Tai-sho* Tomoe Sakade, commander, Kagoshima Prefecture

The DCMS has changed little since the publication of the *Field Manual: Draconis Combine* in 3058. Despite losses suffered in our recent victories over the Clans, the Draconis Combine Mustered Soldiery remains ready and able to take on any challenge to the security and safety of this realm that may arise within the next few years. The following paragraphs provide a brief overview of the DCMS and describe highlights of DCMS actions against the Clans in the Inner Sphere and in Clan space.

In the three years since the publication of the field manual, the Coordinator's reforms have continued to gain ground throughout the Combine military. Many officers and troopers who embraced those tactical and doctrinal changes, whether eagerly or reluctantly, now credit them with the overwhelming success of Operation Bulldog and the liberation of Combine worlds from Clan Smoke Jaguar. Even DCMS units not involved in the recent campaigns against the Clans take immense pride in the achievements of their compatriots, and resistance to innovation has subsequently dwindled to a very few conservative diehards.

In late 3058, *Chu-sa* Griffon Mishune succeeded Oda Hideyoshi as commander of the Otomo. *Tai-sho* Hideyoshi died in his sleep in November of that year, a quiet end to a life of valiant service to the Dragon. The only other major personnel change involved the Ninth Ghost Regiment, whose troops were reassigned to the remaining Ghost Regiments for administrative purposes shortly before the publication of the field manual. The top-ranking officers of the Ninth Ghost joined the ranks of the Otomo. *[I'm not sure how much credence to give this, but I've heard persistent rumors that Hideyoshi died trying to assassinate Theodore. Turned his 'Mech on the Coordinator during Theodore's birthday parade, but got blown to pieces by Tomoe Sakade and a Ninth Ghost 'Mech. Breaking up the Ninth Ghost and giving its officers plum new assignments as part of the Coordinator's bodyguard suggests there may be some truth to the stories. —JC]*

The WarShip-building program that produced the *Kyushu*-class frigate continues to go well, given new impetus by the two Clan WarShips captured during Operation Bulldog. With regard to other materiel, the quantity of salvage taken by DCMS units from the occupation-zone battlefields has greatly mitigated the equipment losses suffered in that often-brutal campaign.

The greatest share of DCMS losses occurred in the OZ operation, which involved the greatest number of Combine units. The Combine sent only three DEST teams to Huntress, and so losses there were minimal. Proportionally, however, the casualties were much higher; most of the DEST teams did not survive the fighting. On Strana Mechty, the First Genyosha took very few casualties. During the first wave of Operation Bulldog, the Third Benjamin Regulars acquitted themselves particularly well, spearheading the assault on Asgard and decimating its occupiers while taking minimal casualties.

The second wave likewise went well for our forces, with the Ryuken-roku proving pivotal in the hard-fought battle for Luzerne. The Ryuken-roku broke a stalemate between the Jaguars and SLDF forces from ComStar and the Federated Commonwealth, turning the tide of battle in the SLDF's favor.

The Smoke Jaguar counterattack, in late July and August of 3059, failed spectacularly in the face of civilian as well as military resistance. On Pesht, the Seventh Sword of Light, the Ryuken-san and the First Kell Hounds shattered the Smoke Jaguar force. On Matamoras, ordinary citizens helped the DCMS garrison blunt the Jaguar offensive until the Ryuken-yon broke the Jaguars with a devastating night-time raid. The Eleventh Alshain lost two lances on Meinacos, but those eight soldiers took an entire Star of Jaguar OmniMechs with them in death. In general, losses to our units were moderate throughout.

Overall, the DCMS regiments ranked among the best of the SLDF units sent against the Clans. Their brilliance, dedication and tenacity are a credit to the Dragon and to every soldier who serves the Draconis Combine.

NOTABLE PERSONALITIES

—Prepared by Ninyu Kerai-Indrahar

The following profiles highlight the principal members of House Kurita.

[It is very interesting that Ninyu did not include Omi Kurita. In light of her relationship to you and her position as Keeper of the Family Honor, as well as daughter of the Coordinator himself, this was no oversight. We must be very careful in interpreting the message he is sending.

As for Ninyu himself, our only concrete facts place him as a companion of Theodore since before the Fourth Succession War, but their relationship has always been troubled. That Subhash himself would adopt Ninyu, however, coupled with the fact that we have been unable to uncover anything significant about his past, is proof enough of his abilities; we must never underestimate him.—JC]

COORDINATOR THEODORE KURITA

Rank/Position: Duke of Luthien/Coordinator of the Draconis Combine
Year of Birth: 2997 (age 64)

Profile:

Since becoming Coordinator of the Draconis Combine in 3053, Theodore Kurita has led his nation into a future that many Combine citizens could never have imagined. Even as Warlord of the DCMS, Theodore refused to be bound by traditions he considered harmful to the realm he would one day lead. In 3034, he made an agreement with ComStar to recognize an independent Rasalhague Prefecture in exchange for Star League-era BattleMechs. Though he weathered a storm of criticism for his action from conservative quarters, the advanced machines proved decisive against FedCom assaults just five years later, in the War of 3039. Theodore similarly showed himself a man of vision on many subsequent occasions, rescinding the prohibition on mercenary units enacted by his father, Takashi Kurita, and launching far-reaching military reforms. Ranging from unit reorganization to tactical innovations to the creation of the famed Ghost Regiments, these reforms would become one of his principal legacies.

When the Clans began cutting a swath through the Inner Sphere in 3050, Theodore was among the first Great House leaders to recognize that this new threat made old enmities irrelevant. He swiftly agreed to an unprecedented nonaggression pact between the Combine and the Federated Commonwealth, proposed during a gathering of Inner Sphere leaders on the Wolf's Dragoons world of Outreach in 3051. In early 3052, he accepted the aid of mercenary units in defending Luthien against a Smoke Jaguar/Nova Cat assault. Six years later, when FedCom Prince Victor Steiner-Davion proposed creating a unified Inner Sphere force to take the war to the Clans, Theodore Kurita was among its most enthusiastic backers.

At the First Whitting Conference, Theodore helped found the new Star League and plan the assault that would drive Clan Smoke Jaguar from the Inner Sphere. In December of that year, he symbolically repudiated the historical hostility between his own realm and the Federated Commonwealth by welcoming

Prince Victor Steiner-Davion on a precedent-setting visit to Luthien, and by publicly giving his blessing to the attachment between Victor and his own daughter Omi. Theodore was elected First Lord of the Star League in November of 3061, and will do everything in his power to safeguard the stability that his people and so many others have fought so hard to attain.

HOHIRO KURITA

Rank/Position: Heir-Designate/Commander of the First Genyosha
Year of Birth: 3023 (age 38)

Profile:

The eldest son and heir of Coordinator Theodore Kurita, Hohiro commands the prestigious First Genyosha Regiment with skill and flair. His experiences during the early years of the Clan War—particularly the loss of his command in the Smoke Jaguar assault on Turtle Bay and his subsequent incarceration in Kurushiiyama Prison—turned him from a green soldier into an able military commander.

Freed from Kurushiiyama by local yakuza in the city of Edo, Hohiro was sent to Wolcott as a liaison to the First Genyosha Regiment. On Wolcott, Hohiro's batchall to the attacking Smoke Jaguar force included a demand for four OmniMechs and twenty-four battle-armor suits if Wolcott's defenders won the engagement. The subsequent defeat of the Jaguars earned the Draconis Combine its first pieces of intact Omni and battlesuit technology, jump-starting that realm's development of its own Clan-style military machines. During the battle for Luthien in 3052, Hohiro fought with the First Genyosha regiment and personally accounted for more than five Clan 'Mech kills. Hohiro acquitted himself equally well during the engagements that marked the end of the Clan war. He led the First Genyosha to victory on Kiamba and Schuyler during Operation Bulldog, and

soundly defeated Clan Blood Spirit in the Great Refusal on Strana Mechty in 3060.

Like his father, Hohiro has shown himself capable of overcoming old hostilities and adapting to new realities. He counts Victor Steiner-Davion among his close friends, and shares with him the goal of maintaining the Star League against any threat it may face. Both politically and militarily, he will make an able successor to Coordinator Theodore when the time comes for him to ascend the Combine throne.

MINORU KURITA

Rank/Position: Bondsman of the Khan of Clan Nova Cat
Year of Birth: 3031 (age 30)

Profile:

The youngest of the Coordinator's three children, thirty-year-old Minoru has spent much of his life out of the spotlight, and so remains an enigma. A mystic rather than a warrior, Minoru is known for his expertise in t'ai chi chuan, kenjitsu and similar martial arts. His consuming interest in these disciplines, along with his less prominent position as a second son, made him a relatively minor player in House Kurita politics until late 3058, when Coordinator Theodore began making serious peace overtures to Clan Nova Cat. As part of this effort to enlist his nation's former foes against the Smoke Jaguars, the Coordinator took the extraordinary step of sending his own son as a peace envoy. Minoru's mystical bent enabled him to fit in well with the spiritually minded Nova Cat Clan; indeed, many Nova Cat warriors took his arrival among them as fulfillment of prophecy. His presence played a large part in convincing the Cats to join the SLDF.

After the end of the Clan war and the creation of the Irece Prefecture, Minoru became a bondsman to Nova Cat Khan Santin West. He remains among the Nova Cats as their official liaison to the rest of the Combine.

CAPELLA RISING: XIN SHENG

" ... Gei-Fu boasts one of the highest percentiles for enrollment in the Capellan Armed Forces, a truly noteworthy contribution to the Xin Sheng effort. A pity that more once-rebellious worlds have not followed your example. Terrible, that they continue to ignore the call of their Capellan heritage or that unjust governments continue to suppress their people's natural desire to rejoin with their brothers and sisters. There never was a more appropriate time than now, during this rebirth of the Confederation ... .This is our time, when all Capellan citizens can once again take pride in their nation and their heritage."

—Excerpt from Chancellor Sun-Tzu Liao's speech on the world of Gei-Fu, Sian Commonality, Capellan Confederation; 23 August 3060

—From the personal journal of Lien-zhang Aris Sung, of the Warrior House Hiritsu

Xin Sheng. New birth. The very sound of the words embodies their meaning; there is a grace to them, an uplift. Our Chancellor has declared this to be the time of Xin Sheng for the entire Capellan Confederation, from the palace chambers of House Liao down to the lowliest street-sweeper. With our lord chosen above all other Great House leaders to serve as First Lord of the Star League—the first to hold that august office in nearly three hundred years—how could this be anything but the right time for a glorious new beginning?

In all walks of Capellan life, Xin Sheng has begun. The Chancellor has decreed political and economic reforms for the benefit of his people, and their effects have already begun to show on several worlds. Planets such as Necromo, which borders the St. Ives Commonality, were reduced almost to penury by the defection of St. Ives from the Confederation thirty years ago. They could not sustain the loss of so many neighboring planets, when the duchess of St. Ives tore her Commonality away and transformed it into the independent Compact. But under Xin Sheng, Necromo is thriving again, and other once-poor worlds cannot be far behind. Not surprisingly, Capellan nationalism is on the rise in many border systems; the people can see the good that their Chancellor and First Lord is doing for them, and they rightly honor him for his efforts on their behalf.

Xin Sheng has also made itself felt in the Capellan Confederation Armed Forces. New recruits are flooding into basic training programs, eager to serve their nation and their lord. Our military manufacturers have begun producing new 'Mech designs such as the *Ti Ts'ang* and the *Yu Huang*, whose incorporation of Chinese symbolism helps to inspire every Capellan MechWarrior to do his best for his nation. These designs also include the latest technological innovations; with them in our ranks, we cannot help but regain what was stolen from us by Hanse Davion during the Fourth Succession War.

I find it most telling that the MechWarriors of Warrior House Imarra, who suffered disgrace thirty years ago through Davion trickery, have adopted the *Ti Ts'ang*—a 'Mech that incorporates a corrected version of the very technology that once brought them to their knees. A Davion lie betrayed them then; through the efforts of a double agent in the pay of Prince Hanse Davion, the Imarra warriors were persuaded to use 'Mechs equipped with triple-strength myomer that was set to fail at a critical moment. Now, the Imarra MechWarriors have taken the symbol of their defeat and turned it into an instrument of victory—for there will be victories aplenty, and soon. I can feel it in my heart every time the Chancellor speaks. We are stronger now than ever before, and we will no longer be trifled with. Not when Chancellor Sun-Tzu Liao sits on the throne of the First Lord, and the once-fearsome Clans are going down to defeat under his wise leadership. The man who conquered the Clans can face any foe, achieve any dream. Who is mighty enough to stand against him? Surely not the Steiner-Davion princelings, one of whom is busy betraying another by stealing his realm.

Certainly the rebels in the so-called Chaos March are not strong enough to defy our lord. Already we have received reports concerning the Disputed Territories; many worlds once lost to us have rejected the illegal regimes that ruled them and returned to the Capellan fold, while others have been liberated by units working for the CCAF. The fight to reclaim what once was ours has begun, and I am confident that we will triumph in the end. I only wish that Capellan blood need not be shed to show our misguided brethren the error of their ways ... .

My new position as head of the Chancellor's honor guard affords me the opportunity to contribute directly to the success of Xin Sheng, in a way I had not even dreamed would be possible. The honor done me by House Master Ty Wu Non, in choosing me for this post, is beyond describing. I can only say that I will discharge my responsibilities as fully as I can, for as long as Chancellor Liao chooses to travel through his realm. I will prepare the way for him, and make certain that no enemies are waiting to strike him down. There is not much I would put past those former Capellans who voluntarily forsook their heritage and their nation to align themselves with a House that came near to destroying the Liao dynasty. And our Chancellor is journeying far too close to them for comfort. If I should fail in my duty to protect him, our nation's rebirth may be over before it has fully begun.

I will do everything in my power to keep that from happening. The Confederation's Xin Sheng is my own, because I am a Capellan.

LIAO COMMONALITY

SARNA COMMONALITY

CAPELLA COMMONALITY

XIN SHENG COMMONALITY

ST. IVES COMPACT

SIAN COMMONALITY

BORDER KEY

_____ *DUCHY BORDERS*

━━━━━ *COMMONALITY BORDERS*

ST. IVES COMPACT
CAPELLAN CONFEDERATION

© 3061 COMSTAR CARTOGRAPHIC CORPS

LEGEND

8 PARSECS

40 PARSECS OR 130.4 LIGHT YEARS
SCALE: 1/8 INCH = 1 PARSEC = 3.26 LIGHT YEARS = 19,164,277,860,000 STATUTE MILES

MAXIMUM JUMP: APPROXIMATELY 30 LIGHT YEARS
FOR NAVIGATIONAL PURPOSES USE 9 PARSECS = 29.34 LY

MATTHEW J. PLOG-PA'

—ComStar intercept, Sun-Tzu Liao to Talon Zahn, 25 May 3058

... I believe I have managed to salvage my plans for the Magistracy, though it was a very near thing. The quality of the evidence used to frame me for the raids on Magistracy worlds by the Marian Hegemony is impressive. I have my suspicions about who perpetrated that little exercise, as well as who is actually supplying the Hegemony with state-of-the-art BattleMechs. And I intend to lead the Magistracy to exactly the same conclusion. One way or another, I will have my alliance with them. I will tame this half-wild Periphery state and turn its military forces toward reconquering my realm. After this enterprise succeeds, I can expand my net to the Taurian Concordat, a obvious choice given their location and current ties to the Magistracy ... though I may have some trouble with their Protector. But that is a problem for the future.

In the end, the Magistracy alliance will cost me very little; technological advisors and educational aid that I can easily spare, a few lances of better 'Mechs than this poor nation can possibly manufacture on its own, a few troops to help put down the Hegemony raiders. My Capellans can do that easily. And in exchange, I begin to make the Magistracy of Canopus dependent on my continued goodwill. Magestrix Emma Centrella will not be able to deny me the use of her troops in the Disputed Territories, where my own available forces are not sufficient. The CCAF could likely take most of the worlds that once belonged to my nation—

but holding them? No ... for that, I need more soldiers. Soldiers I will not have to pay out of the Confederation Treasury, as I would mercenary units. Soldiers who will be working for me for a very long time. A ruler can always find uses for extra troops; I am certain I will think of some, once I have finished reclaiming what rightfully belongs to my House.

I seem to have made an impression on Naomi Centrella, a younger daughter of the Magestrix. Her sister Danai is currently favored as Emma's heir, but that might change. Danai Centrella is a MechWarrior, and warriors die in battle ... . Order full reports to be prepared. For now, it is enough that the Magestrix has agreed to let me prove my innocence of the Hegemony raids. She wants this alliance as badly as I do, needs it more in fact, though she would never admit it. Otherwise she would never have agreed to let me lead Magistracy troops to the Free Worlds League in search of the real culprits. She would have sent me packing on the next DropShip back to the Inner Sphere, doubtless with a few choice curses still ringing in my ears.

I have intrigued her, with my proposal for an alliance. Since arriving here, two weeks ago, I have not been the person she expected. Her curiosity is her weakness, and through it I will harness the Magistracy. The Confederation will be restored, no matter what means I must use to accomplish this. Everything serves xin sheng ... the rebirth of my nation.

THE CAPELLAN CONFEDERATION

[The following material comes from a ComStar ROM operative who intercepted a report from a Word of Blake agent in the Confederation to his superiors on Gibson. It makes interesting reading. The ROM operative noted that she and the Blake agent in question were acolytes together, before the ComStar/Word of Blake schism. She characterized Adept Gong Liu as level-headed and frank to a fault, which means we can probably trust these dispatches up to a point. However, let me stress that none of it has been independently verified. —JC]

TO: Precentor Blane
FROM: Adept Gong Liu
DATE: 18 December 3061
RE: Current Situation in the Capellan Confederation

Excellency,

I regret to report that the fortunes of this once-tattered realm are on the rise, largely due to the unexpectedly impressive abilities of its ruler. By rights, the Capellan Confederation should never have recovered from the loss of nearly half its territory in the Fourth Succession War and the mad policies of former Chancellor Romano Liao. Rather than continue to destabilize, however, the Confederation has begun to rebound over the past decade. Despite a conspicuous lack of resources on almost all fronts—fewer worlds than any other Successor State, a far smaller army and so on—

Chancellor Sun-Tzu Liao has made significant progress in rebuilding his nation. He has even managed to take back some of the worlds lost to the Davion-Steiner military juggernaut thirty years ago, and fully intends to reclaim them all. Thanks to his efforts, the Confederation may soon become a major power once again.

A stable Capellan Confederation does not serve our interests, but that is exactly what Sun-Tzu is creating. Clearly, the Word of Blake has underestimated this man. If we wish to bring back the turmoil of previous years, we will have to deal with Sun-Tzu Liao first.

CHANGING OF THE GUARD

The death of Romano Liao and the accession of her eldest son to the Celestial Throne in 3052 would prove to be a major setback for the Word of Blake's long-term plans, though no one knew this at the time. The Liao family has a reputation for mental instability, and there was no reason to believe Sun-Tzu had escaped that curse. Though he showed no overt symptoms of insanity, he was known for occasional outbursts of temper. Many in the Inner Sphere assumed that the new Chancellor would eventually succumb to madness under the pressures of rulership.

Unexpectedly, however, Sun-Tzu Liao rose to the challenge. Displaying typical Liao cunning, he immediately set about making connections advantageous to himself and his realm. Above all, Sun-Tzu Liao wanted to recapture his nation's lost territory. Aware that the Confederation was too weak militarily to accomplish this, Sun-Tzu looked for a more powerful ally.

THE MARIK CONNECTION

He found that ally in Thomas Marik, Captain-General of the Free Worlds League. Through his engagement to Thomas's daughter Isis, Sun-Tzu received favorable trade agreements and other concessions, including various pieces of military equipment. He used this bounty to shore up both the Capellan economy and his own military, while pressing the Captain-General to solidify the alliance by scheduling the wedding. He also requested direct military aid on several occasions, but initially made little headway.

For several years, Marik used the serious illness of his young son as an excuse to postpone his daughter's wedding to Sun-Tzu. He held off the Chancellor with endless small concessions, which Sun-Tzu used to his realm's best advantage. Chief among these was a battalion's worth of BattleMechs, given as part of Isis Marik's dowry. With them, Sun-Tzu raised and equipped the formidable military unit known as Harloc's Raiders.

SEEDS OF WAR

Meanwhile, Chancellor Liao found ways other than direct military action to begin taking back lost territory. In late January of 3056, a pro-Liao terrorist group calling itself the Zhanzeng de Guang, or War of Light, struck garrison and police forces on the worlds of Aldebaran, Gan Singh, Zurich and Styk. All of these planets lay in the FedCom's Sarna March, which had once been the Capellan Confederation's Sarna Commonality. The Sarna March worlds faced little threat from the Clans, and so FedCom Prince Victor Steiner-Davion had stripped them of troops in order to reinforce the Clan front lines. The Liao-backed terrorists therefore found them easy targets for mayhem.

Throughout 3056 and 3057, Sun-Tzu stepped up the activities of the Zhanzeng de Guang and other guerrilla networks in the area, while continuing to press Thomas Marik for military intervention. New Zhanzeng de Guang cells sprung up on various worlds in the Tikonov region, among them Acamar, Fletcher and the important industrial world of Nanking. The terrorists committed bank robberies, bombings and similiar acts of violence, all intended to destabilize the worlds' Davion governments. As before, however, the Captain-General balked at direct military aid. In response, Sun-Tzu engineered a commando raid on the New Avalon facility where Joshua Marik was receiving treatment. He intended to prove that Joshua was not Thomas's son, but a double installed by Victor Davion—or at least to make Marik believe so. Faced with such an outrage, Thomas would have no choice but to help Sun-Tzu attack the Federated Commonwealth.

At this critical juncture, luck favored the Chancellor. Through another avenue entirely, Thomas Marik learned that his son was dead. The Captain-General's response exceeded his Capellan ally's fondest hopes; Thomas Marik attacked the Sarna March in concert with House Liao. Sun-Tzu's expansionist war had begun.

THE SARNA INVASION

On the day Thomas Marik declared hostilities, Chancellor Liao sent five Warrior House regiments to liberate the world of Liao, ancestral home of his own family. They arrived on 18 September and made short work of the green planetary militia, whom they caught completely by surprise. That same day, the Zhanzeng de Guang overthrew the Davion government of Zurich and took power as the "People's Liberation Party." As the year wore on, Liao and Marik troops took world after world; in the first wave alone, the Capellan army reclaimed all nine of the planets it had targeted. Meanwhile, Marik-backed mercenaries on loan to Sun-Tzu Liao gave crucial military support to anti-Davion rebellions throughout the region.

COREWARD WORLDS

The invasion's initial success prompted Sun-Tzu to press for an accelerated second wave. When Thomas Marik declined, Sun-Tzu turned to other resources. He had spent years creating guerrilla networks on several Sarna worlds, which he now activated. Soon afterward, rebellions broke out on Caph, Keid, New Home, Epsilon Indi and Northwind—the latter the homeworld of the famed mercenary unit the Northwind Highlanders.

Most of these revolts succeeded brilliantly; only the action on Epsilon Indi fizzled, largely because Free Capella agents loyal to Tormano Liao had infiltrated Sun-Tzu's network. The revolt on Keid initially went so well that Thomas Marik chose not to reinforce the world with mercenary troops—a decision that would ultimately lose the planet for the Confederation, when pro-Steiner loyalists replaced the Liaoist regime with the daughter of the deposed local duke. On Northwind, Chancellor Liao pulled a stunning victory from what looked like certain defeat. Only on Nanking and Zurich did he suffer significant reversals.

The Highlander Gambit

Historically, the Northwind Highlanders had served House Liao with distinction and honor. After the Fourth Succession War, however, their allegiance shifted briefly to House Davion, the Liaos' bitter enemy. During that conflict—Davion forces had taken the planet Northwind from House Liao during the Second Succession War—then-Prince Hanse Davion voluntarily ceded the planet back to the Highlanders. This magnanimous gesture won the prince the mercenaries' respect as well as their gratitude, and earned House Davion their exemplary military service.

When Northwind succumbed to Liao-instigated rebellion in early October of 3057, Victor Davion was determined not to lose so valuable an asset. He sent the Third Royal RCT to Northwind with orders to keep the planet—and the Highlanders—in the Davion fold. In a stroke of luck ably exploited by Chancellor Liao, the Third RCT's commander interpreted his orders a shade too literally; when the Highlanders still present on Northwind began arguing over whose side to fight on, the Third attempted to take Northwind by force. The remaining Highlanders, then stationed in the newly formed Lyran Alliance, raced home to liberate their planet. Chancellor Sun-Tzu took immediate advantage of these events, declaring Northwind an independent barony of the Confederation and ceding it permanently to the Highlanders.

Zurich and Nanking

Zurich had seemed firmly in the hands of the Zhanzeng de Guang, backed by the military might of the Black Cobras mercenary battalion. In mid-December, however, Thomas Marik ordered the Black Cobras to Nanking in order to secure the world—and its 'Mech factories—for the Capellan Confederation. The Cobras' departure enabled a pro-Davion counterterrorist group to assassinate the leader of the People's Liberation Party, effectively ending the Liaoist takeover.

Worse yet for Sun-Tzu, the Black Cobras never made it to their destination. Saboteurs had placed explosives on board the unit's DropShips, which exploded as the Cobras were making planetfall onto Nanking. The beleaguered Smithson's Chinese Bandits, a Marik mercenary unit already on the planet, soon surrendered to a Davion counterattack force. Nanking and its factories remained in Federated Commonwealth hands.

SPINWARD WORLDS— THE DISPUTED TERRITORIES

In this region, bordering the Federated Commonwealth, Chancellor Liao supported pro-Capellan movements and leaders wherever he found them. Through these, he retained effective control of worlds that he was still too militarily weak to conquer. Over the next few years, he would use the locals' Liaoist sentiments to frustrate FedCom and Lyran Alliance machinations in the region. He was also buying time for an eventual military solution, as we were soon to learn.

Certain Chaos March worlds claimed outright independence, often joining with others for mutual aid and defense. One such was the Sarna Supremacy, which lay nearest the Confederation border. Unable to absorb the Supremacy militarily, Sun-Tzu finally settled for controlling it through its food supply. In 3058, Liao troops retook the world of Kaifeng—the only Supremacy world with appreciable arable land. Deprived of their breadbasket, the remaining two worlds of the Supremacy have since become dependent on Capellan goodwill for survival.

THE TIKONOV REACHES

Concurrent with the Sarna March invasion, Sun-Tzu Liao took steps to regain other territory lost to the FedCom. The Tikonov Reaches—a former Capellan Commonality of the same name that enjoyed brief independence before its absorption by the FedCom in the 3030s—was his primary target. Pro-Liao resistance cells sprang up throughout the Reaches, aided and abetted by the various agents provocateurs sent into the region to keep things stirred up. Though the activities of these groups gained Sun-Tzu no planets, they did serve to distract the FedCom and the Lyran Alliance, both of whom claimed sovereignty over the Tikonov worlds. Keeping the two larger powers off-balance allowed Sun-Tzu a freer hand in the Sarna March.

THE CHAOS MARCH

By the time the invasion ended, Sun-Tzu Liao had made an impressive start on the reconquest of Capellan territory. Liao troops and mercenary units had retaken several worlds outright, and pro-Capellan sentiment reigned throughout a major portion of what had been the Sarna March. Overall, the Sarna region had become a place where only chaos could truly be said to reign. During the next few years, the Confederation successfully competed with the FedCom and the Lyran Alliance for control of several planets in the Chaos March. Each power backed factions that supported it, but none of the three achieved much lasting success. Chancellor Liao, however, was willing to settle for keeping the situation unstable. As long as the enemy realms did not attain their objectives, he was free to lay long-term plans for the absorption of the entire Chaos March.

THE CAPELLAN REVIVAL

The successes of the Chaos March campaign laid the groundwork for the Confederation's current military, political and economic renaissance. Even before the invasion, Chancellor Liao had launched several reform programs under the rubric of Xin Sheng, or "New Birth." With his ascension to First Lord of the Star League, he received the public relations boost and just enough political power to bring these programs the attention required to succeed. Only in the past two years have these programs begun to pay off. Militarily, recruitment in the Capellan Confederation Armed Forces is up, aided by the Chancellor's revamping of the CCAF's ranking conventions. In addition, the CCAF's 'Mech units are receiving cutting-edge Omni- and BattleMechs created by Capellan designers. The new war machines serve two purposes; inspiring their pilots with Chinese symbolism while using advanced technologies that make each 'Mech a formidable force on the battlefield. In the past two years, he has also added prestigious mercenary units to the regular forces of the CCAF, along with several new line units.

Economically, many poorer Capellan systems are beginning to climb out of recession and depression, making their citizens far less receptive to anti-Liao agitators. Favorable trade agreements with the Free Worlds League, and lately the Lyran Alliance, have also bolstered the Capellan economy as a whole, which in turn has added considerably to the government treasury. Politically, Capellan nationalism is sharply on the rise—not only within the Confederation proper, but also in the Disputed Territories, the Chaos March, and even the former Tikonov and St. Ives Commonalities.

In his drive to reclaim every world over which the Capellan flag once flew, Sun-Tzu Liao has fostered and exploited these sentiments to the fullest. In St. Ives, he has even resorted to military conquest—an unexpected development, but one that Word of Blake might yet turn to advantage.

FIRST LORD OF THE STAR LEAGUE

In November of 3058, Sun-Tzu Liao was chosen as First Lord of the revived Star League—the first Inner Sphere Lord to hold that title since the days of the Blessed Blake. Not surprisingly, he portrayed this honor to his people as yet another facet of Xin Sheng. The re-creation of the Star League became a metaphor for Capellan rebirth, tying nostalgia for the golden age of the original Star League to present-day Capellan nationalism.

The defeat of the Clans during Sun-Tzu's three-year tenure reinforced the Capellans' newfound pride in their nation, despite the fact that Sun-Tzu personally had little to do with the planning and execution of the anti-Clan campaigns. Though the Capellan Confederation did send troops as part of Task Force Serpent, Kingston's Legionnaires are far from the best that the CCAF has to offer. The Confederation's principal role was to keep the supply lines open during the assault on the Smoke Jaguars' Inner Sphere holdings, an obligation it fulfilled admirably. Despite the Confederation's relative lack of military participation, more than one Capellan citizen has since proudly referred to the Chancellor as the "conqueror of the Clans."

Master of Arms

Sun-Tzu's role as military supplier to the SLDF from 3058 to 3060 offered him several ways to reap benefits for the Confederation. Early in his term as First Lord, he used Star

League resources in conjunction with funds from his own treasury to repair, modernize and in some cases rebuild 'Mech production sites on Capellan worlds. He then sold the resulting production to the SLDF coalition force, at sufficient profit to keep the facilities going. As no 'Mechs from these revamped factories went to Capellan units during the Clan offensive, Chancellor Liao could not be accused of using his office to benefit his realm alone. Before long, however, the refurbished 'Mech factories would add significantly to Capellan military strength.

The Shengli Arms factory on the world of Victoria, which our own Order helped finance, was the next step in Chancellor Liao's plan to rearm the CCAF. The Chancellor made the first Shengli production runs available not to the SLDF coalition force as a whole, but only to units with ties to the original SLDF. This action bought him considerable goodwill from the units in question, and also represented the first time that the entire SLDF coalition force had not benefitted from Capellan military production. In retrospect, it appears to have been the first step toward rearming his own forces—an act that would soon have far graver consequences than anyone had predicted.

WAR IN ST. IVES

With his elevation to the First Lordship and the victory over the Clans, Chancellor Liao found it easy to stoke pro-Capellan feeling throughout his former realm. In the Disputed Territories and the Tikonov Reaches, such sentiments sparked civil unrest, as pro-Liao agitators stirred up the citizenry against non-Liao ruling powers. In St. Ives, however, rising Capellan nationalism ran up against the personal popularity of Duchess Candace Liao and her family—especially her son and heir, war hero and Solaris champion Kai Allard-Liao. Sun-Tzu found his efforts blunted, until he experienced a stroke of luck.

In July of 3060, Chancellor Liao embarked on a tour of Capellan worlds on the St. Ives border. Intended to showcase the successes of the Xin Sheng movement, the tour was to have unexpected and far-reaching consequences. At every world he visited, Sun-Tzu made emotional appeals for the reunion of the entire Capellan Confederation and excoriated "oppressive leaders" whom he accused of suppressing "their people's natural desire to rejoin their brethren." Such inflammatory remarks soon came to the ears of the Blackwind Lancers, a large military unit then serving as part of St. Ives' border defenses. The Lancers were known for their hatred of Sun-Tzu, especially the fanatical commanding officer of the Lancers' Second Battalion. Goaded by the Chancellor's thinly veiled threats against the St. Ives Compact, Major Trisha Smithson determined to strike him down.

In August of 3060, the Second Lancers went rogue and dropped onto the world of Hustaing, the next stop on Chancellor Liao's itinerary. They invaded the capital city of Qingliu and attacked the Chancellor's entourage, but their quarry had gone missing. The Lancers would later learn that Sun-Tzu had never gone to Hustaing; he had returned home briefly to Sian, sending his fiancee to Hustaing ahead of him. The attempt to kill Sun-Tzu instead came close to costing Isis Marik her life while leaving its principal target unscathed.

The incident chilled relations between St. Ives and the Free Worlds League, but was to have even worse consequences where the Confederation was concerned. Chancellor Liao demanded and won the disbanding of the Blackwind Lancers, as well as a public apology from Duchess Candace for the conduct of her mercenaries. When the Lancers' demise provoked widespread demonstrations on the world of Denbar, where they had been stationed, Sun-Tzu used the unrest as an excuse to move troops onto several St. Ives border planets. Rather than send Capellan units, which would rightly have been taken as an act of war, the Chancellor used his authority as First Lord to send Marik units under the SLDF banner as "peacekeepers."

The presence of what was essentially an occupying force infuriated St. Ives units on the affected worlds, and skirmishes between the two were inevitable. While Sun-Tzu pointed to the escalating conflict as proof that St. Ives threatened his own nation's sovereignty, Duchess Candace marshaled her political resources in the Star League First Council to expel the SLDF troops. Sun-Tzu's term of office was drawing to a close, and Duchess Candace was confident that a new First Lord would undo the SLDF occupation. Chancellor Liao anticipated her, however. In late 3061, just before resigning the First Lordship, he withdrew the SLDF forces and replaced them with CCAF troops.

The situation in St. Ives remains highly volatile, with no clear indication yet of which side will win out. The St. Ives military is fighting hard for its survival, and may receive aid from the SLDF; though new First Lord Theodore Kurita cannot commit Star League troops without the consent of the First Council, there is nothing to prevent the commander of the SLDF from sending units to St. Ives on "exercises." That commander is ComStar Precentor Martial Victor Steiner-Davion, a close friend of Kai Allard-Liao and a longtime ally of St. Ives; he is likely to do everything in his power to thwart the Capellan Confederation. Chancellor Liao is determined and tenacious, however, and can call on far greater military assets than the tiny St. Ives Compact.

Assuming that Sun-Tzu succeeds in reabsorbing the Compact, he will greatly expand his power. Once he has reclaimed the planets that belonged to his realm in 3028, he may well turn his eye in other directions. Word of Blake should keep a very close eye on the Chancellor of the Capellan Confederation.

The Free Capella Movement

Ironically, the conflict in St. Ives has given the dissident Free Capella movement a proverbial shot in the arm. Free Capella began shifting its focus from political intrigue to social programs under the leadership of Kai Allard-Liao, who took over from his uncle Tormano in 3056. That change in emphasis, along with Xin Sheng-inspired nationalist pride and Sun-Tzu's gains in the Disputed Territories, had done serious damage to Free Capella as a political opposition movement by the time the St. Ives troubles erupted in mid-3060. In late 3061, however, the Confederation's shift from mere "occupation" to open warfare galvanized Free Capella leaders throughout St. Ives and elsewhere. Among them was Mandrinn Tormano Liao, who resigned his position as advisor to Archon Katrina Steiner-Davion in order to turn Free Capella's resources toward liberating St. Ives worlds from Confederation forces.

PERIPHERY MACHINATIONS

As yet another facet of the Capellan revival, Sun-Tzu Liao has made overtures toward the two major Periphery realms—the Magistracy of Canopus and the Taurian Concordat—with an eye to forming an alliance. These efforts, which began in 3058, have since borne fruit. Despite the best our operatives in the Magistracy could do to disrupt matters, Magestrix Emma Centrella agreed to ally her realm with the Confederation. Under the terms of that agreement, Capella's Chancellor can freely deploy Magistracy military units; in exchange, the Magistracy receives ongoing technological aid and funding to upgrade its educational resources.

Throughout 3060 and 3061, the Chancellor has used Magistracy forces to augment his own troops' efforts in the Disputed Territories and the Chaos March. There have even been scattered reports of Magistracy troops involved in the St. Ives conflict. The loss of the Magestrix's eldest daughter, Danai Centrella, in the recent Clan campaign can only smooth the way for even closer ties between the Magistracy and the Confederation. Danai Centrella was no friend of Sun-Tzu Liao's; her death has removed the only real obstacle to the Chancellor's plans for the Canopian state.

The Taurian Concordat was initially far less receptive to Capellan overtures. In an effort to win over Protector Jeffrey Calderon, Chancellor Liao requested a meeting between the Protector, the Magestrix and himself on the world of Detroit. As the site of a new Magistracy production facility made possible by Capellan aid, Detroit was the ideal showcase for the benefits of a Capellan alliance.

The conference was scheduled for December of 3060, but events conspired in Chancellor Liao's favor to make it moot. The crisis on Hustaing and subsequent fallout delayed the Chancellor's arrival, then forced him to postpone the meeting until a later date. Not long afterward, in the New Colony Region, Colony President Sherman Maltin staged a military coup in which he took the Protector and the Magestrix hostage. As ransom, he demanded complete independence for the New Colony Region. Chancellor Liao immediately dispatched Confederation troops under the command of Naomi Centrella, the Canopian heir, to rescue the hostages. After several months of fighting, the coup was put down and the Magestrix freed. Protector Jeffrey Calderon, however, was a casualty of war.

Calderon's successor proved much more amenable to an alliance with the Capellans, especially as he owed his position

CAPELLAN CONFEDERATION ARMED FORCES RANKING CONVENTIONS

New Rank	Old Rank
Commissioned Officers	
Chancellor	Chancellor
Sang-jiang-jun (Senior General)	*
Jiang-jun (General)	Senior Colonel
Sang-shao (Colonel)	Colonel
Zhong-shao (Lieutenant Colonel)	Major
Sao-shao (Major)	Captain
Sang-wei (Captain)	Commander
Sao-wei (Lieutenant)	Subcommander
Enlisted Ranks	
Yi-si-ben-bing (Master Sergeant)	Force Leader
Si-ben-bing (Sergeant)	Lance Sergeant
San-ben-bing (Corporal)	Lance Corporal
Shia-ben-bing (Recruit)	Recruit
Warrior House Ranks	
Shiao-zhang (Lord Colonel)	House Master
Ying-zhang (Lieutenant Colonel [Infantry])	Battalion Leader
Lien-zhang (Major)	Company Leader
Pai-zhang (Captain)	Lance/Platoon Leader
Ban-zhang (Lieutenant)	Squad Leader
Zhang-si (Lance Corporal)	Infantryman

* No equivalent of the new rank existed under the old conventions.

to that realm's timely action. Though he has not yet fully committed himself or his nation, Lord Grover Shraplen is likely to do so in the near future. Such a triple alliance will create a substantial new power bloc, with the Capellan Confederation indisputably in charge.

MILITARY ANALYSIS

—Prepared by *Sang-jiang-jun* Talon Zahn, Strategic Director of the Capellan Confederation Armed Forces

I am pleased to report that the reclamation of Capellan territory is going well on almost all fronts. The Chaos March is an unfortunate exception, but I trust it will not remain so once we have dealt with higher priorities. The combination of irregulars and professional revolutionaries, CCAF troops, mercenary units and troops from the Magistracy Armed Forces has given us the strength we need to take and hold planets against all comers, especially as our major Great House rivals for control in this region are still dealing with the fallout from Archon Katrina Steiner-Davion's assumption of the FedCom throne.

In the Disputed Territories, most of the planets targeted by our operations have been solidly under our control since this past February; we have spent much of the ensuing year consolidating and expanding that power base. Even on Wei and Aldebaran, which held out against CCAF forces until July 3061, active resistance is diminishing. Your Excellency's xin sheng programs deserve much of the credit for the calm in this region; though resistance still exists, large portions of the local populations appear willing to join in the Capellan renaissance. However, I recommend against transferring too many of our units from the Disputed Territories to the St. Ives front. Raids on our supply bases in the Territories by St. Ives troops continue to take a toll, and we would be ill-advised to move troops out of that area wholesale until the raiding parties have been dealt with.

The war to retake the St. Ives Compact is also going well, though slowly. The St. Ives line forces are fighting for their own as well as their realm's survival, and Duchess Liao can call upon the services of several excellent mercenary units. In addition, the recent installation of SLDF peacekeepers by Theodore Kurita has limited our freedom to act on the worlds where those units are deployed. Until there is a political solution to this problem or a new First Lord more responsive to our interests is elected, the peacekeeping forces are likely to pose a significant hurdle.

On the brighter side, however, the St. Ives–Confederation border is almost completely demilitarized. The new Xin Sheng Commonality is a fait accompli that the other House leaders cannot effectively argue with, and our control of such worlds as Indicass, Denbar and Vestallas gives us staging bases from which to pursue the next stage of the invasion. Early indications from the Maskirovka also suggest that your call for Xin Sheng has fallen on receptive ears in more than a few St. Ives units. How many might refuse to fight, or even join the Capellan side, I cannot yet say; that some will, however, is a distinct possibility.

Unlike in the Disputed Territories, however, resistance on many of the border worlds is extremely active. The return of Kai Allard-Liao and his First St. Ives Lancers from Clan space sparked a surge in rebellious acts that our forces have yet to wholly put down. Successful raiding by Cassandra Allard-Liao and the Second St. Ives Lancers has likewise boosted the enemy's morale, and the situation promises to get worse before it gets better. In summary, I believe we can take and hold the St. Ives Compact—but they will make us fight hard for every inch of ground, and many Capellans on both sides will sacrifice their lives for our nation's rebirth.

Per your orders, we have devoted little military attention to our stalled campaigns in the Chaos March. Our irregulars and paramilitaries are doing an admirable job of stirring things up in Tikonov, which should keep Katrina Steiner-Davion occupied and allow us a freer hand in the March once we have completed the St. Ives campaign.

NOTABLE PERSONALITIES

TO: Precentor Blane
FROM: Adept Gong Liu

The following individuals have the greatest potential to affect the unfolding situation in the Capellan Confederation and surrounding territories.

CHANCELLOR SUN-TZU LIAO

Rank/Position: Duke of St. Ives/Chancellor of the Capellan Confederation
Year of Birth: 3031 (age 30)

Profile:
The only son and heir of Romano Liao, Sun-Tzu assumed the Celestial Throne of the Capellan Confederation after his mother's assassination. In the decade since, he has led his nation far more effectively than anyone would have expected, achieving through crafty political maneuvering what he could not hope to accomplish by other means.

Never noted for prowess in a 'Mech, Chancellor Liao excels on the political battlefield. Among his more stellar—and unexpected—achievements in recent years are his tenure as First Lord of the Star League; his calculated generosity in ceding Northwind permanently to the Northwind Highlanders; and the alliance with the Magistracy of Canopus. As the Chancellor's engagement to Isis Marik enters its tenth year, rumors have begun to link him with Naomi Centrella, who is currently leading Magistracy Armed Forces troops within the Capellan Confederation. Though we cannot yet verify any substance behind the stories, the Chancellor's fiancee has lost much of her political usefulness with her father's recent remarriage and the birth of a legitimate heir to the Free Worlds League. For the moment, however, Chancellor Liao appears to be content with the status quo.

DUCHESS CANDACE LIAO

Rank/Position: Duchess of St. Ives/Prime Minister of the St. Ives Compact
Year of Birth: 2988 (age 73)

Profile:
Duchess Candace Liao displays much of her family's craftiness with none of its mental weakness. Ruler of the St. Ives worlds while they were still a Capellan Commonality, the duchess took those worlds with her when she eloped with Davion agent Justin Xiang Allard during the Fourth Succession War. Candace

Liao has maintained close ties with the Davions ever since the formation of the independent St. Ives Compact, and remains a staunch ally of Victor Steiner-Davion.

Known for her keen intelligence and iron will, Duchess Liao is adept at the game of politics. Such survival skills were necessary growing up in a court brimming with lethal intrigues, many of them perpetrated by her unstable sister Romano and their father, the half-mad Chancellor Maximilian Liao. Even in her mid-70s, with her realm threatened by war, Candace remains an influential political player. She may manage to engineer her nation's survival; if not, she will doubtless do everything possible to reclaim it from behind the scenes.

DUKE KAI ALLARD-LIAO

Rank/Position: Heir to the St. Ives Compact/Commander of the First St. Ives Lancers
Year of Birth: 3030 (age 31)

Profile:
The oldest child of Duchess Candace Liao and Justin Allard, the former head of Federated Commonwealth Intelligence, Kai is regarded as the greatest warrior of modern times. Between 3052 and 3056, he successfully held the title of Champion of Solaris—more consecutive years than any MechWarrior before or since. He graduated from the New Avalon Military Academy in 3049 and was assigned to the Tenth Lyran Guards, where he became a close friend of then-Prince Victor Steiner-Davion. During the Clan war, Kai shot to fame in the Second Battle of Twycross, where he destroyed the Falcon Guards Cluster almost singlehandedly in the canyon known as the Great Gash. Though briefly feared lost on the planet Alyina, he survived battle with the Jade Falcons there and went on to become one of the architects of the Inner Sphere's recent victory over the Clan invaders.

During Operation Bulldog, Kai led the St. Ives contingent of the SLDF coalition force. He commanded the assault on Tarazed, and participated in the assaults on Caripare and Schuyler. Afterward, he led his unit, along with the rest of Prince Victor's force, to Clan space. On the Smoke Jaguar homeworld, the SLDF relief force rescued the beleaguered remnants of Task Force Serpent from Jaguar troops bent on retaking the planet. With Huntress once again safely in Inner Sphere hands, Kai and his First St. Ives Lancers accompanied Prince Victor to Strana Mechty, where Kai's unit engaged Clan Wolf forces in the Great Refusal. The Lancers fought the Wolves to a draw, and Kai personally defeated Wolf Khan Vlad Ward in combat.

MAJOR CASSANDRA ALLARD-LIAO

Rank/Position: Major/Commander of the Second St. Ives Lancers
Year of Birth: 3033 (age 28)

Profile:
The eldest of Duchess Candace Liao's twin daughters, Cassandra Allard-Liao is a gifted MechWarrior in her own right, if not so gifted as her brother. With boundless courage and a strong fighting spirit, Cassandra needs only a little political seasoning to make her a truly formidable opponent—or ally. She currently commands the Second St. Ives Lancers, who have spent the past year raiding Capellan supply depots on worlds in the Disputed Territories. Between raids, the Lancers have traveled from world to world in the St. Ives Compact, assisting in planetary defense against Capellan attackers when needed. The unit was last reported on St. Loris, engaged in heavy fighting.

KALI LIAO

Rank/Position: Lady of Highspire/Thuggee cult leader
Year of Birth: 3033 (age 28)

Profile:
The sister of Chancellor Sun-Tzu Liao, Duchess Kali appears to have inherited a double dose of the Liao family madness. Among her less savory exploits, she leads a Thuggee death cult and is thought to have been behind more than one attempted assassination. Her devotion to her brother knows no bounds, but often takes strange forms. She considers herself honor-bound to defend him—usually violently—against any threat to him personally or to the Capellan Confederation; her mental instability, however, often leads her to see threats where there are none. A recent example, if rumors can be believed, is the near-death of Ion Rush, Grand Master of the Capellan Warrior Houses. Officially, Grand Master Rush almost lost his life in a freak gas-main explosion. Unofficially, speculation is rife that Kali Liao attempted to assassinate Rush because of his long-ago ties to Candace Liao, whom Kali regards as a black-hearted traitor.

OPERATION GUERRERO

Field Report
General Helen Thrall, CO, Sirian Lancers
20 December 3057

Captain-General:

The following report sums up the progress of Operation Guerrero since the official cessation of hostilities five days ago. I am gratified to report that the Free Worlds League Military has lived up to its potential throughout this engagement; in my opinion, our forces could have gone further than the rather cautious boundary you set for them. In particular, I refer to the worlds of Sirius and Procyon, which currently lie in the so-called Chaos March. The FWLM has the wherewithal to take and hold those worlds, and in my opinion also has a moral obligation to do so. You are doubtless tired of hearing that, but it is my duty to speak my mind honestly, regardless of what you as my Captain-General might wish to hear. I trust my point is made; I will continue with my report.

FIRST WAVE

Between 16 and 20 September, 3057, Free Worlds League troops jumped into the Callison, Denebola, Marcus, Van Diemen IV, Talitha and Wasat systems via pirate jump points. We chose these six worlds as our first targets because they were the only ones with significant concentrations of FedCom troops, and we wanted to take those units out of the action early. Our forces caught the FedCom by surprise; enemy intelligence operatives apparently assumed that the buildup of Free Worlds League troops on their border was part of the usual unit rotations from interior to border planets.

We struck each target world with three regiments, more than enough to overwhelm the FedCom garrison forces. Prince Victor Davion's single-minded focus on the threat of the Clans had prompted him to move many of his best troops to the Clan front, and SAFE had informed us that most of the rest were engaging in war games in the Tikonov region. The Sixth Free Worlds Legionnaires, Atrean Hussars and Fourth Marik Militia took Denebola without a fight, as the Skye March Militia supposedly defending the planet was away on Caph for exercises. The small remaining planetary militia had no wish to take on three regiments unaided, and surrendered without a shot being fired. The battle for Callison was nearly as painless; the Eleventh Lyran Guards withdrew to Lyran space rather than fight a League force that consisted of the Fourth Free Worlds Legionnaires, First Free Worlds Guards and the Silver Hawk Irregular Falcon unit. Callison's defense was left in the hands of the pro-FedCom planetary militia, which held out for several days before folding.

The rest of the first wave went somewhat less smoothly. Some of the fiercest fighting occurred on Marcus, where the Seventh Free Worlds Legionnaires, Fifth Marik Militia and Twelfth Atrean Dragoons faced the Twelfth FedCom RCT. The Seventh and the Twelfth FedCom, both green units, suffered serious losses when the FedCom commanding officer ordered his single 'Mech regiment to make a suicide charge against our much larger force in order to buy time for evacuation. The Seventh Legionnaires took the brunt of the charge, but managed to hold out long enough for the Fifth Militia and the Twelfth Dragoons to circle behind the enemy. This victory cost the Legionnaires a third of their personnel, including the unit's commanding officer.

The liberation of Van Diemen IV was similarly hard-fought. Though the Tenth and Twenty-third Marik Militias and the Third Oriente Hussars landed as part of the first wave, the planet remained up for grabs until early December, when the First Sirian Lancers were ordered to Van Diemen as reinforcements. Not long after our arrival, the settlement with the FedCom was announced, in which Prince Victor ceded his claim to the world.

The remaining first-wave planets fell to League forces with minimal combat losses. The casualties taken by the Sixth Marik Militia and the Atrean Hussars on Talitha were unfortunately more a result of the long-simmering hostility between those two units than to the efforts of the FedCom troops. On Wasat, the Thirteenth Marik Militia, Fourth Oriente Hussars and Second Sirian Lancers smashed the FedCom's Second Republican Regiment. Some trouble arose later, when you chose to halt Operation Guerrero rather than go on to liberate Sirius and Procyon. The Second Lancers were understandably upset at the abandonment of their homeworlds, and a few individuals unfortunately allowed their emotions to rule them. For the record, however, I wish to protest the deployment of Thirteenth Militia troops as security against Lancer personnel. The Lancers as a whole were never in serious danger of mutiny over the issue of our homeworlds, and the Second does not deserve this blight upon its combat record.

SECOND WAVE

The second wave of Operation Guerrero went nearly as smoothly as the first, though League troops faced more opposition than expected on some worlds. The Third Free Worlds Guards became embroiled in bitter street-to-street fighting with the planetary garrison in Forest City, the capital of Devil's Rock. In just four hours, the Guards lost two lances of 'Mechs to FedCom missiles; total losses amounted to nineteen 'Mechs before the Guards crushed the last resisters. The Third NAIS cadet cadre on Oliver also put up stiffer resistance than expect-

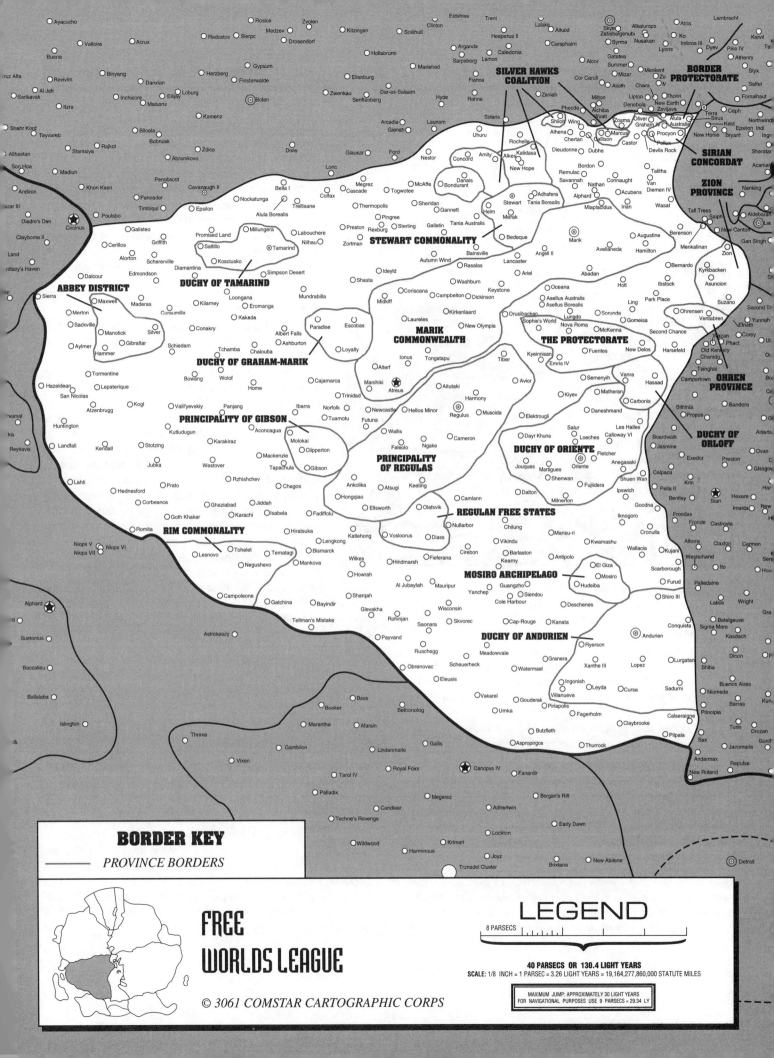

ed, given their inexperience. The Twentieth Marik Militia and the First Orloff Grenadiers found the NAIS unit's oversized aerospace wing a particular problem, but ultimately pushed the FedCom unit offworld.

The Third Sirian Lancers did better on Castor, defeating a handful of planetary militia units in days. Resistance later flared up on the world, but was put down by mid-December. On Zosma, the Ninth Marik Militia easily defeated the FedCom planetary militia.

On Pollux, the Thirty-fourth Marik Militia achieved its objective with a little help from FedCom internal politics. The Thirty-fourth had expected to face seven regiments of planetary militia, but ultimately ended up taking on two: one infantry and one armor. The others either chose to rejoin the League or accepted the offer from Archon Katrina Steiner of the newly formed Lyran Alliance to return peacefully to Lyran territory. Resistance ended within a week of the League units' planetfall.

THE ZION REBELLION

The unpleasant events in the Province of Zion earlier this year appear to have been the only major drawback to Operation Guerrero, at least from a military standpoint. Allowing Capellan troops to stage assaults from the planet Asuncion set the stage for a full-scale rebellion, as the people of Asuncion declared independence rather than accept the presence of so many Capellan units on their world. The citizens of Asuncion have long memories; to them, as to many others in the League, the Capellans will always be the enemy. Asuncion's secession plunged the planet into turmoil, requiring swift action by the FWLM to retake control. Losses among the troops and civilians were thankfully minimal. However, I believe any civilian casualties are too many, especially when the situation might have been avoided.

AFTERMATH

The end of the resistance on Castor marked the cessation of organized hostilities, though a few pro-FedCom partisans doubtless still exist on some of the liberated worlds. The FWLM was wholly engaged in retaking former League possessions; operations assisting the capture of former Capellan worlds were left to various mercenary units, hired by the League and loaned to Chancellor Sun-Tzu Liao. These campaigns met with varying degrees of success; two notable failures were Nanking and Woodstock, both of which remain under FedCom control. The loss of Nanking's 'Mech production facilities would merely have inconvenienced the FedCom military machine, however, while noticeably strengthening a notoriously unstable ally. On balance, events on Nanking may turn out to be a blessing in disguise.

The most serious loss to the League was the damage inflicted on Smithson's Chinese Bandits by the Woodstock Reserve Militia, first on Woodstock and then on Nanking. The FedCom unit crushed an entire Bandits regiment on Woodstock, a loss from which the merc unit will not easily recover. Transferred to Nanking to meet the second half of the Bandits, the Reserve Militia fought them to a stalemate. Burr's Black Cobras arrived to reinforce the Bandits in early December, but Davion saboteurs had planted explosive charges aboard the unit's DropShips. The vessels exploded over the Kallon Industries Factory complex, decimating the Cobras. Shortly afterward, the Bandits surrendered.

Overall, the Free Worlds League gained much and lost little from this operation. We have retaken the worlds lost to the Davions during the Fourth Succession War, provided some of our greener units with valuable combat experience, and suffered comparatively few casualties in the process. Should you decide to press further in the future, the FWLM is still combat-ready, while the opposition promises to be fragmented and disorganized. The entire region of space targeted by League and Capellan invasion forces has become a hotbed of warring factions, where no power holds sway. Making further inroads into this so-called Chaos March would pose no problem for the Free Worlds League Military.

THE FREE WORLDS LEAGUE

TO: Victor Steiner-Davion
FROM: Jerrard Cranston
DATE: 2 January 3062

By most conventional measures, nothing much has been happening in the Free Worlds League since the end of the Sarna March invasion—the brevity of this report is a testament to that fact—and that worries me. Thomas Marik has a new wife who has given him two sons, his realm is militarily quiet and politically stable, and the League economy is booming from sales of military hardware to anyone and everyone. And there sits the Captain-General, apparently content to do nothing but watch the money come pouring in. Where is all that revenue going? Is Thomas really so uninvolved with political business as usual in the Inner Sphere, or is there something else going on beneath the surface?

HISTORICAL BACKGROUND

The decade since the Battle of Tukayyid has been remarkably kind to the Free Worlds League, if not always to its Captain-General. From 3052 through 3056, Thomas Marik kept the promise he'd made to Hanse Davion in 3051. In return for Joshua Marik's medical treatment, the League supplied war materiel to the rest of the Inner Sphere in order to beef up our defenses against the Clans. Meanwhile, Thomas continued to reform his own military. Between 3052 and 3057, he transformed the Free Worlds League Military (FWLM) from a fractious collection of balkanized units, each loyal to their own regional nobles, into a powerful force unified by its common loyalty to the League.

One shining example of this new spirit was the Knights of the Inner Sphere, which Thomas created in 3055. Recruited from the upper echelons of the FWLM, the Knights owe their loyalty to Thomas Marik personally, and are sworn to uphold chivalric ideals both on and off the battlefield. Though their adherence to honorable conduct in warfare swiftly earned them a reputation as "goody two-shoes" from some other quarters of the FWLM, the Knights have since proved themselves to be among the most proficient fighters in the League.

Not long after their formation, the Knights briefly became enmeshed in a guerrilla war against the newly arrived Blakists on Gibson. They initially supported the Gibson Freedom League, until the GFL unleashed a tactical nuclear weapon given them by their backers in the League's Principality of Regulus. The use of that device forced the surrender of the Blakist commander, a renegade Precentor. Thomas Marik ultimately settled the situation by removing the corrupt Countess of Gibson from power and installing one of the Knights, Sir Paul Masters, in her place.

The Knights also contributed immeasurably to the success of our recent campaigns against the Clans, against the Jade Falcons on Coventry and as part of Task Force Serpent. The latter success came at a high cost; of the regiment that landed on Huntress, just over a third survived to see the arrival of the SLDF relief force.

OPERATION GUERRERO

The revamped FWLM got the chance to put its reforms to the test in 3057. Early in that year, Joshua Marik's frail health took a turn for the worse. It soon became clear that his death was inevitable, and so he was allowed to die quietly on 20 May. At the time, we believed Joshua's death meant that Sun-Tzu Liao, through his engagement to Isis Marik, would become the heir to the Free Worlds League throne. Sun-Tzu would then be in a position to launch a bloody war of conquest that the Inner Sphere could not afford. In a well-intentioned but ultimately mistaken attempt to stave off these events, we put a double in Joshua's place. The deception held until late July, when a SAFE agent discovered the substitution. The Captain-General responded by launching a joint assault with Capellan forces against the FedCom's Sarna March.

Despite having the stronger army, Marik was not the primary aggressor in the invasion. That role fell to Sun-Tzu Liao. Sun-Tzu failed to achieve his objective, but came close with the help of Marik-hired mercenary units. He destabilized the entire region, to the point where no major power can claim to hold sway over large sections of the Chaos March. In the years since the invasion, Sun-Tzu has done his best to extend his control in the area, but has apparently been stopped cold by better-organized and -equipped opposition than he expected.

Thomas Marik, with more limited objectives, enjoyed far greater success. In roughly two months, Marik forces targeted and recaptured every world in the Sarna region that the League had lost to the FedCom during the Fourth Succession War. With those worlds once more in the League fold, Marik declared himself satisfied and sued for peace. The FedCom had little choice but to accept the settlement; with half the realm torn away and rechristened the Lyran Alliance, and Lyran units largely neutral during the fighting, Prince Victor was in no position to bargain.

A NEW BEGINNING

In the four years since the end of the Chaos March invasion, Thomas has turned his attentions toward more peaceful pursuits: continuing his military reforms, strengthening the League economy through arms sales and providing the League with a new Marik heir. After the death of his beloved first wife Sophina, Duchess of Oceana, in 3057, many believed that Thomas would never marry again. With no heir save Isis Marik, the League faced the real possibility of seeing Sun-Tzu Liao on its throne. The staggering length of that couple's engagement testified to how little Thomas Marik liked that scenario; since agreeing to the betrothal in 3052, he had used every conceiv-

able excuse to delay the actual marriage. After nine years, only one option remained: to produce a new, legitimate heir to replace Isis Marik.

Theoretically, the Captain-General could have chosen another family member to succeed him—his niece Corrine, for example, or his nephew Photon Brett-Marik. For reasons that are not entirely clear, however, he chose a different course. In December of 3058, Thomas Marik married Sherryl Halas, only child and heir of Duke Christopher Halas of Oriente. Six months later, Sherryl gave birth to a healthy baby boy, christened Janos in honor of his grandfather. Not long afterward, Thomas officially named Janos his heir. A year later, Sherryl produced a second son, Christopher, named for her father.

POLITICAL RAMIFICATIONS

The Captain-General's marriage has further stabilized the historically fractious internal politics of the Free Worlds League by consolidating Thomas' hold over and ties to the powerful Duchy of Oriente. As the Halas family have been among Marik's most vocal backers for some years, this development represents no major change. However, it virtually guarantees that Oriente's support will outlive Duke Christopher and likely even Sherryl Halas—especially if young Janos Marik lives long enough to succeed his father. Should the unexpected happen and the League balkanize again in the future, the marriage alliance offers Thomas Marik—or Janos Marik, potentially—a substantial power base from which to attempt to retake control of the realm.

END OF AN ALLIANCE?

Displaced by her two half-brothers, Isis Marik has ceased to be a valuable piece on the chessboard of Inner Sphere politics. Once a stepping-stone to immense power for Sun-Tzu, she has now become a liability for the Chancellor, and I predict he will rid himself of her whenever he feels it most expedient. At most, he is likely to receive a strongly worded reprimand from Thomas over the cavalier treatment of his daughter; Thomas has never had much use for Isis, and is likely to care what happens to her only because she is a Marik, when all is said and done. His persistent refusal to permit her to marry Sun-Tzu—whom she genuinely appears to love—clearly indicates how little regard Thomas has for his daughter's wishes or happiness. He is unlikely to make Sun-Tzu pay in any meaningful way for jilting her, which Sun-Tzu knows all too well.

The rumor mill these days is linking Sun-Tzu with Naomi Centrella of the Magistracy of Canopus; if the stories are true, Sun-Tzu may already have chosen Isis Marik's replacement. Whether or not there's anything to the gossip, however, the recently forged alliance between the Capellan Confederation and the Magistracy may signal a threat to the Free Worlds League. Sun-Tzu has incorporated several Magistracy Armed Forces units into his own military machine, using them approximately as he does the Capellan Warrior Houses. The MAF units have enabled him to make inroads throughout the Chaos March while simultaneously freeing up CCAF units to make mischief in the St. Ives Compact. Though the bulk of his attention appears to be focused on St. Ives for the moment, Sun-Tzu has nearly sewn up the rimward half of the March, which his people refer to as the Disputed Territories. Once he has this portion of the old Capellan Confederation solidly back under his control, his forces will be just a short jump or two away from the Free Worlds League border. And without his engagement to Isis, Sun-Tzu no longer has any particular motivation to refrain from attacking his onetime ally.

Troop movements in the region over the past few months indicate that Thomas is aware of the potential threat, and is doing what he can to discourage it. He has stepped up the numbers of FWLM units being rotated from interior to border worlds, and is supplying those units with the best possible equipment. Suzano, Ventabren and Harsefeld, all Marik worlds bordering the Confederation proper, were among the first to receive beefed-up planetary garrison forces. Just weeks ago, the buildup reached Zion and Menkalinen, both of which lie close to the Disputed Territories. Meanwhile, Sun-Tzu is reinforcing the Disputed Territory worlds of Aldebaran, Liao and Pleione—three planets that lie very near Marik space. Liao, of course, is the homeworld of Sun-Tzu's ancestors, and resistance to renewed Capellan rule on Aldebaran and Pleione was reportedly quite fierce. Sun-Tzu therefore has ample reason to increase his military presence on all three worlds. We have learned to our cost, however, that Sun-Tzu tends to accomplish several purposes with every move he makes. Reinforcing troublesome worlds while simultaneously massing forces for an eventual assault on the League definitely fits his MO.

WORD OF BLAKE ACTIVITY

Any discussion of Free Worlds League affairs must include the Word of Blake, the reactionary ComStar splinter group that has run League-wide HPG communications ever since Thomas Marik first gave them sanctuary on the League world of Gibson. Uniformly hostile to ComStar, the Word of Blake is also generally ill-disposed toward everything ComStar has accomplished or helped to accomplish since the Schism in late 3052. The Blakists played no part in the recent campaigns against the Clans, nor in the formation of the new Star League. Instead, they have devoted most of the past decade to undermining ComStar, culminating in the capture of Terra in 3058.

THE TAKING OF TERRA

The Word of Blake had plotted for years to take Terra, and finally got its chance with the Chaos March invasion. Though he might not agree, Thomas Marik bears some responsibility for Terra's fall into Blakist hands. In addition to granting the sect a landhold and control over his realm's HPG stations, he also allowed Word of Blake ROM to coordinate some of its operations with his own intelligence agency, SAFE. He did not, however, insist on fully integrating the Word of Blake's sizable and well-equipped militia into the FWLM. Instead, Marik allowed the Blakist militia units to remain independent while taking advantage of League military resources. During the Chaos March inva-

sion, Marik's exclusive use of FWLM and mercenary units left the Blakist militia free to exploit the unfolding situation in the region. Word of Blake used the chaos to move its own forces into position, and by early March of 3058 had driven ComStar from humanity's homeworld.

MARIK AND THE BLAKISTS

The Terra campaign removed the bulk of the Blake militia from the Free Worlds League, which cost Thomas Marik access to men and materiel, but also solved a potentially serious political problem. The Word of Blake's fanaticism and its obvious closeness to Thomas—whom several Blakists considered their "Primus-in-Exile"—had prompted fears of a theocratic takeover, which the militia units' departure greatly assuaged. The Word of Blake remains firmly ensconced in the League, however, controlling League communications and funneling intelligence reports directly to the Captain-General. I believe the Word of Blake was behind the leak that exposed our Joshua Marik double; they apparently revealed a private communication that prompted Thomas to reconfirm the paternity of his "son."

Since the capture of Terra, Word of Blake activity elsewhere has simmered down. In the Free Worlds League, the Blakists are quietly operating the HPG network and generally minding their own business. Outside League borders, Blakist operatives have turned up in the Periphery and in the Chaos March, but even in those regions their activities appear marginal. This lull in operations may be explained by the concentration of Blakist forces on Terra, but the planet has been in their possession for almost four years now. Given the Blakists' predilection for secrecy, I believe their present low level of activity is deceptive. Whatever they're up to, it is more than it appears.

Chaos March Activities

According to recent reports from my people in the Chaos March, known Word of Blake agents have been turning up on various worlds—sometimes meeting with whoever happens to be the planetary authority at the time, sometimes for purposes we can so far only guess at. My sources report meetings between Word of Blake Precentors and government figures in the Styk Commonality, the Terracap Confederation and Epsilon Eridani, though we have not yet discovered the substance of those talks. The ComStar/Word of Blake file contains the additional details.

The most disturbing incident occurred on Hsien, which has spent most of its brief independence precariously balanced between three opposing factions. Shortly after a Word of Blake delegation left that world this past October, a new round of fighting broke out that left the leaders of Dendeez Province in effective control of the planet. They have since invited the Word of Blake to take over the administration of Hsien's HPG stations from ComStar.

Given the close ties between the Word of Blake and Thomas Marik, it is possible that the recent Blakist travels in the region are intended to test the waters for a possible Marik offensive in the Chaos March. Sun-Tzu Liao is having a fair amount of trouble reconquering the region, and the Captain-General may have decided to take advantage of that difficulty.

Operations Within the League

Though the Word of Blake appears to be doing nothing more sinister than fulfilling its HPG service contract, there are a few indications of other happenings beneath the surface. Precentor Martial Cameron St. Jamais, leader of the radical Toyama sect within the Word of Blake since the death of Precentor Demona Aziz in 3058, has made an unusual number of trips across the Free Worlds League over the past nine months, including stops on Gibson and Atreus. He reportedly spent several hours closeted with Precentor Blane of Gibson, and on Atreus received a private audience with Precentor Malcolm Kane at the Captain-General's court. On his other journeys to League planets, he has likewise made a point of meeting with high-ranking Blakist Precentors. The subject of these meetings remains unknown, but the sheer number and frequency, and the very fact that he is traveling himself rather than sending a representative, serve as a red flag indicating that something's afoot.

St. Jamais may be acting as a courier, carrying messages that the Word of Blake does not wish to entrust to its own HPG network. If the Blakists are up to something they wish to keep from ComStar, HPG transmissions are not necessarily a completely safe option. Alternatively, St. Jamais may be sounding out his fellow Blakists about some action on the Toyama's agenda.

In a worrisome development, the Word of Blake has recently begun hiring mercenary units. Much of the Blake Militia remains on Terra, so the Word of Blake does have a legitimate interest in shoring up its defenses within the Free Worlds League. However, additional troubling possibilities also exist. The Blakists may be building up for an eventual takeover of the League; they already control its communications, and Thomas Marik's apparent absorption in his personal life may have made him a liability in the eyes of the more fanatical-minded. Alternatively, Marik may be working hand-in-glove with the Word of Blake on whatever scheme is afoot, and his apparent lack of interest in anything outside of his new family is designed to lull suspicion. We will continue to monitor the situation, and will send you updates whenever we have them.

NOTABLE PERSONALITIES

The following are briefings on individuals to watch for, especially if the Free Worlds League should destabilize in the near future. I don't expect that to happen as long as Thomas Marik remains alive and in good health, but he is seventy-two years old, and his heir is not yet three—not an ideal situation in the Inner Sphere, where political intrigue is as much a part of the air as oxygen.

CAPTAIN-GENERAL THOMAS MARIK

Rank/Position: Duke of Atreus/Captain-General of the Free Worlds League
Year of Birth: 2990 (age 72)

Profile:
The man that most of the Inner Sphere knows as Thomas Marik has served as Captain-General of the Free Worlds League for almost thirty years. He was believed to have died in the bomb blast that claimed his father and older brother in 3035; his unexpected reappearance in 3036 raised a few eyebrows, but also represented deliverance from his cousin Duncan Marik's incompetent leadership. Therefore, no one felt inclined to inquire too deeply into the miracle of Thomas's survival.

Thomas Marik's transformation from introspective ComStar acolyte to the deft political and military leader of an often-fractured nation has been astonishing, to say the least. Over the past three decades, Marik has launched several important reforms of the League military and government, among them the famous Addendum to the Incorporation that centralized power in the Captain-Generalcy. Soon after passing the Addendum, Thomas Marik led League forces in conquering the rebellious Duchy of Andurien, thereby ending the civil war into which Duncan Marik had led the realm.

In the years since, Marik has presided over an increasingly stable and prosperous nation. The death of his beloved son in 3057 was a personal blow, but he has since remarried and sired two new legitimate heirs. Despite the burns that disfigure his face and arms, he is a remarkably well-preserved seventy-two, and stands every chance of living to see his infant son come of age.

DUCHESS ISIS MARIK

Rank/Position: Duchess/Fiancée to Chancellor Sun-Tzu Liao
Year of Birth: 3035 (age 26)

Profile:
The illegitimate daughter of Thomas Marik, Isis was the heir to the Free Worlds League throne until the birth of her half-brothers. Even in third place, however, Duchess Isis can still function as a player in Inner Sphere politics. Janos Marik is very young, and the Captain-General is no longer so. Thomas and his wife may or may not have more legitimate children; in the meantime, the League would be faced with a child Captain-General should anything happen to Thomas in the near future. As a grown woman with some grasp of statecraft, Isis might well look like a reasonable alternative to many Free Worlds nobles; alternatively, she might be chosen as regent during Janos Marik's minority. Either way, she could potentially wield considerable

power over League affairs.

On a more personal note, Isis Marik has changed greatly for the better since her first appearance among the Inner Sphere's young royals on Outreach in 3051. Flighty and self-centered then, she was apparently dazzled by her own sudden leap into prominence. She has since matured into a thoughtful young woman, with graceful manners and a sense of responsibility to the people she had expected one day to govern. With the exception of his machinations in St. Ives, I believe we owe much of Sun-Tzu's unexpectedly solid performance as First Lord to Isis's influence. She genuinely cares for him, and appears to have bent over backwards to help him acquit himself responsibly.

By all accounts, Isis has also honed her political instincts, though she seems to have little taste for intrigue. She is capable, intelligent and a reasonably good judge of character, the latter possibly from her own experience. Having grown up being valued for her parentage rather than herself, she doubtless quickly learned to spot those interested in befriending her for their own advantage. In terms of our efforts to preserve the Star League, I believe she is a potential ally to be cultivated.

LIEUTENANT-COLONEL PHOTON BRETT-MARIK

Rank/Position: Lieutenant-Colonel/Executive Officer of the Second Free Worlds Guard
Year of Birth: 3015 (age 47)

Profile:
Currently serving as executive officer of the Second Free Worlds Guard, Photon Brett-Marik is Thomas Marik's nephew. His mother Therese Marik's elopement with Jeremy Brett, a junior officer in the FWLM, led the Marik family to disown her and placed both of her sons outside the accepted line of succession. Photon's somewhat irregular status, however, would be little obstacle to factions in search of a figurehead should Thomas Marik die before his legitimate heir comes of age.

To his credit, Lieutenant-Colonel Brett-Marik has so far shown no inclination toward political intrigue, nor has he capitalized on his Marik connections—in fact, just the opposite. To avoid the appearance of nepotism, Brett-Marik used the pseudonym Urien Domei upon enlisting in the FWLM in 3033. Not until 3048, when he received the prestigious Order of the Saber for his participation in a raid on the FedCom world of Dixie in 3050, did his true identity become public knowledge. Thomas Marik presented the award to him under his real name, at which point Urien Domei ceased to exist. Since then, Photon Brett-Marik has served ably as executive officer in the Second Free Worlds Guards, with apparently little interest in anything else.

FORCE COMMANDER CORINNE MARIK

Rank/Position: Force Commander/Executive Officer of the Second Free Worlds Legionnaires
Year of Birth: 3023 (age 38)

Profile:
The daughter of Thomas Marik's brother Paul, thirty-eight-year-old Corinne Marik was until recently second in line for the Captain-Generalcy. Janos Marik's birth bumped her one step further down the ladder, and the birth of Christopher pushed her further still. Any subsequent children born to Thomas and Sherryl will likely put Corinne out of the running altogether. The extent to which she cares about this remains an open question. Unlike her father, who has often and forcefully refused to have anything to do with rulership, Corinne exhibits a keen interest in politics, and in the past has dabbled in affairs beyond her legitimate concerns.

As the executive officer of the Second Free Worlds Legionnaires, Corinne occupies a prominent position with ample opportunity for building a power base. During the first few years after the forging of the Liao-Marik alliance, when fears of "the Liao" inheriting the League through marriage were at their height, Corinne became a focus for various anti-Liao factions interested in promoting her above Isis Marik as the next heir to the throne. Whether Corinne knew of or approved of this attention is in doubt; by all accounts from those serving with her, since attaining the executive officer's position she has devoted herself to the demands of her job. With the likelihood of Isis's marriage receding, political interest in Corinne Marik should drop off correspondingly. If she has been cultivating the anti-Liaoists as a personal power base, her following should remain the same or even increase.

Let me emphasize, however, that I do not consider Corinne Marik to be an imminent threat to the Captain-General. Even at the height of her fling with politics, she did not demonstrate the kind of naked ambition for power that would suggest a potential usurper. She is most likely to become a power player only if something should happen to Thomas Marik while Janos is still a child. In that case, she might well become a rival to Isis. Her stint in the military has taught her leadership, and her political abilities appear solid; combined with an existing power base, Corinne Marik could become a formidable contender for the League throne.

ADMIRAL HEATHER ALEXANDER

Rank/Position: Admiral/Director of Military Intelligence
Year of Birth: 3012 (age 50)

Profile:

As the person responsible for coordinating the League's extensive foreign and domestic intelligence operations, Admiral Heather Alexander is a woman to watch. Highly intelligent and as crafty as a Liao, the admiral knows very well that information is a formidable weapon. There isn't much she doesn't know about, and even less that gets past her. After more than thirty years in the intelligence field, holding positions from field operative all the way up to her current rank, she is well-versed in the tricks of the espionage trade.

Among other things, Admiral Alexander controls the League's so-called liberation units, small bands of irregulars outside the regular FWLM chain of command. Drawn from the ranks of dispossessed MechWarriors, special-forces troopers, other League citizens and even a few foreign nationals, these units are trained to infiltrate enemy worlds and cause chaos. Sabotage and terrorism are their stock in trade, which they use to soften up target planets for a larger FWLM invasion. Having such forces at her disposal could make the Director of Military Intelligence a formidable ally—or enemy—in a factional fight.

GENERAL HELEN THRALL

Rank/Position: General/Commander of the Sirian Lancers
Year of Birth: 3000 (age 62)

Profile:

General Thrall of the Sirian Lancers has been a vocal critic of the Captain-General's policies since the Chaos March invasion, when he declined to take the Lancers' homeworlds of Sirius and Procyon. The general and her Lancers vehemently protested this, especially after communications with the two planets abruptly ceased a few weeks later. When reports reached the League in mid-3058 of death camps and killing fields, an incensed General Thrall informed the League high command that her three regiments would attack the Sirian Holds as soon as they could arrange transport, with or without officialdom's blessing.

The Lancers liberated their homeworlds in early October of 3058, but what they found there permanently soured their relationship with Thomas Marik and the Free Worlds League. The Sirian Holds had fallen under the sway of a mad ComStar adept, and the delay in retaking the planets had given the madman time to execute tens of thousands. So bitter were the feelings of betrayal that talk of secession sprang up, and it has yet to die down. The only thing holding the Sirian worlds in the League is their need for assistance in rebuilding, which grows less and less acute with each passing month.

General Thrall has already committed her own personal act of secession. In late 3058, she publicly announced her intention to withold the Lancers' services from the FWLM the next time it called upon them. Thomas Marik has made no attempt yet to bring the general or her troops to heel, even though the situation is going into its fourth year. He may be playing a waiting game, believing that the Lancers will think better of their position; alternatively, he may be allowing them to make the first move before cracking down. Or he may simply believe that there is no reason to pour more gasoline on the fire until the issue actually comes up.

Having spent the past few years as senior officer of the military junta that rules the Sirian Holds, General Thrall has essentially made herself a petty head of state. Once she feels that her worlds no longer need League assistance, she may well declare independence. Whether Thomas Marik or his successor will allow her to keep it remains to be seen.

THE FALCON AND THE WOLF

[Victor: This revealing summary of the conflict the Clans called the Refusal War and the following report on the Clans come from Phelan Kell, as requested. His sources are excellent and his grasp of the situation sound. The SLDF won a colossal victory over the Clans, but anyone tempted to believe the Clan threat wholly gone should read this analysis and think twice. —JC]

In June of 3057, growing tensions between the Crusader and Warden factions of the Clans led to a protracted Trial of Refusal between two of the most powerful Clans on either side—the Warden-minded Wolves and the fanatically Crusader Jade Falcons. That conflict, later called the Refusal War, decimated both Clans and led to a Warden-Crusader schism in Clan Wolf. Under the last orders given to me by ilKhan Ulric Kerensky, I led the Warden Wolves to sanctuary in the Inner Sphere, where we now live as Clan Wolf (in Exile). The rest of Clan Wolf, overwhelmingly Crusader, remains a distinct threat to the Inner Sphere under the leadership of Khan Vladimir Ward—an ambitious and talented warrior who has made no secret of his desire to continue expanding his Clan's territory at the expense of the reborn Star League.

THE ROOTS OF CONFLICT

The Refusal War stemmed directly from the Truce of Tukayyid. The brevity of the average Clan warrior's military career meant that warriors who came of age during the Truce would likely be past the peak of their fighting abilities by the time the truce elapsed, and would get few chances to face combat before then. The problem was especially acute in Clan Wolf, and many Wolves ardently supported the Crusaders' call to break the truce. Crusaders within the Wolf Clan took advantage of the deepening split between them and the Wardens to attempt to force ilKhan Ulric Kerensky to repudiate the truce he had negotiated and resume the invasion.

In June of 3057, Wolf Loremaster Dalk Carns accused Ulric Kerensky of high treason. According to the charges, ilKhan Ulric had colluded with ComStar leaders to engineer the Clans' defeat on Tukayyid. Secondly, he elevated me to the post of Clan Wolf's saKhan. Finally, they characterized the truce as an attempt to destroy Clan Wolf's genetic heritage by effectively barring three generations of Wolf warriors from any combat more hazardous than training exercises or the occasional raid.

The first two charges Ulric easily disproved. The third, however, proved explosive. Ulric ordered the charge forwarded to the Grand Council and promised to answer it in a month's time.

He used that month to set plans in motion that would ensure the survival of the true Wolf Clan, no matter what the ultimate outcome of the trial.

TRIAL OF REFUSAL

On 8 August 3057 began ilKhan Ulric Kerensky's genocide trial. Khan Elias Crichell of Clan Jade Falcon insisted on playing prosecutor. Crichell painted a damning portrait of a conspiracy between Ulric, Precentor Martial Anastasius Focht of ComStar, Wolf Khan Natasha Kerensky and myself to establish a tainted Star League with Prince Victor Steiner-Davion as First Lord, and Crichell's wild speculations proved more effective than my defense. Sixteen Clans declared Ulric's guilt, stripping him of the ilKhanship and demoting him to the rank of Star colonel. In response, Ulric demanded a Trial of Refusal against Clan Jade Falcon. His bid; the entire Wolf Clan Touman.

The Falcons had wrongly assumed that Ulric would not contest the verdict—and with their forces poised to sweep down on the Inner Sphere the minute the Truce of Tukayyid was officially declared void, a large-scale Trial was the last thing they wanted. But the Falcons had no choice but to agree to the conflict that would prove their downfall.

PLOTS WITHIN PLOTS

After the Council adjourned, Ulric, Natasha and I retreated to Ulric's command center on Tamar to plot our battle strategy. There, Ulric revealed his scheme to cripple the Crusaders' power while ensuring the long-term survival of the best representatives of Wolf Clan's proud heritage. By virtually destroying the Falcons and the Crusader Wolves through inter-Clan warfare, Ulric would tear the heart out of the Crusader movement and protect the Inner Sphere, as Aleksandr Kerensky had directed almost three centuries ago.

To ensure the survival of the Wolf Clan, Ulric ordered me to take the bulk of the Warden warriors, along with Clan Wolf's genetic legacy and a third of its equipment and civilians, to a safe haven in the Inner Sphere. I accepted this role reluctantly, knowing that the greater good of the Clan depended on it. The departure of my forces after a few early battles would severely weaken those left behind, but I still had hopes that Ulric and Natasha might yet pull off a military miracle.

SUDETEN

To foster the illusion that the Wolves had committed their entire Touman to the Refusal War, my forces attacked Sudeten.

Using an ambush and aerospace fighter support, Delta's warriors destroyed or captured almost all of the Falcon 'Mechs while taking moderate casualties.

On the strength of this victory, I attempted to persuade my fellow Wolf Khans to allow my forces to stay and fight with the rest of our Clan, but to no avail. A week after the battle for Sudeten, my people left Clan space. We headed for the one place in the Inner Sphere that I knew would welcome us: Arc-Royal, homeworld of the Kell Hounds.

RED OCTOBER

Throughout the month of October, Wolf Clan forces pressed the Jade Falcons hard on several worlds, among them Zoetermeer, Baker 3, Devin and Evciler. The Wolves won on Zoetermeer and Baker 3, taking losses but demolishing the opposing Falcons. The battle for Devin went harder for the Wolves. Khan Natasha's Clusters won, but lost nearly half their 'Mechs and equipment and close to a quarter of their personnel.

Evciler was an equally hard-won victory; overwhelming Falcon opposition, as well as adverse environmental conditions, seemed likely to hand the Falcons their first win of the war. In the end, however, the pits in which the Falcon 'Mechs had hidden amid the ice-covered landscape of Evciler's southern polar continent weakened the ice beneath them, and the heat from weapons fire did the rest. The ice cracked and sent Falcon 'Mechs into the frigid waters below; the ensuing confusion gave the Wolves time to mount an effective counterattack and eke out a narrow victory.

TWYCROSS AND WOTAN

In early December, Khan Natasha Kerensky led her battered troops in an assault on Twycross, site of the Jade Falcons' most humiliating defeat against the Inner Sphere. This time, the Falcons achieved a stunning victory, inflicting heavy casualties on the Wolf units and ultimately forcing them to withdraw. Among the casualties was Khan Natasha Kerensky.

Three days later, the remnants of Ulric's and Natasha's forces arrived on Wotan, numbering a little more than a Galaxy but roughly equal to the Falcon force that had dug itself in around the capital city of Borealtown. The battle for the city was brutal, with both sides taking 80 percent casualties. SaKhan Vandervahn Chistu challenged Ulric Kerensky to a duel, but actually set a trap. The missile barrage that greeted Ulric's arrival in the center of the city killed him and two others of his accompanying Star, and Chistu's forces destroyed the rest. Unfortunately for Khan Chistu, one Wolf warrior—Star Captain Vlad—survived, along with evidence of Chistu's treachery.

MORGES

Meanwhile, the Jade Falcons pursued my own forces to the Lyran Alliance world of Morges. The entire Falcon force dropped onto Morges on 13 December, into the teeth of dug-in Wolf and Kell Hounds troops. After several days of brutal fighting, the Falcons drove us toward our fallback position but needed to resupply, and in so doing presented the Wolves with a chance to make a devastating counterattack.

The initial counterassault caught the Falcons by surprise, and their commander called for reinforcements. Wolf and Kell Hounds aerospace fighters unleashed a rain of death on the incoming Falcon units, decimating the Falcon aerospace flights even as they scrambled from their DropShips. The air barrage destroyed the Falcon ground units as well, bringing the Refusal War to a bloody end.

AFTERMATH

Though the Refusal War came close to destroying both Clans that fought it, Ulric Kerensky had achieved his objectives. The Falcons' power was shattered and the Wolf Clan survived, albeit in two mutually opposed pieces. Though the Crusader Wolf Clan was temporarily Absorbed by Clan Jade Falcon, Vlad Ward's return with a recording of saKhan Chistu's *dezgra* actions on Wotan forced the Grand Council to nullify the Absorption. Vlad Ward then killed both Jade Falcon Khans in single combat, after which he announced the resurrection of Clan Wolf with himself as its Khan. In the years since, both halves of Clan Wolf as well as Clan Jade Falcon have largely devoted themselves to rebuilding.

In Clan space, the Crusaders recently fought a series of inter-Clan engagements dubbed "Harvest Trials" to quickly beef up their Toumans. The Wolf Khan has already stated his Clan will not abide by the results of the Great Refusal. The Jade Falcons, with one of the few victories in the Trial, will undoubtedly find a way to bend the results to their liking. Both Clans believe the invasion of the Inner Sphere has just begun, and the other Clans will undoubtedly follow suit.

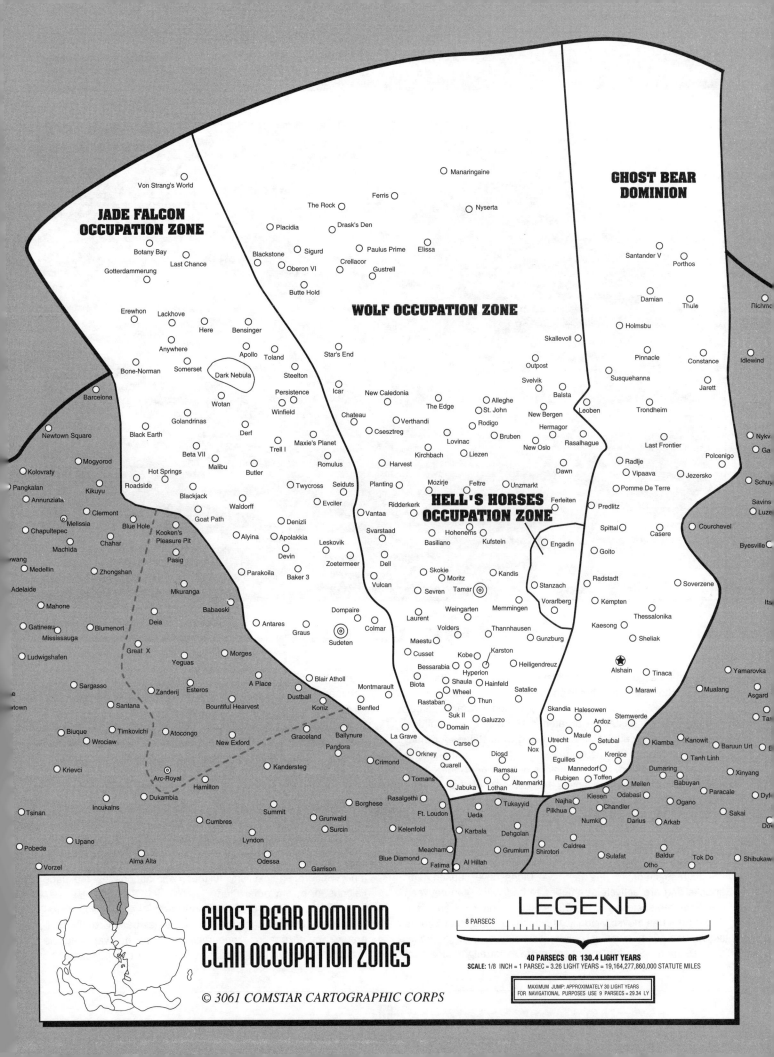

GHOST BEAR DOMINION

JADE FALCON OCCUPATION ZONE

○ Von Strang's World

○ Botany Bay
Last Chance ○
Gotterdammerung ○

Erewhon ○ Lackhove ○
○ Here ○ Bensinger
Anywhere ○
○ Apollo
Bone-Norman ○ Somerset ○ Toland ○
○ Barcelona Dark Nebula
○ Wotan Steelton ○
Persistence ○
Newtown Square ○ Golandrinas ○ Winfield ○
Black Earth ○ Derf ○
○ Kolovraty Beta VII ○ Trell I ○
Pangkalan ○ Malibu ○ Maxie's Planet ○
Mogyorod ○ Hot Springs ○ Butler ○
○ Annunziata Kikuyu ○ Roadside ○ Romulus ○
Clermont ○ Blackjack ○ Twycross ○ Seiduts ○
Melissa ◎ Waldorff ○ Evciler ○
Chapultepec ○ Blue Hole ○ Goat Path ○ Denizli ○
Machida ○ Chahar ○ Kooken's Alyina ○ Apolakkia ○ Leskovik ○
Pasig ○ Devin ○ Zoetermeer ○
Medellin ○ Zhongshan ○ Parakoila ○ Baker 3 ○
Adelaide Mkuranga ○
Mahone ○ Babaeski ○
Gatineau ○ Deia ○ Antares ○ Graus ○ Colmar ○
Mississauga ○ Blumenort ○ Sudeten ◎
Ludwigshafen ○ Great X ○ Morges ○ Dompaire ○
Yeguas ○
Sargasso ○ Zanderij ○ Esteros ○ A Place ○ Montmarault ○
town ○ Santana ○ Bountiful Hearvest Blair Atholl ○ Benfled ○
Biuque ○ Timkovichi ○ Atocongo ○ Graceland ○ Ballynure ○ Dustball ○
Wrociaw ○ New Exford ○ Pandora ○ Koniz ○
Krievci ○ Kandersteg ○ Crimond ○ La Grave
Arc-Royal ◎ Hamilton ○ Orkney ○
Tsinan ○ Incukalns ○ Dukambia ○ Tomans ○
Borghese ○ Rasalgethi ○
Summit ○ Ft. Loudon ○
Cumbres ○ Grunwald ○ Surcin ○ Kelenfold ○
Pobeda ○ Upano ○ Lyndon ○
Vorzel ○ Alma Alta ○ Odessa ○ Garrison ○ Blue Diamond ○

WOLF OCCUPATION ZONE

○ Manaringaine
Ferris ○
The Rock ○ Nyserta ○
○ Placidia Drask's Den ○
Blackstone ○ Sigurd ○ Paulus Prime ○ Elissa ○
Oberon VI ○ Crellacor ○ Gustrell ○
Butte Hold ○

Star's End ○
Icar ○ New Caledonia ○
Chateau ○ Verthandi ○
Csesztreg ○
The Edge ○ Alleghe ○ St. John ○
Rodigo ○
Lovinac ○ Bruben ○
Kirchbach ○ Liezen ○ New Oslo ○
Harvest ○
Planting ○ Mozirje ○ Feltre ○ Unzmarkt ○

HELL'S HORSES OCCUPATION ZONE

Ridderkerk ○ Ferleiten ○
Vantaa ○
Svarstaad ○ Hohenems ○
Basiliano ○ Kufstein ○ Engadin ○
Dell ○ Skokie ○ Moritz ○ Kandis ○
Vulcan ○ Sevren ○ Tamar ◎ Stanzach ○
Weingarten ○ Vorarlberg ○
Laurent ○ Memmingen ○
Volders ○ Thannhausen ○
Maestu ○ Kobe ○ Karston Gunzburg ○
Cusset ○ Heiligendreuz ○
Bessarabia ○ Hyperion ○
Biota ○ Shaula ○ Hainfeld ○
Rastaban ○ Wheel ○ Thun ○ Satalice ○
Suk II ○ Galuzzo ○
Domain ○
Carse ○ Nox ○
Diosd ○
Quarell ○ Ramsau ○
Jabuka ○ Lothan ○ Altenmarkt ○

GHOST BEAR DOMINION

Santander V ○ Porthos ○
Damian ○ Thule ○
Holmsbu ○
Skallevoll ○ Pinnacle ○ Constance ○
Outpost ○ Susquehanna ○ Jarett ○
Svelvik ○ Balsta ○
New Bergen ○ Leoben ○ Trondheim ○
Hermagor ○
Rasalhague ○ Last Frontier ○
Dawn ○ Radlje ○
Vipaava ○ Jezersko ○
Pomme De Terre ○
Predlitz ○
Spittal ○ Casere ○
Goito ○
Radstadt ○
Kempten ○ Thessalonika ○
Kaesong ○ Sheliak ○
Alshain ★ Tinaca ○
Marawi ○
Skandia ○ Halesowen ○ Stemwerde ○
Ardoz ○
Utrecht ○ Maule ○ Setubal ○ Kiamba ○ Kanowit ○
Eguilles ○ Krenice ○ Tanh Linh ○
Mannedorf ○ Toffen ○ Dumaring ○
Rubigen ○ Meilen ○ Babuyan ○ Paracale ○
Kiesen ○ Odabasi ○ Ogano ○ Sakai ○
Najha ○ Chandler ○
Tukayyid ○ Pilkhua ○ Numki ○ Darius ○ Arkab ○
Ueda ○ Dehgolan ○ Caldrea ○
Karbala ○ Grumium ○ Shirotori ○ Sulafat ○ Baldur ○ Tok Do ○
Meacham ○ Fatima ○ Al Hillah ○

Richm○
Nyk○ Ga○
Idlewind ○
Schuy○
Savins ○ Luze○
Courchevel ○
Byesville ○
Soverzene ○ Ita○
Yamarovka ○
Mualang ○ Asgard ○
Ta○
El○
Xinyang ○
Dyfe○
Do○
Shibukaw○

○ Krwang
○ Medellin
Adelaide

**GHOST BEAR DOMINION
CLAN OCCUPATION ZONES**

© 3061 COMSTAR CARTOGRAPHIC CORPS

LEGEND

8 PARSECS

40 PARSECS OR 130.4 LIGHT YEARS
SCALE: 1/8 INCH = 1 PARSEC = 3.26 LIGHT YEARS = 19,164,277,860,000 STATUTE MILES

MAXIMUM JUMP: APPROXIMATELY 30 LIGHT YEARS
FOR NAVIGATIONAL PURPOSES USE 9 PARSECS = 29.34 LY

THE CLANS

In the decade since ComStar's defeat of the Clans on Tukayyid, the status quo between us and the Inner Sphere has undergone several unexpected transformations. What began as a fragile truce constantly threatened by raiding and political pressures has become a permanent end to hostilities for many Clans. The reborn Star League need not fear the renewal of a unified Clan invasion, and the nations of the Inner Sphere have developed sufficiently advanced technologies of war to fight individual Clans with far greater odds of victory than were possible when the invasion began. No longer will any Clan be able to cut a swath of destruction through every Inner Sphere unit in its path; any more attempts at conquest will be bitterly contested, and the cost on both sides will be high.

In recognition of this fact, two Clans have ceased their attacks and are actively attempting to bridge the gap between the disparate societies of the Clans and the Inner Sphere. Clan Ghost Bear has moved virtually all personnel to its Inner Sphere occupation zone, retaining only token holdings in Clan space. Clan Diamond Shark's merchant caste is strengthening that

Clan's ties to Inner Sphere worlds, forging bonds of peaceful commerce with Inner Sphere citizens and governments.

Two additional Clans have gone a step beyond ceasing their attacks, and have completely thrown in their lot with the Inner Sphere. Clan Nova Cat has joined the Star League Defense Force, and its people are busy building new lives in the Draconis Combine. Clan Wolf (in exile) has spent much of the past four years settling into the Arc-Royal Defense Cordon. Centered on the Kell Hounds' stronghold of Arc-Royal on the spinward side of the Lyran Alliance, the autonomous ARDC spans the border between the Alliance and the Jade Falcon occupation zone. Together with the Kell Hounds, the Wolf (in exile) Touman stands ready to defend the ARDC and the entire Inner Sphere against any further depredations by the Jade Falcons, or by any other Clan.

Certain invading Clans have suffered stark reversals of fortune since Tukayyid. Clan Smoke Jaguar has been virtually obliterated, its occupation zone reclaimed and its war machine razed. The few surviving Jaguar warriors are either bondsmen or bandits, if one believes the rumors. Clan Steel Viper, once an adjunct invading Clan, recently retreated to Clan space to lick its wounds after gravely underestimating Clan Jade Falcon. The Vipers may yet rise again, but at the moment are fully occupied teaching the home Clans that, although they retreated from the Inner Sphere, the difference between the combat prowess of the home Clans and those who actually participated in the invasion is significant.

The SLDF victory in the Trial of Refusal on Strana Mechty, while undoubtedly a triumph, has not ended the Clan threat forever. The Crusader Wolves have refused to abide by the results, and it is doubtful whether the Falcons will abide by the results for long. Additionally, some of the Clans currently pursuing peaceful coexistence with the Inner Sphere may not always remain that way. The following analysis, beginning with my own Wolves (in exile), sums up the strengths, weaknesses and degree of danger posed to the Star League by each of the Clans with significant Inner Sphere operations.

CLAN WOLF (IN EXILE)

The exiled Wolves arrived in Lyran Alliance space on 20 November 3057, in the Morges system. The planetary defense had been turned over to the Kell Hounds, which saved my forces the necessity of fighting our way in. We defeated the pursuing Jade Falcons with help from the Kell Hounds, and in late December joined our strength to theirs when Morgan Kell formed the ARDC. The ARDC has become our home, and every one of us will fight to the death to defend it.

WARDENS OF THE INNER SPHERE

The Wolves (in exile) spent most of 3058 recovering from the Refusal War and beginning to put down roots on Arc-Royal. In his capacity as Arc-Royal's Grand Duke, my father granted us a virtually uninhabited continent on the planet, where our civilian castes immediately set about building a Clan society.

In mid-3058, Star Captain Ragnar (formerly Prince Ragnar Magnusson of the Free Rasalhague Republic) was our Clan's contribution to Prince Victor Steiner-Davion's Coventry attack force. Ragnar's understanding of Clan ways provided the crucial information that allowed the Falcons to accept hegira from Prince Victor and withdraw from Coventry without loss of honor. Meanwhile, I and my Wolves accompanied Kell Hound units on tours of the ARDC, sometimes clashing with Jade Falcon units that had slipped out of the occupation zone. What we lacked in numbers, the Wolves (in exile) made up for in ferocious combat, proving that we had not lost our fighting edge.

Later that same year, I participated in the military planning sessions against Clan Smoke Jaguar at the first Whitting Conference, and in 3059 led three Clusters against the Sixth Jaguar Dragoons on Labrea as part of Operation Bulldog. Fighting under the banner of the Star League, the Fourth Wolf Guards, First Wolf Legion and First Wolf Strike Grenadiers

defeated the Dragoons and took the survivors as bondsmen. Two additional Wolf Clusters also participated in the assault on the Smoke Jaguar OZ, defeating Jaguar forces on six other worlds and playing an instrumental role in clean-up operations.

Our clear willingness to shed Wolf blood in the Inner Sphere's defense went a long way toward earning us acceptance from our neighbors, though a few conflicts with Inner Sphere extremists continue to plague the Wolves. Most of these have so far been attributed to Ragnarok terrorists opposed to the Wolf capture of Prince Ragnar Magnusson, though suspicion of us likely still lingers among some populations in or near the ARDC. The people of Arc-Royal, following their Grand Duke's example, seem largely content to live and let live.

As for the exiled Wolves, the process of building a new life in the Inner Sphere has been both exhilarating and troubling. Many Clansmen, bred to unquestioning acceptance of their own superiority, find it hard to conceive of living as the mere equals of Inner Sphere citizens. Exposure to the Kell Hounds, whose military prowess is second to very few, is slowly eradicating the worst of this attitude, but a certain proportion of my Wolf warriors are likely to suffer from this "superiority complex" all their lives. Many Wolves from the lower castes, by contrast, see great advantages in becoming part of the Inner Sphere. Regardless, the Wolves (in exile) believe it their duty to protect and preserve the Inner Sphere, as Ulric charged us to do in his last command.

MILITARY ASSETS

The Sixth Jaguar Dragoons—captured nearly intact—have added significantly to the still-understrength Wolf (in exile) Touman. With the addition of the Sixth, Alpha Galaxy is close to full strength. Epsilon Garrison Galaxy is the most understrength, containing only three Trinaries per Cluster, as opposed to the five per Cluster deployed prior to the battle of Tukayyid. The oldest of the sibko cadets who accompanied us into exile have recently come of age, and stand to make promising warriors. Two of Omega Garrison Galaxy's Clusters are permanently stationed on Arc-Royal to protect the Wolf (in exile) stronghold against attack by other Clans, especially those with forces in Inner Sphere occupation zones. Given that most other Clans regard the Wolves (in exile) as an abomination, cadets placed in Omega are likely to receive more combat experience than they might wish for. In the meantime, their own superiors and the Kell Hounds are providing excellent training, and I am reasonably confident that my Clan will be able to fulfill its obligations to the Inner Sphere.

With regard to equipment, the first of the exiled Wolves' new 'Mech designs entered service in 3060, and our trade agreements with the Kell Hounds have netted us much-needed machines and supplies. In addition, Wolf scientists and technicians working in tandem with the Kell Hounds recently produced a new OmniMech based on Inner Sphere technology. So versatile is this 'Mech that some Wolf garrison warriors have traded in their Clan BattleMechs for it.

Our action against Clan Ghost Bear on Utrecht in late 3060 gained us badly needed materiel and resources with which to continue rebuilding, while costing us few casualties. The First Wolf Guards challenged the Bears for the contents of a newly arrived "ark" ship—a new *Leviathan*-class WarShip—among those contents prefab buildings and equipment for building factory complexes. The Ghost Bears accepted the challenge and allowed us safcon, which contributed greatly to the low casualty rate. One significant loss, however, was the capture of Star Captain Ragnar by the Third Bear Guard. His skill and insight will be sorely missed among the exiled Wolf Clan.

CLAN WOLF

Despite the SLDF's victory in the Strana Mechty Trial, Khan Vladimir Ward's Wolf Clan remains an increasingly potent threat to the Star League. Over the past four years, Khan Vlad has turned his ambition and drive toward ensuring his Wolves' political survival and beefing up the Wolf Touman. He has made excellent progress on both fronts, forging an alliance of convenience with Clan Jade Falcon to stave off other Clans' calls for Absorption and adding to his military forces through the Harvest Trials. As yet, he still lacks the strength to come against the Inner Sphere in force. That he intends to do so, however, is beyond doubt. He has announced his intention to continue the Great Crusade until Clan Wolf takes Terra, and I see no reason to believe that he has changed his mind.

CRUSADERS' RISE

The history of Clan Wolf since the Refusal War demonstrates the ability of the Wolves—Crusader and Warden alike—to adapt, survive and triumph over every setback. The Jade Falcons had intended the war to end Clan Wolf's existence; in the first few days after the final battle on Wotan, the Falcon Khans indulged in political maneuvers designed to obliterate their longtime rival. Recasting the Trial of Refusal as a Trial of Absorption, they claimed all surviving Crusader Wolves as isorla. They also Abjured the Warden Wolves, who were beyond the reach of the Falcons' shattered military forces.

They reckoned without Star Captain Vlad of the Wards. Found alive in his buried 'Mech three days after the conflict on Wotan, Vlad had the battlerom of the ambush in which Ulric Kerensky died, and brought his proof of Ulric's murder to the senior Falcon Khan. In exchange for bringing down the overly ambitious saKhan Chistu, Khan Crichell agreed to give Vlad the Ward Bloodright belonging to me, and also a Clan of his own from which to build a power base. With Khan Crichell's sanction, Vlad challenged Chistu to a Trial of Refusal and killed him. Crichell then turned his bargain with Vlad to what he thought was his own advantage. Rather than resurrect Clan Wolf, Crichell declared the formation of the Jade Wolf Clan, with Vlad as its new Khan.

Clan Jade Wolf was short-lived, however. Furious at Crichell's duplicity, Vlad Ward took his first opportunity to destroy him. He got it less than three weeks later, during an impromptu Grand Council meeting to elect a new ilKhan. When Crichell won the close vote, Vlad challenged him to a Trial of Refusal, disputing his fitness to be ilKhan on the grounds that he was not a warrior. Vlad killed Khan Crichell in hand-to-hand combat, whereupon he declared the Jade Wolves dead and a "new breed" of Clan Wolf revived in their place. After his ruthless performance against Khan Crichell, no one cared to dispute Vlad's actions. Since that day, Vlad Ward has served as Khan of the Wolf Clan.

His first action to strengthen his Clan was a lightning strike on Kiamba in the Smoke Jaguar occupation zone. An impressive show of strength, the assault demonstrated to all the Clans that the Wolf still had sharp teeth. He also began recruiting warriors from the lower castes in order to quickly fill out the depleted Wolf Touman, placing the new recruits in garrison units and moving former garrison troops up to front-line and second-line status. His next move was political rather than military, making common cause with Marthe Pryde of Clan Jade Falcon against other Clans. Elected Khan of Clan Jade Falcon shortly after Crichell's death, Marthe Pryde joined with Vlad against an attempt to engineer the Absorption of Clans Jade Falcon and Wolf.

The most significant result of the Wolf/Jade Falcon "alliance" was the Harvest Trials, proposed by Khan Ward and backed by Khan Pryde as a way of quickly adding combat-seasoned troops to their Toumans. These Trials of Possession for Crusader units from other Clans offered a chance at battlefield glory to many among the home Clans who desperately wanted a piece of the Inner Sphere action. Overall, the Harvest Trials proved an astounding success for Clan Wolf, swelling the front-line ranks with fervent Crusader units eager to crush the Inner Sphere "barbarians." Then, just as the Wolves appeared ready to renew the invasion, the SLDF attacked the Smoke Jaguars on multiple fronts.

The overwhelming Star League victory against what had been a powerful Crusader Clan apparently persuaded Khan Vlad to bide his time and rebuild for a little longer. The fact that his forces on Strana Mechty had to settle for a draw rather than a victory, and that he himself was defeated by "mere freebirth" Kai Allard-Liao, most likely also added to his newfound caution. Khan Vlad is as ambitious as he is talented, and he aspires to become an ilKhan who will take a prominent place in history. When he does move against the Inner Sphere, it will be with the most overwhelming force he can muster. In the meantime, we can likely expect sporadic Wolf raids as Vlad puts his units through their paces.

THE WOLVES AND THE BEARS

Another factor in Vlad's calculations is Clan Ghost Bear. In recent months, the Ghost Bears have taken three worlds in the Wolf occupation zone, possibly to keep the Wolf Clan in line after Vlad's public refusal to end the Inner Sphere invasion. In response, it appears Vlad has found a unique, if surprising solution.

During the Harvest Trials, Khan Malavai Fletcher of Clan Hell's Horses offered Vlad a proposal he could not refuse. Instead of battling Wolf units for something both Clans ultimately wanted, he proposed a contract with the Wolves, allowing Khan Ward to bid Horses troops into the invasion force without having to first win them away from their native Clan. The Twelfth Mechanized Cavalry became the first unit to work under this contract.

This working relationship seems to have convinced Vlad that the Wolves could work well alongside Clan Hell's Horses, if need be. Shortly after the Ghost Bears won hard-fought Trials of Possession for the Wolf worlds of Leoben, Skandia and Radstadt, Clan Hell's Horse's forces suddenly appeared and declared Trials of Possession for the Wolf worlds of Engadin, Stanzach and Vorarlberg. The subsequent battles and quick acceptance of hegira for Wolf withdrawal, however, appear too convenient, especially considering that all three worlds now held by Hell's Horse's warriors form an effective barrier against the Bear forces on Radstadt. My best estimation is that Vlad realized he could not obtain such a large force from the Hell's Horses by contract, but recognized them as the lesser of two evils. Knowing the enmity that exists between the Horses and the Bears, he felt a few worlds would be a small price to pay for the beginnings of a secure border against an opponent that outnumbers him four to one.

With this bold stroke, however, Vlad may have sowed the seeds of his own undoing. The home Crusader Clans, led by the Ice Hellions, are already demanding that the Grand Council intervene, as Clan Hell's Horses did not fight any Trials for the right to invade the Inner Sphere. So far, Vlad has squashed these objections by stating that, like the Ghost Bears, the Wolves own the Inner Sphere worlds they hold and so the Horses have simply taken Wolf worlds. Only time will tell whether this argument will satisfy the home Crusaders, or simpy give them the impetus to embark on their own campaigns to capture Wolf worlds in the Inner Sphere.

Regardless of Vlad's reasoning, the Bears' aggression is helping to keep Clan Wolf bottled up for the moment, until Vlad can either persuade them to cease their attacks (unlikely) or build up sufficient Hell's Horses units along his border to wall off their attacks. In either case, he knows he will have to balance the prize of holding the Bears at arm's length against allowing more Hell's Horses units into his occupation zone. Of course, now that Clan Hell's Horses have their own foothold in the Inner Sphere, Vlad may not have any choice in the matter.

MILITARY ASSETS

Khan Vlad has rebuilt all four of his front-line Galaxies since the Refusal War, using salvage taken on Wotan and promoting entire units of upper-quality garrison troops. Delta Galaxy, newly created from an entire garrison Galaxy plus front-line troops, has gone from just above second-line to front-line quality within the past two years under the able leadership of Galaxy Commander Katya Kerensky. The Wolves currently field four front-line Galaxies and two full garrison Galaxies, with a third being built.

CLAN JADE FALCON

Like the Crusader Wolves, the Jade Falcons have made great strides toward rebuilding their shattered Touman since the end of the Refusal War. The attack on Coventry, like the Wolf assault on Kiamba just a few months before, reminded other Clans that the Jade Falcons remained a force to be reckoned with and cost them negligible casualties. The Falcons also did well in the Harvest Trials, suffering losses only to Clans Fire Mandrill and Blood Spirit.

Marthe Pryde has served admirably as Khan of the Jade Falcons for the past four years. A staunch believer in the superiority of her Clan above all others, she intends to see it hailed as the ilClan. As her forces were one of only two Clan units to win their battle against the SLDF, Khan Pryde believes that their victory gives her Clan the right to bend the Crusaders' defeat to suit the Falcon agenda, which means she will most likely resume the Inner Sphere invasion as soon as she considers the time to be right.

THE ROAD TO CIVIL WAR

Despite the Falcons' insistence on outward conformity to Clan tradition, this Clan has a history of defining that tradition to suit its own desires. After ilKhan Ulric Kerensky signed the Truce of Tukayyid, tradition dictated that the Falcons abide by the word of their supreme war leader and accept the treaty. They obeyed the letter of this law, but violated its spirit. In 3054 and 3055, Clan Jade Falcon created and equipped a "bandit" unit under the leadership of a woman who called herself the Red Corsair. The Red Corsair raided several Lyran worlds above the Tukayyid truce line, essentially daring the Inner Sphere to send forces to apprehend her. Had they done so, the Jade Falcons would have pointed to the Inner Sphere incursion as a violation of the truce, rendering it null and void. IlKhan Ulric sent the Thirteenth Wolf Solahma after the alleged bandits, but the Thirteenth's commander, Conal Ward, was in league with the Corsair. His forces made no serious effort to capture or kill her, and on more than one occasion actively fought on her side against both Inner Sphere defenders and other Wolf units. The Corsair's forces eventually fell to the Kell Hounds on Arc-Royal, and the Corsair herself died on the world of Elissa.

With the failure of their bandit plot, the Jade Falcons turned to other means of breaking the truce. These means led to the Refusal War, in many ways a Pyrrhic victory for the Falcons. They had succeeded in breaking the Truce of Tukayyid, but in the process had left themselves too weak to exploit their achievement. Before they could rebuild sufficiently to renew the invasion, the SLDF launched its assault on Clan Smoke Jaguar, culminating in the 3060 Trial of Refusal on Strana Mechty. The unified Clan invasion of the Inner Sphere was over; Clan Jade Falcon would have to renew hostilities on its own, facing Inner Sphere units far superior in equipment and tactics to those the Jade Falcons had decimated roughly a decade earlier.

FALCON VS. VIPER

Fortunately for the Inner Sphere, the Falcons are not yet militarily capable of launching a renewed assault. Their recent clashes with Clan Steel Viper in the Falcon occupation zone cost them troops and 'Mechs they could ill afford to lose, which may have been the Vipers' secondary objective all along. The enmity between these two Clans runs bitter and deep; though the Vipers would doubtless have preferred to take Falcon territory, their successful interference with the Falcons' larger plans likely offers them some comfort. From the Falcon point of view, however, successfully kicking the hated Steel Vipers all the way back to Clan space is just one more proof of Falcon superiority. This Clan is riding high on its own military prowess, and its leaders are therefore more likely to give the go-ahead for assaults on the Inner Sphere despite their still-limited numbers.

MILITARY ASSETS

The Falcon Touman presently consists of ten Galaxies, three Galaxies short of full strength. Roughly a quarter of those Galaxies comprise full-strength Trinaries; only Falcon losses to the Steel Vipers kept that number from being higher. Khan Pryde has moved aggressively since the Refusal War to bulk out the Clan's military forces, graduating unprecedented numbers of cadets early in order to avoid more than minimal recruitment from the lower castes. That Khan Pryde recruited any lower-caste freeborns at all testifies to her determination to bring the Falcons back to full fighting strength as swiftly as possible; the Falcons' general attitude toward freeborns, which Khan Pryde shares, ranges from scorn to outright loathing.

Successes in the Harvest Trials have also added greatly to the Jade Falcons' strength, netting them experienced trueborn warriors from several other Clans. The units involved in the Harvest Trials are among those that most ardently desire war against the Inner Sphere, especially against the "false" Star League. Pressure from these units to renew the invasion, in addition to her own ambition and pride in her Clan, are likely to make Khan Pryde move against the Inner Sphere sooner rather than later.

CLAN HELL'S HORSES

Formerly only a Home Clan, the Hell's Horses have recently acquired the former Wolf worlds of Engadin, Stanzach and Vorarlberg, each garrisoned by a Cluster from Gamma Galaxy. It appears as if Vlad has made a decision to allow Clan Hell's Horses to stage Trials of Possession for worlds in the Wolf occupation zone in exchange for securing the Wolf border against Clan Ghost Bear. The Horses have little love for the Bears, and so future fighting is likely to be bitter and bloody. Whether more Hell's Horses units will appear in the Inner Sphere, or take more worlds for themselves, will depend on the fighting in Clan space.

The Trials of Possession between the Clans for the holdings of the Ghost Bears, Smoke Jaguars and Nova Cats that began nearly three years ago are still flaring up now and then.

The Hell's Horses, like almost every Clan, flexed their muscles in attacking and holding portions of several worlds against other Clans. Assigning a whole Galaxy to what effectively is an invasion corridor in the Inner Sphere may stretch their forces beyond what they can hold. If the fighting in Clan space dies down completely, however, we will assuredly see more Hell's Horses in the Inner Sphere

CLAN GHOST BEAR

In an unprecedented move, the Ghost Bears have relocated virtually all of their people and assets to their Inner Sphere occupation zone, now called the Ghost Bear Dominion. They have made the world of Alshain their capital, and apparently regard the Inner Sphere as their permanent new home. Recent Ghost Bear attacks on Wolf-held worlds, three of which they had captured by late 3061 (Leoben, Skandia and Radstadt), appear intended to safeguard the Inner Sphere against further Wolf depredations in accordance with the results of the Great Refusal.

THE CONQUERORS COME HOME

Though no one knew it at the time, the Ghost Bears apparently began laying the groundwork for their "third Exodus" not long after Tukayyid. Even before Tukayyid, Ghost Bear Khan Bjorn Jorgensson was making efforts to place local governments in the Bear OZ back in charge of their own people, with minimal oversight from the Clan. After Tukayyid, this process intensified. At the same time, in an effort to boost commerce, the Ghost Bears began several ambitious industrial expansion projects, which kept employment rates up and the local populations relatively peaceful while simultaneously enhancing the Bear Touman. The Bear merchant caste was also permitted limited trade with the Inner Sphere under strict warrior supervision.

By 3054, however, the half-years'-long delay between the Inner Sphere and the Clan homeworlds was beginning to seriously hamper the Ghost Bears' efforts to expand industry and trade in the occupation zone. Ghost Bear warriors and civilians still living on marginal Kerensky Cluster worlds began to resent their counterparts in the Inner Sphere, who enjoyed far better conditions on more than thirty worlds. In an effort to unite his people, Khan Jorgensson proposed to move the entire Clan permanently into the Inner Sphere. The proposition passed with more than the necessary two-thirds majority of the warrior caste, and in early 3055 the Bears set their operation in motion. They conducted the move in secrecy, most likely to prevent predation against Ghost Bear holdings or vessels.

When Victor Steiner-Davion and the SLDF arrived on Strana Mechty, conventional wisdom suggested that the Ghost Bears would defend their actions in the Trial as eagerly as any of their fellow Crusader Clans. Conventional wisdom, as often happens, was wrong. Khan Jorgensson refused to take part in the Trial, then went on to chide the Crusaders for their self-deceiving belief in innate Clan superiority. He ended by declaring the Ghost Bears a Warden Clan, and stated that the Crusader Clans

should defend "the invasion that has defined them and will destroy them." This political realignment brought consequences, among them a hasty call for the Bears' Abjuration when their move to the Inner Sphere became obvious. The Grand Council voted down that proposal, however, essentially granting the Ghost Bears the right to relocate wherever they wished.

Thus far, the Ghost Bears have made no threatening moves against their Inner Sphere neighbors—partly because they are fully occupied in building their Inner Sphere "nation," and also partly because of their newfound Warden convictions. Not every Ghost Bear warrior necessarily holds these Warden views, however. The Ghost Bear tradition of family-like bonds and extreme loyalty to their leaders makes it unlikely that any Crusader warriors or unit commanders will challenge their Khan's decisions in the near future. However, the sheer size of the Ghost Bear Touman and a lingering desire for glory in battle may pose problems further down the line, especially if any Combine Warlords or DCMS units decide to reclaim Ghost Bear worlds. For the moment, the Bears seem to be turning their military might toward preventing territorial expansion by Clans Wolf and Jade Falcon. The Bears regard the Great Refusal as binding on all the combatants, and see any violation of it as a stain on Clan honor.

MILITARY ASSETS

The Ghost Bear Touman, the largest among the Clans, contains five front-line OmniMech Galaxies and eight second-line Galaxies. Including the elite Keshiks, this Clan possesses roughly fifty-eight Clusters. Unlike many of their fellow Clans, the Bears have engaged in little combat since Tukayyid, and so have not depleted their military resources. In addition, the Ghost Bears developed a remarkably advanced logistical network during their relocation to the Inner Sphere, which now admirably serves the needs of a large military stationed across so many worlds.

Ghost Bear 'Mech units emphasize strength, relying on their abundant heavy and assault 'Mechs to deliver devastating firepower. They also make excellent use of Elementals; only Clan Hell's Horses makes more effective use of battle-armored infantry. Since the end of the Ghost Bear "Exodus," the fourteen-WarShip Bear fleet mainly protects key Inner Sphere worlds and escorts JumpShips carrying important cargo near hostile borders.

CLAN NOVA CAT

Within the past decade, Clan Nova Cat has undergone a change almost as unexpected as the demise of Clan Smoke Jaguar. From an adjunct invading Clan with strong Crusader convictions, the Nova Cats have become part and parcel of the Inner Sphere. Abjured in Clan space, they have made a new home in the Draconis Combine and joined their Touman to the SLDF.

The battle for Tukayyid came close to destroying the Nova Cats' invasion force, and so the Clan devoted the following several years to consolidating and rebuilding its Inner Sphere pres-

ence. Sobered by the extent of their defeat and lacking the strength to raid Inner Sphere worlds above the truce line, the Cats instead focused on holding the fifteen worlds they possessed in the Smoke Jaguar/Nova Cat occupation zone.

Of the worlds grudgingly ceded to them by Clan Smoke Jaguar, only two made major efforts to overthrow their weakened conquerors. The remaining four saw the Nova Cats as a welcome change from the brutal Smoke Jaguars, and chose to leave well enough alone. Of the worlds the Cats took on their own, Teniente was the least stable. Resistance units backed by Combine troops on-planet continued to give the Cats trouble long after those troops had departed. The loyal citizens of Teniente knew that the Nova Cats had come close to capturing the heir to the Combine throne, and did not feel inclined to forgive them that affront. The people of Caripare, by contrast, which was jointly administered by Clans Nova Cat and Smoke Jaguar, supported the Nova Cats in preference to the harshness of Jaguar rule. On most other Nova Cat worlds, resistance proved well within the Clan's capabilities to handle.

After the Inner Sphere victory at Coventry, the Nova Cat Khans began receiving peaceful overtures from the Coordinator of the Draconis Combine. The Combine and the Cats shared a devotion to warfare as a spiritual discipline, and the Coordinator's choice of his mystic-minded younger son Minoru as envoy to the Cats cemented this common ground. Over the next few months, Minoru persuaded the Nova Cat Khans to aid the newly formed SLDF in an assault on Clan Smoke Jaguar by refraining from attacking the Star League force being sent against the occupation zone. By offering token resistance against the SLDF on Nova Cat worlds, the Cats could satisfy the dictates of Clan honor while ensuring that the Inner Sphere would have more units to throw at the Cats' most hated Clan enemy.

Unknown to the Combine's leaders, the Nova Cats were predisposed to accept the Kurita proposals. Not long before Minoru's arrival, Clan Oathmaster Biccon Winters had experienced visions in which a dragon severely mauled a nova cat, and a nova cat and a dragon together killed a smoke jaguar. The Nova Cat Khans therefore took the Combine's proposed alliance as the fulfillment of prophecy.

CATS AGAINST THE JAGUAR

The Nova Cats fought almost all of their token battles against DCMS units. Nova Cat commanders voluntarily revealed the numbers and quality of their defending troops, and in several cases bargained down their forces to the point that no actual fighting took place. Of the nine first-wave targets, actual combat took place only on Kanowit and Avon, whose position at the leading edge of Clan conquests demanded a show of serious contention. By contrast, on Sawyer—the targeted world farthest away from the Cats' front lines—the Nova Cat garrison commander lost to the wing commander of the Third Night Stalkers in an aerospace fighter simulator.

The Nova Cat commanders on Avon decided to stage the battle for that world as a series of Trials of Position against

Kurita forces. Defeat meant that the Nova Cats would be absorbed into the Draconis Combine and redeployed as SLDF units—a harbinger of things to come. The Clan officers also bid themselves down to lesser 'Mechs or those with a slight design flaw that the DCMS troopers could exploit. Despite these intentional handicaps, the Nova Cats came close to winning on Avon; their warriors crippled at least three SLDF 'Mechs in each Trial. Following the SLDF's narrow victory, the Clusters on Avon became the SLDF Nova Cats, and assisted in major battles against the Jaguars on that world in the assault's second wave.

Having surrendered the Nova Cat halves of Avon and Caripare, the Cats and the SLDF used them as staging bases from which to hit Jaguar forces on those worlds. Actual 'Mech combat between the Cats and the SLDF took place only on Mualang; on the remaining five targeted worlds, DCMS forces prevailed with personal combat or token challenges. On Bjarred, a coin toss between Star Colonel Olivia Drummond and *Tai-sa* Katherine Oltion gave the SLDF its victory. Given the right to make the call, Drummond chose the edge. After this no-lose "battle," Drummond's forces became Bjarred's new DCMS garrison.

By 7 July 3059, all targeted worlds lost to Clan Nova Cat were once again the property of the Draconis Combine. As the SLDF assault proceeded without them, the Nova Cats were left to ponder just how far they wished to take their alliance with the fledgling Star League.

The Great Refusal

At the Grand Council on Strana Mechty in April of 3060, the Nova Cat Khans followed the Ghost Bears in their refusal to fight for the Crusader cause. A day later, Nova Cat Khans Lucien Carns and Severen Leroux came to the SLDF's field headquarters with a startling request: to fight Clan Ice Hellion alongside the SLDF in the Trial of Refusal. Based on a vision, the Khans were convinced that Clan Nova Cat must oppose the Ice Hellions, or the SLDF would lose. Prince Victor granted their request, and the Nova Cats went on to thrash Clan Ice Hellion in a fierce battle that claimed the lives of both Cat Khans and nearly killed Ice Hellion Khan Asa Taney. By this action and the word of Khan Carns, the Nova Cats pledged themselves to the Star League and gave their military forces to Victor to command—on Strana Mechty and wherever they might be needed in the future.

JOINING THE COMBINE

Soon after the SLDF's triumphant return to the Inner Sphere in 3061, Coordinator Theodore Kurita granted Clan Nova Cat its own prefecture within his realm. This proved fortuitous, as the Nova Cat population had already begun relocating to the Inner Sphere worlds under Nova Cat control, due to their Abjuration.

Becoming part of the Star League would not be as easy as moving from one set of planets to another, however. Despite shedding blood on behalf of the SLDF, the Cats soon found that many Combine citizens still saw them as "the Clan enemy." From the Nova Cat point of view, this suspicion is understandable, but misplaced. After the events of 3059 and 3060, including the deaths of both Khans who had led the Clan through Operation Revival, most of the Nova Cat rank and file see their Clan as having been reborn into a new life. Their actions during the Inner Sphere invasion are part of the old life, and should therefore be disregarded. They wish to be judged only by their recent acts in support of the Star League, which to them mark the beginning of their newfound enlightenment.

It is a mark of the Cats' devotion to their new path that Nova Cat units were the clear aggressors in only one of the incidents between Nova Cat and DCMS troops that have occurred since the Cats' arrival. On Avon, the Nova Cats challenged the Fourth Pesht Regulars to a series of duels. The Nova Cat garrison unit had failed to quash guerrilla resistance by the Third and Eleventh Regulars on Teniente in 3052; unable to challenge those units to a grudge match, the Cats settled for the Fourth Regulars instead. The Fourth's executive officer was badly wounded in one duel, which prompted the Eleventh Alshain Avengers to launch a retaliatory strike against a Nova Cat lance.

The Nova Cats, already smarting from being fought to a draw by the First Shin Legion on Cyrenacia, saw the Eleventh Alshain's action as dishonorable. Their reverence for the Star League fortunately made them reluctant to engage in an all-out assault on its DCMS representatives, which bought Coordinator Theodore Kurita some breathing space in which to more permanently deal with the problem. The Irece Prefecture was his solution, effectively separating the Clan from the rest of the Combine so that tempers could simmer down.

Despite these flare-ups, the Cats as a whole seem inclined to grant their Combine neighbors the time to come around. Individual Cat warriors may chafe under a continued hostility they see as undeserved, but so far the Clan has remained remarkably docile. Given time, the tensions between the Nova Cats and the rest of the Combine should work themselves out. For the moment, however, the risk of additional incidents remains. Coordinator Theodore is using considerable political capital to persuade his people to accept his unprecedented action; as long as he remains at the Combine's helm, his will and vision should prevail.

CLAN DIAMOND SHARK

Like Clan Ghost Bear, Clan Diamond Shark has chosen to create closer ties with the Inner Sphere, though in a very different way. After losing nearly two front-line Galaxies on Tukayyid, the Sharks concluded that their Clan's best interests lay in other battlefields—specifically, economic ones. The Diamond Shark merchant caste, historically an influential player in that Clan, has spent most of the past decade forging economic ties with Periphery and Inner Sphere worlds, both within and outside the Clan occupation zones. As renewed warfare would be staggeringly bad for business, the Sharks are unlikely to pose a military threat any time in the near future, even without taking into consideration their strong Warden leanings.

The ascension of the Diamond Shark merchants began with the military setbacks of the early 3050s. Soon after the devastating losses on Tukayyid, the Diamond Sharks lost their staging world to Clan Ghost Bear, and with it much of its garrison Galaxy. The Diamond Sharks pulled all military assets back to the homeworlds, where they still had vast holdings to protect. Luckily, the treason trial of Ulric Kerensky and the Refusal War

occupied the attention of most Clans long enough for the Sharks to recover.

Khan Ian Hawker, a Crusader blowhard somewhat out of place in this largely Warden Clan, devoted himself to political damage control rather than taking charge of rebuilding the Diamond Shark Touman—possibly because he did not wish to preside over an effort so heavily dependent on freeborn warriors, whom he despised as unworthy. In the absence of direct leadership by both Diamond Shark Khans, effective control of the Clan passed to Angus Labov, a retired trueborn warrior who had become head of the Diamond Sharks' merchant council. Determined to restore the Diamond Shark touman by every means at his disposal, Labov sent his fellow merchants to drive hard bargains in the Clan occupation zones as well as the homeworlds, with an eye to large profit margins or military concessions. WarShips began protecting merchant convoys, as well as harassing the merchant shipping of other Clans. Before long, Labov's efforts had largely bridged the gap between warrior and merchant, forwarding the goals of both castes.

The Harvest Trials accelerated the rise of the merchant caste. Losses to Clans Jade Falcon and Wolf cost the Sharks many a Crusader-minded unit, leaving fewer conservative warriors to oppose the developing new order. Angus Labov, who had returned to active warrior duty, joined the Touman as a Star colonel, which lent an air of official authority to the changes he had wrought.

Meanwhile, the SLDF launched its assault on Clan Smoke Jaguar. The Jaguars' staggering losses, accompanied by the failure of Khan Hawker's scheme to lead a strike force in their support, confirmed in the minds of most Diamond Shark warriors the folly of continuing hostilities. When Victor Davion and the SLDF arrived on Strana Mechty, Hawker bowed to the will of his Clan and voted along Warden lines, though undoubtedly he hoped for a Clan victory. After the dust settled, the Clans found themselves unexpectedly at peace. A disillusioned Khan Hawker chose death rather than life without war; saKhan Barbara Sennet became Khan, and Angus Labov was elected saKhan.

RECENT GAINS

The death of the Smoke Jaguars, the Abjuration of the Nova Cats and the voluntary withdrawal of the Ghost Bears to the Inner Sphere left unclaimed large swaths of territory in Clan space that had formerly belonged to all three Clans. With the invasion defunct, Clan warriors in search of combat began fighting each other for those holdings. The Ghost Bears had given several worlds to the Diamond Sharks, which the Sharks soon found themselves defending. Though forced to surrender territory to the Jade Falcons, the Sharks held on to the valuable world of Paxon. They also leased several *Potemkin*-class troop transports to Clan Nova Cat and entered into a contract to defend that fleeing Clan. On the Nova Cat capital of Barcella, the Diamond Sharks helped tie up the Ice Hellions and Jade Falcons, and were rewarded with a large portion of the planet. According to reliable reports, the fighting on Barcella has yet to settle down.

Meanwhile, the merchants continued with plans of their own. Beginning in January of last year, with Chandrasekhar Kurita as their marketing representative, Clan Diamond Shark opened formal, but secret, trade negotiations with the Draconis Combine. In addition to various non-military items, the Diamond Sharks have reportedly included stripped-down versions of their new *Ha Otoko* BattleMechs. Already the Sharks have begun to see profit from this endeavor, and stand to make even more if they can negotiate similar deals with other Inner Sphere powers.

With their increasing ties to Inner Sphere merchants and dealers, the Diamond Sharks seem likely to integrate successfully into Inner Sphere society, if they choose that path for themselves in the future. This of course, is assuming that society will let them. Powerful business interests in certain areas are likely to make known their dislike of Clan competition. The most immediate threat in this regard will probably come from Combine hard-liners already opposed to their Coordinator's "coddling" of Clan Nova Cat; they are the most likely to resent "gaijin Clanners" cutting into their profits, and any action they take against Diamond Shark merchant interests will have the side benefit of hurting the Coordinator.

CLAN STEEL VIPER

On the face of it, Clan Steel Viper no longer poses a credible military threat to the Inner Sphere. A reserve invading Clan to begin with, the Vipers were handed their heads by the Com Guards on Tukayyid and never really recovered from that defeat. The failure of their recent bid to take over the Jade Falcon/Steel Viper occupation zone forced the Vipers' wholesale departure for Clan space, where they are shoring up their Touman and biding their time. They have not lost their belief in their own superiority, however, and the hatred between the Vipers and the Jade Falcons has only grown more bitter with the events of the past year. Should Clan Steel Viper regain sufficient strength to challenge the Falcons again, they are likely to do so—and a Steel Viper victory would be as bad or worse than a Falcon one for any Inner Sphere worlds that these Clans might choose to make their battlefields.

WAR AGAINST THE FALCON

The debacle on Tukayyid cost the Steel Vipers their senior Khan—not to glorious death in combat, but to the humilation of resignation. Acknowledging her responsibility for her Clan's disastrous defeat, Khan Natalie Breen stepped down in favor of then-saKhan Perigard Zalman. Zalman chose to restore the Vipers' pride via an assault on Jade Falcon possessions in the two Clans' shared occupation zone.

The Vipers had taken fewer casualties than most Clans on Tukayyid, and so initially did well against the Jade Falcon military. Barely a month after Tukayyid, the Vipers took three OZ worlds from the Falcons, and had taken another six by mid-3055. Khan Zalman then ordered a halt to the assault rather than overextend his forces, and the Vipers turned to sporadic

raiding of Federated Commonwealth border worlds. Meanwhile, they used the resources of their OZ planets to expand their military and economic base.

What had begun as a low-intensity war against the Jade Falcons turned into a major military endeavor in 3061, more than three years after the Refusal War. The depletion of the Falcon Touman in that conflict temporarily made the Vipers the stronger Clan; Khan Zalman, apparently with advice from former Khan Breen, took advantage of the chance to put his Clan on top permanently. Internal troubles had prevented the Vipers from acting when the Falcons were at their lowest ebb, however. By the time Zalman launched major operations, the Falcons had begun to rebuild. Unluckily for the Vipers, their Khan chose to ignore the warning he might have taken from Falcon exploits on Coventry. His Clan therefore faced an opponent stronger than they had expected.

Initially, the Steel Vipers claimed impressive successes. After several weeks of fierce fighting, they had taken a string of worlds from Toland to Quarell, and believed they had the Falcons on the run. However, they had reckoned without the granite resolve of Khan Marthe Pryde, whose tireless efforts to rebuild the Falcon Touman were finally beginning to pay off. Khan Pryde regarded the Viper assault as a larger-scale Coventry—a chance for her troops to hone their skills in battle. Her units exceeded her expectations, and before long the tide began to turn in the Falcons' favor. The Jade Falcons ultimately prevailed, forcing the Vipers to withdraw from the Inner Sphere rather than face total war against the rival Clan they had thought such easy prey.

CURRENT ACTIVITIES

For the moment, the Steel Vipers are fully occupied holding their Clan space territory against expansion-minded home Clans. They are unlikely to pose a major danger to the Star League anytime soon, but may become a real threat in the longer term. Their desire for revenge against the Jade Falcons burns brightly, as does their conviction that they alone are destined to re-establish the "true" Star League. They regard the present Star League's existence as a personal insult, and would gladly see it destroyed. Of all the invading Clans, the Steel Vipers most closely resemble the Smoke Jaguars in their contempt for freeborns and everything associated with them; that mere "freebirth scum" have dared to unite under the banner of the revered Star League only proves the Inner Sphere's barbarity in their eyes. Once they rebuild, they are likely to target the "sham" Star League with the same enthusiasm as the Jade Falcon occupation zone.

Unable to move in force against either the Falcons or the Inner Sphere, the Steel Vipers will likely settle for destabilizing both regions through sporadic raiding. Any Viper interference with the Falcons works to the Inner Sphere's advantage, as dealing with it will tie up Jade Falcon military resources. Lack of access will make the Vipers less likely to raid Inner Sphere worlds; they no longer have any staging bases in the Falcon OZ, and the remaining Clans with Inner Sphere territory are unlikely to permit Viper military action from within their borders. One possible exception to this is Clan Wolf, which may see advantages in making minor trouble for the Falcons despite the two Clans' recent detente.

HOME CLANS

Though the home Clans in general are unlikely to pose much danger to the Inner Sphere in the near future, knowledge of their recent activities may offer useful insights into Clan politics and thinking. Like the invading Clans, the home Clans are divided into Warden and Crusader camps. Among the Crusader Clans are the Blood Spirits, Fire Mandrills, Ice Hellions and Star Adders; the Warden Clans include the Cloud Cobras, Coyotes, Goliath Scorpions and Snow Ravens.

CLAN BLOOD SPIRIT

Reclusive and deeply wary of its fellow Clans, Clan Blood Spirit had virtually ceased all contact with them by the time of the Great Refusal. For centuries, the Blood Spirits have felt slighted by the other Clans. They blamed their troubles principally on Clan Burrock, whose near-constant raiding had consistently kept them from building up their military forces. In 3059, when evidence of Burrock dealings with the bandit caste came to light, the Spirits fully expected to be granted the right to Absorb their ancient enemy. After the Grand Council gave that right to Clan Star Adder instead, the incensed Blood Spirits launched their own preemptive attacks against Clan Burrock holdings, only to find their Touman savaged at the hands of both the Star Adders and Burrocks. Mortified by their defeat, the Clan voted to isolate themselves as completely as possible from other Clans. They withdrew to their enclave on the world of York, releasing their holdings in the Pentagon worlds and leaving only a token force on Strana Mechty.

The Blood Spirits' belief in their own superiority rivals that of any other Clan, and so their defeat in the Great Refusal dealt them a profound shock. Only with great reluctance did the warriors of Clan Blood Spirit, and especially their Khan, admit they had dramatically underestimated the Inner Sphere.

For now, they remain cloistered on York, building up their Touman as best they can and biding their time. Though their numbers are small compared to such Clans as the Star Adders, Jade Falcons or Ghost Bears, their determination to survive and overcome all obstacles is astonishing. They have vowed that they will come when the Inner Sphere least expects them and will pull down the Star League, regardless of the results of the Great Refusal.

CLAN FIRE MANDRILL

Clan Fire Mandrill suffered severe losses in the Hellion's Fury campaign that convulsed Clan space during the early waves of the Inner Sphere invasion. The Mandrills' disorganized and often quarreling

Kindraa (divisions among the Clan dividing Bloodname houses) were unable to mount a coordinated defense, and plans to retaliate against Clan Ice Hellion fell apart amid squabbles over who would command a proposed multi-Kindraa strike force. The Fire Mandrills have slowly rebuilt since then, as old rivalries faded somewhat in the face of intermittent Absorption threats from other Clans. The home Clans were also preparing for the possibility of a renewed invasion, and this time the Fire Mandrills were determined to be among the invaders. Mandrill units sent Harvest Trial challenges to Clans Wolf and Jade Falcon, but fought only Falcon forces; Clan Wolf, having taken the fanatically loyal Mandrills as bondsmen in the past, knew better than to attempt integration of Mandrill units into its ranks.

After losing to Capellan troops on Strana Mechty, Clan Fire Mandrill chose to continue rebuilding and to keep its military campaigns in Clan space. The Mandrills are among the many Clans contesting for Smoke Jaguar, Nova Cat and Ghost Bear territory, keeping their forces busy for the time being.

CLAN ICE HELLION

Known throughout the Clans for fighting better battles with words than with 'Mechs, Clan Ice Hellion lived up to that dubious reputation with its defeat on Strana Mechty. The Hellions managed to kill both Nova Cat Khans only because the Cat leaders took the brunt of the fighting on themselves; Khan Severn Leroux personally shot down the Hellion Khan's aerospace fighter. Before the Great Refusal, the Hellions' best-known recent exploit was the Hellions' Fury campaign—a temper tantrum masquerading as a military campaign, launched against the other home Clans after the Hellions failed to win a place in the Inner Sphere invasion force. The Fury campaign netted the Hellions considerable land and resources, but cost them both of their Khans and much of the goodwill their fellow Clans had previously shown them. The shocking defeat of the invading Clans on Tukayyid mitigated the other home Clans' resentment somewhat, allowing Khan Asa Taney to build support among them for a bid to either join or replace the invaders. That effort fizzled, however, when the Grand Council rejected Taney's call to Absorb the Wolves and Jade Falcons in the aftermath of the Refusal War.

Taney's close call in the Great Refusal has added to his political difficulties, strengthening the hand of those Hellion warriors who prefer territorial expansion in Clan space to a new Inner Sphere invasion. Given those circumstances, it is highly unlikely that the Ice Hellions will launch a solo attack on the Inner Sphere.

CLAN STAR ADDER

Clan Star Adder is among the stronger of the home Clans militarily after having Absorbed Clan Burrock in 3059. The Adders have nearly finished integrating Burrock units into their own Touman, and the

Clan is looking for somewhere to flex its newfound muscle. The Adder victory in the Great Refusal fired the pride of many Star Adder warriors, some of whom have begun to agitate for a campaign against the "false" Star League—this time with Clan Star Adder leading the way. However, the Adder Touman is still stretched somewhat thin defending the Clan's considerable holdings as well as meeting Clan Burrock's defense contract with Clan Cloud Cobra. The Adders may become a threat if the pro-invasion faction gains ascendancy, but likely not until then.

CLAN CLOUD COBRA

The Cloud Cobras tend to keep to themselves. Only Clan Coyote has managed to draw them out by engaging them in a long-standing feud. Few others have had much contact with them since the Clans' inception. Those who know anything about the Cloud Cobras tend to disregard them because of their small numbers or their devotion to what they call the Way—a religious tendency that resembles the mystical oddities of Clan Nova Cat.

The Cloud Cobras are far more clever than is generally assumed, and their belief in the Way is proof. A great many Cobras genuinely believe in and follow their own version of the Way. A few, however, use it to their own advantage, following the letter of their laws but not the spirit. When combined with the political acumen of their Khans, this willingness to fit their beliefs to the circumstances leads many other Clans to label the Cloud Cobras as opportunists.

Two recent incidents demonstrate the Cobra's opportunistic tendencies. The first is their success in disavowing their dealings with Clan Burrock when that Clan was absorbed by Clan Star Adder in 3059. They also took advantage of their recent victories in the War of Possession, in which they supported the Nova Cats' withdrawal following their Abjuration, by occupying the planets they were defending. Their religious bent and willingness to take advantage of opportunities when they appear make the Cloud Cobras a dangerous foe.

CLAN COYOTE

Warden from the beginning, Clan Coyote was one of the few to side with the Wolves when charges were brought against ilKhan Ulric Kerensky in 3057. They chose not to intervene when the Inner Sphere attacked Clan Smoke Jaguar, and sided with Clan Ghost Bear in declaring the Strana Mechty Trial a matter for the Crusader Clans to decide. In the past two years, the Coyotes fought for former Nova Cat and Smoke Jaguar territory on Brim, Huntress and Londerholm. The latter campaign gained the Coyotes a portion of the planet, though they are still wrestling with Clan Ice Hellion for control of the world. On Huntress, Clan Coyote won possession of the Jaguars' ProtoMech technology and withdrew.

The destruction of the Smoke Jaguars and the defeat on Strana Mechty have badly shaken some Clans, but not Clan Coyote. Visionaries in this Clan point out that the Crusaders have borne the brunt of the recent losses, and predict a bright future for the remaining Clans under wiser Warden guidance. Clan Coyote intends to be a leader toward that future, and may even attempt rapprochement with the Star League.

CLAN GOLIATH SCORPION

Despite its Warden leanings, Clan Goliath Scorpion forces fought at Tukayyid—one Star of Scorpion 'Mechs, led by the Scorpion saKhan. SaKhan Posavatz had accompanied the Steel Vipers to the Inner Sphere, promising to return with Star League treasures he claimed would elevate the Scorpions to the position of ilClan. He and his unit unfortunately disappeared on Tukayyid, lost during the fighting at Devil's Bath.

While the invading Clans were off in the Inner Sphere, the Scorpions consolidated their strength in Clan space. Khan Suvorov initiated strikes throughout the Kerensky Cluster to probe neighboring Clans' defenses, and in the process made significant gains on the world of Tokasha. After the Refusal War, the Scorpion saKhan helped Clan Wolf strengthen its depleted forces through the Harvest Trials. To make room for new recruits, the Scorpions bid away an entire Trinary of Crusader-minded warriors to their longtime Wolf allies. The Scorpions recently gained former Jaguar territory on Huntress, and are in the process of developing ProtoMechs. They have also recently unveiled a technological innovation of their own: Undine battlearmor, meant for underwater operations. The Scorpions are in a position to strike out across human-occupied space, and believe it is incumbent upon them to help shape the Star League's rebirth in one way or another. Whether that will mean military action at some point in the future depends largely upon how we treat them, and on how well we live up to the Scorpions' interpretation of the old Star League's ideals.

CLAN SNOW RAVEN

Clan Snow Raven profited hugely from the invasion of the Inner Sphere, contracting out parts of its immense naval fleet to other Clans. The Ravens stayed out of the infighting that followed in Tukayyid's wake, choosing not to support the "Home Clan coalition" forged by the ambitious Ice Hellion Khan. The Harvest Trials proved the Ravens right, especially after they lost two Clusters to the Jade Falcons and several smaller units to the Wolves.

These setbacks were balanced by gains from an unusual source. The Snow Ravens discovered Clan Ghost Bear's move to the Inner Sphere some time before it became common knowledge, when the Ghost Bears sought the Ravens' aid in converting their *Leviathan*-class WarShips into arks suitable for large-scale civilian transport. In return, the Bears gave the Ravens numerous asteroid mines and most of the world of Bearclaw. The Ravens clashed with the Hell's Horses over Bearclaw soon afterward, but retained control of the planet. After the Smoke

Jaguars' demise, the Ravens took control of large areas of Circe; they gained even more territory on that world from the Nova Cats, whose flight to the Inner Sphere they aided. The Ravens lent ships to the Nova Cats, screened their retreat and escorted them through the Deep Periphery.

The Snow Ravens' recent territorial gains and growing power have made other home Clans sit up and take notice of them. The Cloud Cobras accepted their aid against Clan Steel Viper on the world of Homer, in exchange for a portion of the Jaguar enclave there. The Goliath Scorpions likewise looked to Raven expertise to shore up their aerospace arm; the Snow Ravens' reputation for air and naval superiority has not diminished throughout the centuries of that Clan's existence. Such influence is a new and enjoyable experience for the Snow Ravens, and they will likely do whatever is necessary to keep it.

NOTABLE PERSONALITIES

The following individuals are among those with the greatest power to aid or harm the Star League in the near future.

KHAN BJORN JORGENSSON

Rank/Position: Khan, Clan Ghost Bear/Commander of Ourse Keshik
Year of Birth: 3023 (age 38)

Profile:
Bred in a MechWarrior sibko, the current Khan of Clan Ghost Bear failed his initial Trial of Position and became an aerospace pilot after tests showed aptitude for that branch. In an exceptional display of talent for his new calling, Bjorn Jorgen-sson passed his second Trial of Position and scored three kills, which earned him the initial rank of Star captain. He served with distinction in the 140th Striker Cluster during the Inner Sphere invasion and earned the rank of Star colonel between the second and third waves, shortly before becoming Khan.

Large and muscular compared to typical Clan aerospace pilots, Khan Jorgensson allegedly pilots a *Kirghiz* because it is the only fighter big enough to accommodate him. He tends to be soft-spoken, allowing his saKhan to do most of the talking in Council. When Jorgensson speaks, he generally has something of serious import to say; for example, he declined on behalf of his Clan to fight in the Great Refusal.

STAR COLONEL RAGNAR

Rank/Position: Star Colonel/Commander of the First Rasalhague Bears
Year of Birth: 3036 (age 25)

Profile:
Once known as Ragnar Magnusson, Star Colonel Ragnar was captured by Clan Wolf early in the Inner Sphere invasion. By dint of hard work and exceptional ability, he soon earned warrior status and the rank of Star captain. He accompanied the Wolves (in exile) to the Inner Sphere after the Refusal War, and his insight into Clan customs proved vital in the Inner Sphere's victory on Coventry against Clan Jade Falcon.

In late 3060, he was captured by Clan Ghost Bear as he led his Star of 'Mechs against the Third Bear Guards in a Wolf raid on Utrecht. As in Clan Wolf, his rise to warrior status was outstandingly fast; he now serves as Star Colonel of the First Rasalhague Bears Cluster. As a former prince of Rasalhague, his insight into the hearts and minds of that realm's conquered citizens should aid Clan Ghost Bear in its ongoing efforts to forge ties between the people of Rasalhague and their Clan rulers.

KHAN VLADIMIR WARD

Rank/Position: Khan, Clan Wolf/Commander of Alpha Galaxy
Year of Birth: 3026 (age 35)

Profile:
Vladimir Ward's rise to the top of Clan Wolf began after the Clans' defeat at Tukayyid, when he became the leader of the disaffected Crusader faction among Clan Wolf's younger warriors. In 3057, Vlad saw an opportunity to achieve the glory he believed the Truce of Tukayyid had denied him. Along with then-Loremaster Dalk Carns and fellow Star Captain Marialle Radick, Vlad conducted a secret internal investigation of ilKhan Ulric Kerensky. That investigation culminated in charges of treason and genocide against the ilKhan, which in turn led to the decimation and schism of Clan Wolf in the Refusal War.

On Wotan, Vlad was one of five MechWarriors who escorted Ulric to the site chosen by Vandervahn Chistu for a duel against the ilKhan. The duel never took place; instead, Chistu called in missile fire to destroy Ulric and his escort. Vlad survived the ambush, along with recorded evidence of Chistu's treachery. Vlad used that evidence to extort from Falcon Khan Elias Crichell the Bloodright of Ward and the resurrection of Clan Wolf. Crichell gave him the Bloodname, but revived the Wolf Clan as the Jade Wolves—an act of political calculation that cost him his life. Vlad Ward killed Crichell in single combat, then announced the reformation of Clan Wolf.

Since assuming the Wolf Khanship, Vlad Ward has rebuilt his Clan's battered touman with single-minded efficiency. His détente with Clan Jade Falcon, instigation of the Harvest Trials and attempts to gain territory abandoned by the Nova Cats, Smoke Jaguars and Ghost Bears are all directed toward the goal of renewing the Crusader Wolves' strength so that they can once again invade the Inner Sphere.

KHAN MARTHE PRYDE

Rank/Position: Khan, Clan Jade Falcon/Commander of the Turkina Keshik
Year of Birth: 3010 (age 51)

Profile:
Formerly a Star colonel and saKhan, Marthe Pryde became Khan of Clan Jade Falcon after the deaths of her predecessors at the hands of Vlad Ward. A canny military strategist with an eye to the long term, Marthe Pryde is determined to restore her Clan to its former prominence. She has served with distinction throughout her career, leading her unit in several impressive victories. The latest of these, over the Com Guard component of the SLDF on Strana Mechty, is a sobering reminder of just how tough Falcon troops can be. The Khan's accomplishments, spanning almost half a decade, are well on the way to rivaling those of her famed sibling among the Jade Falcons, the maverick Aidan Pryde of the Falcon Guards.

Though widely respected, Khan Pryde rarely forms friendships, even with her peers. Capable, fiercely intelligent and utterly dedicated to the advancement of her Clan, Marthe Pryde has few weaknesses. Even her legendary temper, a frequent problem in her younger days, has largely yielded to her iron-willed desire to regain her Clan's former glory. Though she retains her lifelong distaste for the Clans' often-Byzantine politics, she has become almost as adept in that arena as she is behind the controls of a 'Mech. Her recent alliance with the Crusader Wolves—an act of bridge-building that most other Jade Falcons could scarcely have brought themselves to consider—has done much to preserve the Falcon Clan and proved Marthe Pryde a dangerously visionary leader.

KHAN SANTIN WEST

Rank/Position: Khan, Clan Nova Cat/Commander of the NovaStar Keshik
Year of Birth: 3031 (age 30)

Profile:
Santin West became Khan of Clan Nova Cat in early 3060, after the previous Khans died in the Great Refusal. Though somewhat on the short side for an Elemental, Santin's stature has never proved a handicap in battle. He attained the rank of Star captain in his first Trial of Position, winning out over a fellow Elemental with considerably greater height and reach. He later won the Bloodname of West and the rank of Star colonel under similar circumstances.

During the Inner Sphere invasion, Santin West fought Combine troops on Caripare and on several other worlds, racking up an impressive number of 'Mech kills. On Luthien in 3052, he survived the destruction of his unit in the Kadoguchi Valley at the hands of the Kell Hounds. Later that same year, he battled the Com Guards 244th Division on Tukayyid. His next major engagement against Inner Sphere forces came in 3058, when Star Colonel West led his 179th Striker Cluster against what he believed was Clan Smoke Jaguar's newly formed Tau Galaxy on the worlds of Tarnby and Wayside V. In fact, the "Smoke Jaguars" who had hit Nova Cat targets on Tarnby were part of Stirling's Fusiliers, a regiment of the famed Northwind Highlanders mercenary unit. West, fired by a vision he had experienced of two great cats battling to the death, was eager to engage and defeat the Jaguar force. The false Jaguars fought him to a standstill on Tarnby, however, forcing him to break off and renew the combat elsewhere.

He got his chance on Wayside V, to which the Nova Cats had followed the Highlander unit from Tarnby. The Cats deployed from their DropShips to face the real Jaguar Tau Galaxy, at the Jaguars' hidden base—exactly as the Highlander masqueraders had intended. With a little unexpected help from the Fusiliers, the 179th defeated the Jaguar force.

By strict Clan tradition, the mercenaries' aid left the Cats' victory tainted, and Star Colonel West would have been within his rights to destroy the Fusiliers. He chose instead to act in accordance with a higher honor, sparing the Fusiliers rather than obliterating them in a fight that would have needlessly decimated his own battered unit as well. This action demonstrated a flexibility of mind that will serve him well as the first Khan of the SLDF-affiliated Nova Cat Clan.

THE FALL OF TERRA

—Post-battle report by Trent Arian, Precentor Martial, Word of Blake, 16 April 3058

Precentor Blane,

Attached is a comprehensive summary of our successful campaign for Terra. Though a few Com Guard bases and facilities remain sealed as of this date, the Word of Blake has achieved its goals of suspending the Terran Assembly and restricting access to Terra's archives, and is firmly in control of the planet. We expect to mop up the last resistance within the week. Humanity's homeworld once again belongs to its true spiritual heirs.

OPENING MOVES

The campaign for Terra, code-named Operation Odysseus, began with a singular stroke of luck. Thomas Marik's 3057 war in the Chaos March left the region of space near Terra in turmoil, with countless factions battling for power on planet after planet. The constant fighting created a surge in demand for mercenary troops, with a corresponding rise in pay. Among the mercenary units tempted by these proverbial greener pastures was Brion's Legion, which made up nearly half the strength of the Terran Defense Force. In late 3057, the Legion terminated its contract with ComStar and left Terra for Pleione in the Tikonov Reaches. The unit's departure left a gigantic hole in Terra's defenses. Faced with the choice of moving one of its Com Guard units away from the Clan front or hiring another mercenary unit, ComStar chose the latter course. In so doing, they gave us our opportunity and sealed their own fate.

THE SHADOW LANCERS

Among the mercenary units ComStar considered was the Twenty-first Centauri Lancers, a unit with a sterling reputation and connections all the way back to the Star League. Subtle maneuvering by our agents in ComStar helped to ensure that the Lancers were hired. Precentor Suzanne Mulvanery, commander of the First Division of the Word of Blake, then set Phase Two of our plan in motion. Accompanied by elements of the Sixth Division, Mulvanery led the First to the Lancers' homeworld of Nestor and placed the mercenaries' dependents under the Word of Blake's protection. With the Centauri Lancers' non-military personnel safely transferred to Gibson, Precentor Mulvanery made the returning mercenaries the proverbial offer they could not refuse. If the Lancers agreed to keep a low profile for the next few months,

they would be reunited with their families at the end of that time. If not, the First and Sixth Divisions would destroy them, and the fate of their dependents would be up for grabs. Prudently, the Lancers agreed to our request.

While the First and Sixth reorganized and equipped themselves to match the real Lancers, Word of Blake operatives within ComStar took steps to ensure that the false Lancers could pass the expected security checks. It helped that Precentor Martial Anastasius Focht was off conducting war games on Tukayyid. We also timed our infiltration of the Terran Defense Force to coincide with the regular rotation of veteran Com Guards from Terra to Tukayyid. The Shadow Lancers made planetfall on Terra in January 3058, as scheduled, and took up residence at the Bowling Green, Kentucky facility recently vacated by Brion's Legion.

Over the next few days, our forces prepared for their role in the coming takeover. Despite surveillance by ComStar ROM agents, the Shadow Lancers successfully contacted Word of Blake sympathizers within ComStar, the Com Guards and the Branch of Terran Affairs. Orders were given and personnel placed precisely where needed. This part of Operation Odysseus took just under two months to complete, assisted somewhat by the Jade Falcon attack on Coventry in February. The Clan assault further distracted Focht and Com Guard leaders, giving our people more room to maneuver.

By the end of February, all the necessary pieces were in place and the timetable set. Once again, luck worked in our favor; a spate of bad weather flared up across the North American continent, confining many Terran defense units to base. At that point we made our move.

OUTBREAK OF WAR

Hostilities began in earnest on 28 February 3058, when two Shadow Lancer aerospace fighters shot down the DropShip of the Terran Defense Force commander as it approached Bowling Green. Precentor Lisa Koenigs-Cober was unfortunately one of the two survivors, though there was little she could do to stop us at that point. At the same time, Word of Blake agents all across Terra began operations against various Com Guards sites. The single most effective of these had actually been carried out some time before, during a post-Schism overhaul of ComStar's computerized base security. Posing as a civilian computer systems engineer, agent Satoshi Fujishima had installed a "backdoor" that gave him almost

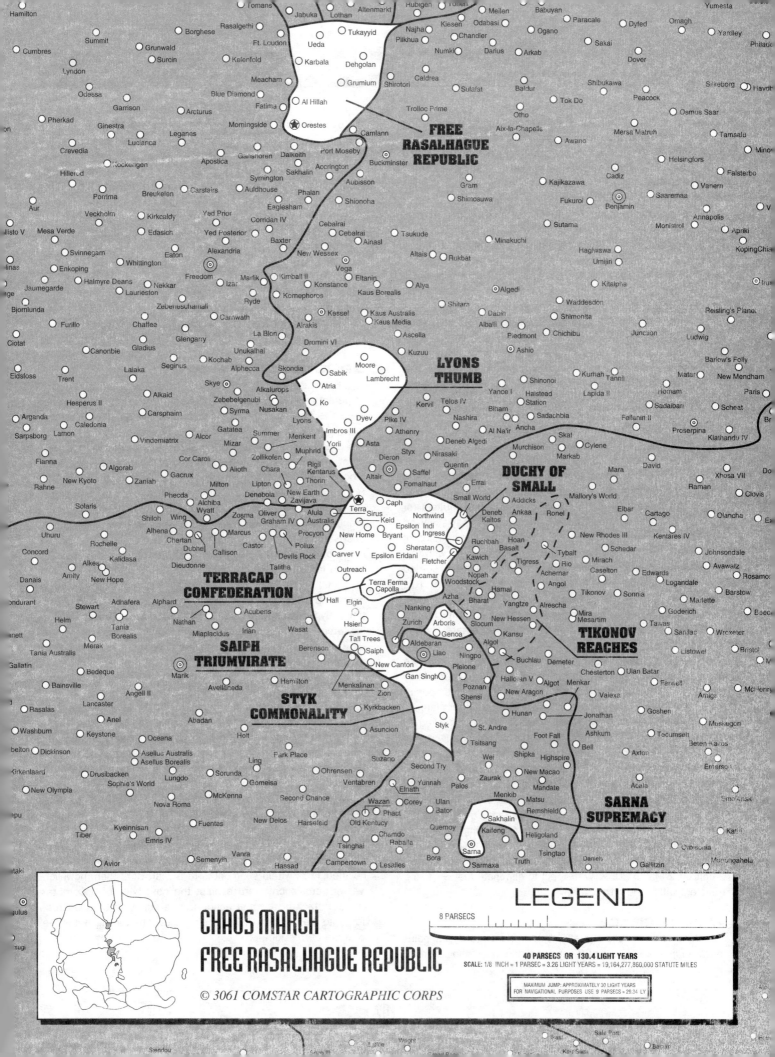

unlimited access to ComStar's Terran computer systems. Upon receiving word that the attack was underway, Fujishima sent a command sequence via this backdoor to all Com Guard and Terran Security Force installations. The sequence informed each facility that it was being overrun by enemy forces and locked each into autonomous mode. As planned, the defense systems assumed that all ComStar personnel present were hostile, and trapped several Com Guard troops within their bases. Fujishima's stratagem effectively neutralized some two hundred Com Guard and TerraSec bases, greatly simplifying our task.

Meanwhile, we also took other measures to minimize resistance. Word of Blake infiltrators assassinated key ComStar officers and administrators, while aerospace fighters and ground forces attacked Com Guard armories, barracks, 'Mech hangars and other vital sites. To neutralize ComStar ROM's heavily fortified HQ, our ROM operatives resorted to a powerful nerve agent. Within thirty minutes, this multi-pronged surprise attack had reduced Terra's formidable defense forces into a scattered, leaderless mass incapable of mounting an effective counterattack.

ASSAULT ON HILTON HEAD

At ComStar's Hilton Head Island headquarters in North America, we expected—and got—stiff resistance from Primus Sharilar Mori's bodyguard unit, made up of light armor and infantry. Fortunately, the system-wide computer lockdown prevented Hilton Head personnel from broadcasting requests for help to Terran or offworld garrison forces; had they received such reinforcements, Hilton Head might yet be in the hands of the enemy. The Shadow Lancers' armor unit, charged with taking Hilton Head, soon abandoned its frontal assault and settled into positions from which it could bombard the complex. This tactic softened up Hilton Head's defenders for subsequent Lancer attacks. Before our forces could take the facility, however, Precentor Koenigs-Cober and one of her lancemates turned up unexpectedly and disrupted the Lancer armor's ongoing assault. Com Guard troops used the distraction to evacuate Sharilar Mori and remove or destroy valuable equipment. They also set several booby traps, which killed a large number of Lancers when they finally took the facility just 24 hours later.

Of the three remaining North American bases attacked by the Shadow Lancers, only the Salina facility put up significant resistance. Our forces greatly outnumbered the 201st Com Guard Division, however, and soon forced them to withdraw. They broke through our encirclement, at which point elements of the Shadow Lancers set out in pursuit. After forcing the 201st to fight several rearguard actions, the Lancers pinned them against another Word of Blake force heading southward from Washington state. Though a few Com Guard 'Mechs escaped the final battle, the 201st Division ceased to exist as a unit on 2 March 3058. We expect to eliminate the remaining resisters within the next few days.

WAR IN SPACE

Our invasion flotilla arrived in-system via a pirate jump point in trans-lunar orbit late on 28 February, and made short work of the Com Guards' defending vessels. As the Word of Blake fleet reached Terran orbit, Blake commandos seized control of the remaining ComStar Space Defense System sites, which operated independently from the general-security computer system. Most of these assaults succeeded admirably, with the glaring exception of the protracted battle fought over the Santo Tomas laser battery in the Andes mountain range. Fortunately, Word of Blake forces captured Santo Tomas before it could pose any major threat to the invasion fleet.

Other off-planet battles went less well for the Word of Blake. Though we succeeded in capturing the War Academy on Mars by 2 March, only six ComStar 'Mechs survived that battle. The Blake naval force sent to take the Titan shipyards was actually beaten back by the Com Guards, leaving the yards firmly in ComStar's control.

GROUND CAMPAIGN

By midday on 1 March, the flotilla had begun to land troops at primary and secondary sites across Terra. Among the former were the Com Guards' Sandhurst headquarters in the British Isles, the seat of Terran government in Geneva and the Court of the Star League in Washington state. Approximately one regiment of Word of Blake troops landed at Sandhurst, while combined-arms battalions made planetfall at Geneva and Unity City. Secondary invasion forces, varying from a lance to two companies in size, landed at the Ecole Militaire in Paris, numerous key manufacturing and research sites, and several Com Guard bases known to have escaped the computer lockdown. Though some of our troops initially met fierce resistance, the assaults by and large were stunningly successful. By the time I arrived on-planet on the evening of 1 March, I had only to establish a command post from which to oversee the mopping-up operations. By 5 March, we had destroyed the bulk of Terra's defending forces and consolidated our control over the planet. The battle for Terra was over, and the planet once more in the hands of its rightful caretakers.

AFTERMATH

Since the official end of hostilities on 7 March, the Word of Blake Militia has begun to rebuild using salvage and the contents of Com Guard storehouses. Guerrilla groups on all three inhabited planets in the Terran system continue to harass our forces whenever they can, but the damage they can do is limited. Terra now lies under martial law.

Word of Blake ROM is spearheading our efforts to quell resistance among Terra's population, hunting down suspected ComStar sympathizers, Com Guards in hiding and representatives of hostile foreign intelligence services. Though rooting out all resistance is likely to take some time, I fully expect to see a pacified Terra within six months to a year. Until then, however, we will remain on guard against the possibility of a ComStar counterattack or terrorist action by the surviving Com Guards. To quote the Blessed Blake, one can never be too vigilant in the defense of freedom.

COMSTAR & THE WORD OF BLAKE

[This section begins with several transmissions between Word of Blake operatives and their higher-ups, which my people and ComStar ROM managed to intercept. Though unfortunately scant on detail, they do tell us that there's something going on in the Chaos March, and I'd bet it isn't good. For the ComStar section, I've compiled several reports from the heads of the various ComStar branches; they should bring you up to speed on the current situation and the resources at your disposal. —JC]

WORD OF BLAKE: SCHEMES AND MACHINATIONS

TO: Precentor Blane, Gibson, Free Worlds League
FROM: Adept Talman Dysart
DATE: 29 October 3061
RE: Styk Commonality—Status Report

During the past week I have visited both Styk Commonality worlds, and am pleased to report that local leaders appear uniformly receptive to our proposals. They have not yet accepted, but they have given us a fair hearing and asked several ques-

tions that indicate a high degree of interest. I expect an affirmative reply within the next couple of days.

As you directed, I requested a tour of the Tao Mechworks and several other industrial facilities on Styk. Though not on the cutting edge of manufacturing technology, they are nonetheless quite serviceable and can generate considerable output per quarter. Any improvements we can offer will be welcomed, but we need not offer much. I have not yet determined how many displaced FedCom personnel are still working at Tao, however, or in what positions. Since the nationalization of the facility in late 3059, the Styk government has made a point of ferreting out those it labels "foreign nationals," among whom were large numbers of former FedCom citizens. According to my guides, the bulk of the Mechworks' labor force is now native to the Commonality, and will follow the dictates of its government rather than acting on behalf of some foreign power. I cannot, however, rule out the possibility that FedCom sympathizers or even loyalist partisans of the former FedCom prince might leak word of our activities to their superiors.

Ambassador Dartain assures me that his government can stall any action by the Federated Commonwealth almost indefinitely, especially since that realm's recent change in government. The leaders of the Commonality have been "in negotiations" with the Commonwealth concerning trade agreements since 3058, and have dragged those talks out long enough to retain independence for almost the past four years. To continue forestalling military action in this way poses no problem, provided we can offer the Styk government certain assurances. Apparently, the reclamation of the Commonality's resources and industrial base remain low on the list of Archon Katrina Steiner-Davion's priorities, which leaves us ample room to maneuver.

I will report again when I receive the government's answer. In the meantime, please advise the proper course of action in case of a refusal; I do not consider this a realistic possibility, but it is best to prepare for all contingencies.

[This communiqué suggests several possibilities. The obvious one is a military build-up, with the Blakists offering the Commonality minor technological improvements (under Word of Blake control, of course) in exchange for military manufacturing output. Most of the materiel produced by Tao Mechworks and others has been going to the FedCom and the Free Worlds League, but shipments to the FedCom have been dropping off in the past couple of years. Most of the League shipments have found their way into units deployed in the Duchy of Andurien, in keeping with the pro-Andurien slant of the Styk regime. The Humphreys family, hereditary rulers of Andurien and bitterly opposed to the Liao-Marik alliance, are propping up the Styk government financially, though persuasive evidence indicates that the Word of Blake is kicking in some cash as well. Thomas Marik is not among the Humphreys' favorite people just now, nor is anyone connected with him. If the Word of Blake wants a larger share of Styk's military output going into its own storehouses, a separate deal makes sense.

The Blakists may also be offering direct military aid, which the Commonality would surely welcome. The tiny state's defenders consist of a few mercenary units, reportedly of respectable size and quality, but nowhere near enough to stand against a determined assault by a House military. At most, they could hope to hold off a small House force for an indefinite period of time, which is what they seem to have done with Sun-Tzu Liao's troops. Fortunately for the Styk Commonality, Sun-Tzu is occupied on so many fronts that he hasn't enough spare units to launch an all-out attack.

The most farfetched scenario has the Word of Blake attempting some sort of political alliance or even an outright takeover of the Styk Commonality, above and beyond a simple tech-for-supplies swap. Hints of such an alliance are there, though they can also be interpreted in other ways. Controlling the Styk Commonality would give the Word of Blake a foothold in the Chaos March, though why they would want one remains a mystery. Attempting to branch out from Terra and recreate the old Terran Hegemony, perhaps? Like I said, it's farfetched ... but just about anything is possible with these guys. —JC]

TO: Precentor Blane, Gibson, Free Worlds League
FROM: Precentor Melva Kingman
DATE: 10 November 3061
RE: Status Report, Terracap Confederation

My meeting with the surviving former leaders of the Capollan government has been most productive. They are anxious to stabilize their planet, and would like to see the mercenary thugs responsible for its current chaos gone. They have few resources to fall back on, however. Negotiations with the Federated Commonwealth in late 3058 came to nothing, and most of the mercenary units hired to liberate Capolla from the Fist of Mokal in early 3059 left the planet shortly after their victory. Few stayed long enough to see the liberation undone by pirate attacks and Mokal-led raids, and the resulting state of anarchy has depleted those units that did remain. Under such circumstances, any offer we can make them will look attractive.

Before their abrupt departure from Capolla, the Fist had managed to extract a fair amount of valuable ore from the planet's extensive mines, some of which remains in storehouses guarded by this or that local strongman. The Word of Blake's HPG maintenance contract with the Terracap Confederation government remains valid on Capolla despite the near-constant turnovers of power there, as all sides have a vested interest in keeping lines of communication open. The movements of our technicians provide a perfect cover for further operations on Capolla and Terra Firma; we await only your word to put the next phase of our plan in motion.

On Terra Firma, the Fist remains firmly in control, aided by its paramilitary death squads. The principal surviving pro-FedCom loyalist movement has long since given up on getting any aid from its parent realm, and is now seeking simple independence from the Fist dictatorship. They will work with anyone who will bring them closer to that goal. The surviving Liaoist factions are more problematic; rumors have reached them of the Capellan Confederation's recent renaissance, and they are far less amenable to our overtures than they were this time last year. Many of them are convinced that Sun-Tzu Liao will soon send troops to liberate Terra Firma, and are determined to hold out until then.

Per your last orders, we will continue to contact resistance groups on Terra Firma. The results will be in my next status report.

[Interestingly enough, one of the "former Capollan leaders" took ship for Styk ten days after the date of this transmission. He arrived at Styk's major spaceport, where he was met by a government-issue hovercar and taken to the White Palace—the seat of government for the Styk Commonality. My people have spotted him once in the capital since; we don't know whether he is still there. Unfortunately, we also have no hard data on what he came to Styk to discuss, or with whom. The timing makes it probable that it has something to do with whatever went on between the deposed Capollan authorities and the Word of Blake—but again, we have no specifics.

My guess: an offer of protection or backing against various warlords on Capolla, either direct military aid or finances with which to buy troops and equipment. Or it could be something as prosaic as agreeing to shut down all the HPGs on Terra Firma, which would make it infinitely easier for others to drive out the Fist of Mokal. Presumably a regime heavily beholden to the Word of Blake would then take over on Terra Firma, and would be in an excellent position to dictate terms to the Capollans. However, I'm not certain what the Word of Blake hopes to gain from such an arrangement. The Terracap Confederation has little to offer anyone; all but the most desperate merc units shun the place because the low pay isn't worth the hazards. —JC]

TO: Precentor Blane, Gibson, Free Worlds League
FROM: Adept Roman DiMassi
DATE: 2 December 3061
RE: Epsilon Eridani—Status Report

Matters are progressing well here; I have made several useful contacts in the city of Dori, and most have expressed at least guarded interest in our proposals. A few walk away upon learning who we are—some because they prefer not to work with "a gang of fanatics," as one put it, others because they still remember Operation Scorpion and equate us with Primus Myndo Waterly's failed attempt to redeem civilization. Most, however, look first to their purses, where we measure up quite well. Our work here should be finished within two months, at the rate things are going. I have also learned the names of several dealers—some based on Epsilon E, others based elsewhere—whose merchandise makes them suitable for our purposes. Attached are the names and brief descriptions of the most likely candidates; hopefully, this information will be sufficient for ROM to come up with a fuller profile of each. Extra leverage can be very useful when dealing with these people.

I met Duke Benton briefly, though I have not yet spoken frankly with him. I thought it best to take the measure of the man before doing so, and ascertain just how deeply his commitment to Epsilon E's independence runs. He is an excellent leader of men, with immense personal integrity and charisma. He would make a persuasive advocate for our cause, provided we can convince him of its justness. Toward the Word of Blake in general, he appears wary, though not hostile. He is among those who distrust "fanatics," and he has little taste for politics outside of his own planet. If he sees our activities as political meddling, he is unlikely to want anything to do with them. At the same time, however, he will not hinder us unless he believes we pose a danger to his world.

Epsilon Eridani's HPG stations may offer us a way to get what we need here, with or without the duke's cooperation. As one of the few safe havens in the Chaos March, Epsilon E is a thriving center of commerce, which depends upon swift and easy communication. The sheer amount of business that takes place on this planet entails heavy HPG use, which is currently enriching the coffers of the ComStar heretics. If we can offer a better deal—to Duke Benton or to a sufficient number of prominent local businessmen—we can likely engineer ComStar's departure.

I will continue my inquiries and report back in two weeks.

[Unfortunately, we haven't yet managed to crack the encryption on the attached files, so we don't know what "dealers" DiMassi is referring to. Arms dealers are the obvious choice, but is the Word of Blake interested in buying or selling—or both? What are they offering or asking for in exchange, and what is their ultimate goal in connecting with these people? We don't know yet, and I'm afraid I can't even venture a good guess at this point. As to the other "contacts," they could be just about anyone, though I'd guess merc commanders. I have people watching DiMassi closely; they should be able to get me some hard data on which commanders DiMassi talked to, as well as which were receptive. —JC]

[The following reports offer some interesting insights into Word of Blake thinking. They appear convinced that things will be heating up on Terra in the near future, now that the Clans are no longer consuming most of ComStar's attention and military manpower. If you're planning something, count me in. —JC]

Field Report: Precentor Randolph Kanni, Commander, Word of Blake Third Division; Nairobi, Africa Command
To: Precentor Martial Cameron St. Jamais
Date: 28 June 3061
Eyes Only

First, I would like to congratulate you on your recent rise in rank. Your exploits are quickly becoming legendary; thus you must be worthy of the power you now wield. I fervently hope that the office you currently hold does not put too much strain upon you, as all activities on Terra that are adverse to us will reflect poorly upon you with the Ruling Conclave.

Unfortunately, I regret to report that we have not completely stamped out all guerrilla raids in our sector of operations. Though the 201st Division was finally destroyed in late 3059, I believe that a handful of units from that Division were able to excape into Africa and are conducting a very small, but effective guerrilla campaign. We have even begun to receive aid from the civilian population in our efforts to track down these last rebels. I personally believe their aid is a trap that will spring on us if we are not careful, regardless of their masks of sincerity.

However, I would request your personal presence, in an effort to bolster the flagging spirits of my Third Division and to see firsthand what we have accomplished, despite the constant raids. Regardless, I assure you that all guerrilla activity will cease by the new year.

Reply To: Precentor Randolph Kanni, Nairobi
From: Precentor Martial Cameron St. Jamais
Date: 2 July 3061
Re: Request for Additional Troops

I have read your latest field report, but am unfortunately unable to accede to your request for my personal visit. Duties take me elsewhere, as I begin to redeploy our current forces and shore up our static defences.

Do whatever is necessary to eradicate the guerrilla activity.

The enemy cannot be allowed to once more gain a foothold on Terra. I have complete faith that you and your Division will do your duty.

Confidential: Eyes Only
From: Precentor ROM Alexander Kernoff
To: Adept Julia Holloway

My dear Julia,

You will have heard by now of the appointment of Victor Steiner-Davion as the new Precentor Martial of ComStar. Will it surprise you to know that I find this no cause for rejoicing? Anastasius Focht was a wily enemy, but we knew his ways and could therefore predict him to a certain extent. Also—though he would never admit it—his age was catching up to him. Distracted by the Clans, he was short-sighted enough to ignore us—a misstep that dropped the homeworld of humankind into our laps. The former Prince of the Federated Commonwealth is a young man, with as keen a sense of strategy and tactics as Focht at his best. He is also likely to devote far more of his attention to the Word of Blake as a primary threat to his precious sham Star League, now that he has broken the back of the Clan war machine. I fear we face a more formidable antagonist than many of our brethren are willing to grant.

I am certain that Victor Davion will attempt to infiltrate his own people into our organization, as ComStar has done ever since the Schism of 3052. Your previous efforts to root out the traitors in our midst have had admirable results; I ask you now to redouble them, until not a single ComStar agent remains among us. Pay particular attention to the newer acolytes and adepts; I have reason to believe that Focht and Precentor Victoria Parrdeau have planted agents among them in order to make information-gathering easier for Focht's successor. The reports on the Second Whitting Conference make it clear that Focht had planned Victor's ascension for some time; he had ample opportunity to coordinate operations with Parrdeau against us.

I would also like you to compile a complete dossier on Victor Steiner-Davion. We need to know as much as possible about the man we will be forced to deal with over the next several years. Any information may be significant, so do not confine yourself to his extensive public record. I want everything we can get, down to his favorite color and whether he favors a nightcap before retiring.

Please attend to these matters with dispatch; we cannot afford leaks to ComStar, especially now. The time prophesied is nearly at hand.

I await your complete report. Blake's blessing be with you. *[The profile Holloway drew up as part of your dossier appears further on in this file. You ought to find it amusing. You might want to run this one past Precentor ROM Parrdeau or Primus Mori, or even Focht, for their guesses as to which prophesy they might be referring.*

The next communiqué raises several questions. Why is the Word of Blake hiring mercenary units, given the quality and numbers of their own militia? Unless they expect the Blake Militia to be tied up somewhere, and they need additional troops for some other purpose at the same time ... . —JC]

Outreach, 12 December 3061
TO: Precentor Martial Cameron St. Jamais
FROM: Precentor Helen Schlegel

Following is the update you requested on the Outreach mission. I am pleased to report partial success; of the two most viable units I have approached so far, Smithson's Chinese Bandits has accepted our contract. After the Bandit's devastating losses during Operation Guerrero, they traveled to Outreach, and though they have always been a reliable unit, their time on Outreach had yet to yield them a contract. Their desperation to sign a contract plus the large incentives we're offering effectively combined to overcome any misgivings they may have felt.

I was unfortunately less successful with the Vanguard Legion, who until recently were employed by the Draconis Combine. Though not an A-rated unit, the Vanguard Legion is a respectable outfit with excellent combat capabilities and a reputation for sticking to a contract no matter what the circumstances. Such a unit would have made a useful addition to our roster. However, they appear to take their cue from their previous employers regarding the Word of Blake; the Vanguard's commanding officer, Colonel Chad Allen, was warily polite throughout our meeting. I do not think he trusted my description of the mission, or the Word of Blake in general; it may only have been the generous terms that induced him to give us a hearing.

I will be contacting several more mercenary units during the rest of my stay, notably the Fifty-first Dark Panzer Jaegers and Sathen's Snipers—both of which, though relatively new, have begun to make a name for themselves (though neither are as well-regarded as Smithson's or the Vanguard). Despite the setback with the latter, I have every confidence that we will find enough takers to suit our needs.

COMSTAR

FROM: Precentor ROM Victoria Parrdeau
TO: Precentor Martial Victor Steiner-Davion
DATE: 17 December 3061
RE: Current Status of ComStar ROM

Anastasius Focht was good enough to inform me of his planned retirement just before he departed for the Second Whitting Conference, and so I am able to offer you a fairly comprehensive summary of the current state of ComStar ROM. We are still compiling a more detailed report; however, the following summation should give you a reasonably clear idea of our current strengths, weaknesses and operations.

Ever since the Schism, ComStar ROM has been hampered by smaller numbers than its Word of Blake counterpart—a situation unfortunately exacerbated by the ascension of a Word of Blake operative to commanding officer of the counterintelligence division in late 3057. Evidence suggests that Demi-Precentor Michelle Ellingham, who succeeded the late Precentor Damien Constantine, engineered his assassination specifically to assume his post. During her brief but catastrophic tenure, she identified large numbers of our people within the Word of Blake, and was likely responsible for the deaths of twenty-two ComStar ROM agents. In the years since the Blakists' 3058 takeover of Terra, we have been systematically rooting out Ellingham's network of Blakist informants and sympathizers. We have made excellent progress, but I do not believe the job is done. I have also instituted recruitment programs, within ComStar's other branches and outside the organization. These have begun to bear fruit, but slowly; the creation of top-notch intelligence personnel is a time-consuming business, especially when the utmost caution is necessary to avoid infiltration.

On a more positive note, the bulk of our agents still within the Word of Blake have survived that organization's recent purge, and are consequently in a position to give us useful intelligence on Blakist activities. Our people in the Chaos March emerged completely unscathed, and are keenly observing all Word of Blake activities in that region. Fuller details of their dispatches will be included in the complete report, which should be on its way to you shortly. We are also gradually extending ComStar's presence in the Chaos March, a welcome change after the loss of several HPG stations to the Capellan takeover of several March worlds this past year. Chancellor Sun-Tzu Liao's increasing reliance on the Word of Blake for HPG maintenance has effectively made Capellan space hostile territory for ComStar.

On Terra, ROM agents have made contact with several surviving Com Guards and other resistance leaders. Though Word of Blake has managed to gain almost undisputed control over all of Terra, these surviving units are doing what they can to sting and distract them. However, the recent Star League victory over the Clans has considerably raised ComStar's stock among the ordinary citizens of Terra; that, coupled with the unrelenting rigidity of the Word of Blake regime, is helping to expand the anti-Blakist environment that we can exploit.

Overall, opportunities for future action look promising. I look forward to extended discussions with you after receipt of the complete ComStar ROM readiness report.

FROM: Precentor Malcolm Duncan, ComStar Divisions and Placement
TO: Precentor Martial Victor Steiner-Davion
RE: Summary of Status Report—Com Guards, 3062

As this new year gets underway, the Com Guards stand ready to safeguard the Star League should we be called upon to do so. We are still feeling our way as part of the SLDF, and have not entirely established our place in the chain of command with regard to non-ComStar units. Problems are minor, however, and should shortly work themselves out.

The First and Second Armies remain deployed in Combine space, where they have been stationed since 3055. The Twelfth Army likewise remains stationed in Free Rasalhague. The rest of the Com Guards have shifted around considerably over the past six years, in response to such major events as the invasion of the Chaos March and the SLDF campaigns against the Clans.

The Seventh Army, formerly deployed on Talitha, Devil's Rock, Pollux and Sirius, was asked to leave following the reconquest of those planets by Marik forces. Various divisions of the Sixth, Fifth and Eighth Armies received similar invitations in late 3057 and 3058, when the Free Worlds League absorbed Sirius, Procyon, Pella II, Castor and Callison. All of these units were transferred to the Clan fronts in Rasalhague, the Draconis Combine and the Lyran Alliance. Had some of them been sent instead to Terra, they might have proved sufficient to turn the tide when the Word of Blake struck; however, twenty-twenty hindsight is a luxury few military commanders can afford. The units already on Terra at that time were decimated in the fighting. Their survivors have since waged a surprisingly effective guerrilla campaign against the Blakist forces, given their small numbers.

Com Guard deployments in the Capellan Confederation have not changed, despite the Word of Blake's inroads in that nation. Having extorted from ComStar the right to deploy the Com Guards near the St. Ives border in the early 3050s, Sun-Tzu apparently sees no reason to deprive those worlds of their Com Guard garrison forces. The Com Guard divisions in question have so far remained neutral in the St. Ives-Capellan conflict, as we have no legal authority for taking action.

Deployments in the Chaos March unfortunately remain up for grabs as a result of our ongoing struggle with the Word of Blake for influence in that region. One recent major loss was the world of New Home, which fell into the Blakist camp in 3058. The conquest of Terra in that same year luckily forced the Word of Blake to pull back somewhat in the Chaos March while it consolidated its hold on humanity's homeworld. Though the Blakists have recently begun extending new feelers into the March, they have not yet had time to make serious gains at ComStar's expense.

A part of Third Army's Second Division sustained high casualties on Huntress, and the forces that accompanied you to Strana Mechty suffered casualties as well in their unfortunate defeat by Clan Jade Falcon. The Second is rebuilding slowly but steadily, however; additional details are contained in the complete report to follow.

At this point, I cannot predict what will happen to the divisions currently stationed on FedCom and Lyran Alliance worlds, especially those on New Avalon and Tharkad. Archon Katrina made no changes when she formed the Lyran Alliance in 3057; I gather, however, that family politics have turned her bitterly against you. Whether your assumption of the Precentor Martial's office will cause her to reconsider her realm's relationship with ComStar in general, or the placement of the Com Guards specifically, remains an open question. For the moment, our forces remain stationed on the capital worlds and on the Lyran border with the Clan occupation zones.

THE FREE RASALHAGUE REPUBLIC

Reports from the Twelfth Army in what remains of the Free Rasalhague Republic indicate a troubling trend. Where once the people of Rasalhague welcomed the Com Guards' presence as security against further Clan advances, they have now begun to resent us as a drain on their limited resources. Also, with the end of organized Clan hostilities, Clan Ghost Bear has been taking pains to integrate the Clan and Inner Sphere populations of its worlds. Word of these developments, passed from former Rasalhagians to their friends and relatives in the Republic, has done much to humanize the Ghost Bears in Rasalhagian eyes. Between those who resent their nation's status as a ComStar protectorate and those who wonder if life wouldn't be better under Clan Ghost Bear after all, the tide of anti-ComStar feeling is growing.

The retirement of Haakon Magnusson following the Second Whitting Conference and the subsequent elections that followed dramatically demonstrates this fact. When votes were tallied from the election, a clear majority of the Republic Parliament had voted for captured Ragnar Magnusson—currently a Star colonel with Clan Ghost Bear. An emergency meeting of Parliament confirmed that Ragnar was their Elected Prince, and a second election was held, in which Christian Månsdotter was elected as the Elected Prince Regent, and acts in that office until such a time as Ragnar returns. The implications of this act are tremendous.

We are certainly not yet at the point of revolution in the streets, but this critical situation bears careful watching and smooth diplomacy.

FROM: Precentor Padraig O Bhaoil, Director, Explorer Service
TO: Precentor Martial Victor Steiner-Davion
RE: Status Report Summary, Explorer Corps

The two most significant recent events that have affected Explorer Corps operations are the loss of Terra to the Word of Blake and the delivery of the so-called Exodus Road to the Inner Sphere. Both occurred in 3058, though the Corps was not informed of the latter until several months after the fact.

The loss of Terra cost the Corps a certain number of facilities in the Terran system, as well as the full use of its shipyards on the Jovian moon of Titan. Though ComStar held onto Titan for almost four more years, the close proximity of Word of Blake forces had essentially made them "enemy territory" as far as our ability to repair and refit our ships was concerned. That all changed in early December of 3061, when Precentor Klaus Hettig, who was in charge of the shipyards, ordered them cleared of all ComStar personnel in a false evacuation and then defected to the Word of Blake. This sudden defection, along with that of several other high-ranking Com Guard members, was the result of your assumption of the rank of Precentor Martial of ComStar. As in the case of Hettig, it is our belief that he resented the fact that Focht would place a complete outsider in charge of the military arm of ComStar and chose a most drastic measure of showing his disappointment. Unfortunately, this now leaves the entire Sol system completely in the hands of Word of Blake

Fortunately, the Corps had moved Coreward Operations and much of the DES staff to Columbus in 3053 when I assumed the directorship, which greatly minimized the impact of losing our Terran facilities five years later. We were therefore able to continue our search for the Clan homeworlds with minimal interruption.

The assembled leaders of the Inner Sphere received a "road map" to the Smoke Jaguar world of Huntress at the first Whitting Conference, which prompted them to plan an assault on that planet. The overriding need for secrecy prompted then-Precentor Martial Anastasius Focht to keep the Corps in the dark about the Exodus Road; our DCMS counterparts remained similarly uninformed. We therefore continued our exploratory mission, unaware that there would soon be no need for it.

Information taken from databases on Huntress gave the SLDF the location of the other Clan homeworlds, including the Clan capital of Strana Mechty. The Explorer Corps learned of this discovery along with the rest of the Inner Sphere, when the SLDF returned home triumphant in early 3061. Since then, we have turned our efforts toward general exploration. No longer bound by a driving necessity to discover the home of our enemies, we can instead seek out suitable worlds for colonization, track down lost colonies from earlier eras, and expand the Inner Sphere's overall knowledge of the universe. We have spent the past year changing the focus of our operations in these directions.

Personally, I look forward to serving as the director of a true "explorer" corps, whose principal purpose is to expand the horizons of human knowledge. Perhaps this new beginning for the Explorer Corps is a good omen for the new Star League.

NOTABLE PERSONALITIES

[With the exception of your own write-up, the following ComStar and Word of Blake personality profiles come from Captain Lars Dressel of Wolf's Dragoons, the man in charge of monitoring and analyzing ComStar's doings. His sources are excellent and his analysis second to none. —JC]

PRIMUS SHARILAR MORI

Rank/Position: Primus of ComStar
Year of Birth: 2997 (age 64)

Profile:

Sharilar Mori has risen admirably to the many unexpected twists and turns that her career in ComStar has taken. Though she initially joined the Blessed Order of ComStar as an agent of the Draconis Combine's Internal Security Force, over the years she came to appreciate ComStar's worth as a stabilizing force in the Inner Sphere. In an eerie echo of events to come, she succeeded Myndo Waterly as Precentor Dieron—a position she used to slip information to the Draconis Combine concerning the Clans and Operation Scorpion.

Operation Scorpion was Primus Myndo Waterly's attempt at a ComStar takeover of the Inner Sphere after the Com Guards' narrow victory on Tukayyid. The scheme cost the Primus her life and caused the schism of the old ComStar order. Precentor Martial Anastasius Focht, who took it upon himself to eliminate Waterly, chose Sharilar Mori to succeed her as Primus of a new ComStar—one without the overtly religious trappings and often-blind missionary zeal of its predecessor.

Though she had acted primarily on behalf of the Draconis Combine, Sharilar Mori's undermining of Operation Scorpion at considerable personal risk showed her to be unhampered by Primus Waterly's fanaticism and willing to place the good of the Inner Sphere ahead of other considerations. In addition, her remarkably rapid rise to the First Circuit showed her to be a skilled politician. Primus Mori has used all of these qualities to the benefit of ComStar and the Inner Sphere nations throughout the past decade, and is firmly committed to the success of the new Star League.

PRECENTOR ROM VICTORIA PARRDEAU

Rank/Position: Precentor ROM
Year of Birth: 3017 (age 44)

Profile:

Victoria Parrdeau has served as ComStar's Precentor ROM since 3054, and has spent her tenure rebuilding ComStar's intelligence arm after multiple setbacks. To this task she brings the same steely determination that she showed as a member of the Com Guards, fighting against Clan Smoke Jaguar on Tukayyid.

The Schism cost the new ComStar a shockingly high percentage of its ROM operatives, the bulk of whom defected to the Word of Blake. Between 3054 and 3057, Precentor Parrdeau made admirable progress in shoring up ROM's tattered ranks, despite an ongoing covert war between ComStar ROM and its Word of Blake counterpart. In late 3057, however, Word of Blake operative Michelle Ellingham became head of ComStar's counterintelligence division. She identified several ComStar ROM operatives within the Word of Blake and created a network of Blakist sympathizers within ComStar ROM that Precentor Parrdeau has yet to completely eradicate.

Parrdeau's organization could ill afford the loss of its agents, or the intense focus on finding moles after Ellingham's departure. These setbacks go a long way toward explaining the failure of ComStar ROM to pick up on warning signals that a Blakist takeover of Terra was imminent, or to recognize the Blakist "Shadow Lancers" as impostors when they arrived on Terra in early 3058. The Word of Blake took no chances when moving against ComStar ROM's Terran headquarters outside Cairo; they gassed the compound with a nerve agent, costing ComStar ROM still more personnel.

Undaunted, Precentor ROM Parrdeau remains as committed as ever to rebuilding her organization and using it to further ComStar's interests. She is a staunch backer of the Star League, and will do everything in her power to keep the Word of Blake from undermining it.

PRECENTOR XIX PADRAIG O BHAOIL

Rank/Position: Director, Explorer Service/Commander, Coreward Operations Area
Year of Birth: 3002 (age 59)

Profile:

Originally a Lyran native, Padraig O Bhaoil grew up expecting to take up the family shipping business. A regular passenger on his father's merchant JumpShip *Eala* during his youth, Padraig learned to love spacefaring at an early age. When the *Eala* suffered catastrophic drive failure and was lost with all hands, Padraig turned to ComStar as an outlet for his spacer's skills, and spent the first ten years of his career aboard various couri-

er vessels. When the Explorer Corps was expanded in the early 3030s, O Bhaoil joined up and quickly rose to command of the *Free Spirit*, a *Magellan*-Class explorer ship.

In 3048, O Bhaoil took the *Spirit* on an extended three-year mission spinward of the Inner Sphere, arriving back in the Outworlds Alliance shortly before the Battle of Luthien against Clans Smoke Jaguar and Nova Cat. Shocked by news of the Clans' arrival and conquests, he set out swiftly for Terra and arrived in late January of 3052. His ship was immediately pressed into service ferrying troops to Tukayyid, a position that gave him and his crew ringside seats for that epic battle from the system's nadir jump point.

Never much taken with ComStar's mysticism, O Bhaoil chose to stay on in the secularized ComStar after the Schism. As the most senior captain in the service, he was the logical choice to become its director when ComStar and the Draconis Combine began their joint search for the Clan homeworlds. With the abrupt end of the Clan war, Precentor O Bhaoil is free to turn his organization toward his first love—exploration for its own sake. Though pushing sixty, he has stated his intention to venture on exploratory missions himself rather than "letting everyone else have all the fun."

PRECENTOR MARTIAL VICTOR STEINER-DAVION

Rank/Position: Precentor Martial, ComStar/ Commanding General, Star League Defense Force
Year of Birth: 3030 (age 31)

Profile:

The first of the bastardized Steiner-Davion line, Victor Steiner-Davion was groomed to serve as Archon Prince of the Federated Commonwealth. Throughout his formative years, he was educated in the twin arts of politics and warfare; he excelled at the latter, but appeared hopeless at the former. The young Victor was a soldier's soldier; other aspects of governing tended to elude him. The untimely death of his mother thrust Victor onto throne before he had a chance to acquire much political seasoning, and turned the blunt manner of the battlefield commander into a liability that would ultimately lead to the downfall of his cobbled-together nation.

During the Clan war, Victor fought the Clans on various worlds. His unit's defeat in its first Clan engagement, on

Trellwan in April of 3050, must have come as a terrible shock to a young princeling unused to failure. Displaying the iron determination that would later make him such a formidable war leader, Victor set out to learn everything he could about the Clan enemy. Though he suffered subsequent defeats in other battles, he learned something from each one. He ultimately applied those lessons with devastating effect, leading the SLDF to victory against the Clans on Strana Mechty in 3060.

In the meantime, however, Victor's lack of political finesse caused him no end of trouble off the battlefield. His bungled handling of Skye secessionist leanings during the early 3050s, as well as his rumored involvement in several assassinations, greatly damaged his reputation among his Lyran subjects. By the time the Prince made his ill-fated decision to substitute a double for the dying Joshua Marik, Victor's image had become so tarnished among Lyrans that they welcomed the secession of their territory from the FedCom that same year.

Victor seems to have finally begun learning from his political mistakes during the past few years, though apparently too little and too late to save his realm. His unexpectedly masterful leadership of the SLDF coalition force that drove the Smoke Jaguars from the Inner Sphere demonstrated a newfound talent for diplomacy and political maneuvering. None of this prevented his sister Katrina from assuming control of the rest of the FedCom while Victor was off fighting the Clans; however, it stands to make him a formidable opponent as ComStar's Precentor Martial.

Victor's close friendship with Kai Allard-Liao, heir to the St. Ives Compact, may provide an exploitable weakness. The escalating conflict between St. Ives and the Capellan Confederation is likely to distract the new Precentor Martial's attention in the coming months, leaving him less apt to notice our activities. ComStar's becoming more deeply mired in the St. Ives affair may even uspet the shaky political balance of the pseudo-Star League, as its various member-states take sides for or against the Confederation. Technically, the Precentor Martial cannot deploy troops without the consent of a majority of the Star League states; if he attempts to do so anyway, the resulting political fallout will cause trouble for ComStar. The people of the Inner Sphere still remember Operation Scorpion, and will not take kindly to the "reformed" ComStar once again meddling too deeply in their affairs.

PRECENTOR WILLIAM BLANE OF GIBSON

Rank/Position: Precentor
Year of Birth: 2992 (age 70)

Profile:

William Blane of Gibson essentially serves as Primus of the Word of Blake, though he continues to eschew the formal title. An apparent moderate among the reactionaries, he has successfully held the organization's often-quarrelsome factions together for the past decade. Intelligent and level-headed, he is a politician rather than a fanatic, which earns him no points with the ultra-radicals but also gives him the necessary skills to deal with them. Blane also gives the Word of Blake a veneer of respectability. His affable manner and apparent reasonableness have done much to earn the Word of Blake a measure of trust in the Free Worlds League, the Capellan Confederation and even some Periphery realms. Wherever possible, Blane has parlayed this trust into HPG maintenance contracts designed to funnel much-needed monies into Word of Blake coffers.

Blane's long-term friendship with Captain-General Thomas Marik ensured that the Word of Blake would find sanctuary within the Free Worlds League. From the sect's landhold on Gibson, Blane spent five years carefully planning and then directing the conquest of Terra; he is also likely a prime mover behind other Blakist machinations that have yet to be discovered. The death of Precentor Demona Aziz in 3058 removed Blane's most serious rival for power, though there are some indications that the ultra-radical Sixth of June faction considers him a liability. Whether they will attempt to remove him from power remains an open question.

PRECENTOR MARTIAL CAMERON ST. JAMAIS

Rank/Position: Precentor Martial of Word of Blake
Year of Birth: 3027 (age 34)

Profile:

Despite having served as the Word of Blake's Precentor Martial for just more than half a year, Cameron St. Jamais has already greatly increased Blakist military activity throughout the Terran system. In addition to building up Word of Blake forces at key sites on Terra and on Mars, he has also begun hiring mer-

cenary units. Known as a fanatic even in an organization of extremists, St. Jamais would do literally anything he believed necessary to prevent humanity's homeworld from falling into "heretic" hands.

St. Jamais rose rapidly through the Word of Blake's ranks after the Schism, aided by his close friendship with the powerful Precentor Demona Aziz. One story alleges that the two of them were lovers on Gibson, though ComStar ROM has yet to verify this rumor. After Aziz's unexpected demise, St. Jamais took her place as leader of the Toyama. According to persistent rumors, he is also the leader of an even more extremist splinter group within the Toyama—the Sixth of June, a terrorist movement dedicated to destroying human civilization by assassinating the leaders of the Great Houses and the Periphery states. The Sixth of June takes its name from the date of Myndo Waterly's death, and its members revere her memory.

Whether or not St. Jamais heads up this terrorist group, he is certainly a formidable opponent. Highly intelligent and politically astute—not to mention his membership in the Com Guard's special forces unit, Blake's Wrath, before the schism—he has a gift for intrigue and an unshakable sense of his own righteousness. He will use any means to further his warped view of humanity's "greater good," including cold-blooded murder. Placing such a man in charge of the Word of Blake Militia suggests that the Word of Blake is gearing up to make some sort of move against the Star League, which most of their members consider a sham. Precisely what they intend, however, remains a mystery.

[St. Jamais spent much of 3058 traveling around the Periphery, though we have little data on what he actually did there. He turned up on Alphard in the Marian Hegemony, the Magistracy world of Marantha and the planet Astrokaszy within the space of six weeks, during which time he allegedly crossed paths with the mercenary unit Avanti's Angels. One rumor links St. Jamais to the Hegemony raids on Magistracy worlds in that year, though that conclusion remains speculative at best.

The Sixth of June connection raisesa truly frightening possibility. We don't have anywhere near a complete list of the people St. Jamais met with on his recent progress through the Free Worlds League, nor do we how many Sixth of June cells there are or where they are located. If St. Jamais is the terrorist group's leader, he may be using his frequent trips to touch base with his organization, or to prime them for action in the near future. —JC]

THE BEST LAID PLANS ...

—Excerpt from the unpublished memoirs of Emma Centrella, Magestrix, Magistracy of Canopus; 30 August 3061

Rulers of nations learn to deal with the unexpected. You have to, or you don't survive for long. And with all the times that the unexpected has occurred in my life, you'd think nothing much could surprise me anymore.

I'd pin what happened at the Detroit Conference on Sun-Tzu Liao if I could. He is far more than he appears to be; I could see that when he first came to the Magistracy with his proposals of alliance. He even benefits from what happened; the man most likely to take the Concordat's helm will probably be far more amenable to Sun-Tzu's agenda than Jeff Calderon was. But to have engineered the events on Detroit would take someone even more Machiavellian than I suspect Sun-Tzu of being. No, the straightforward explanation is the more likely one—that some Steiner-Davion or other took steps to sabotage the three-way alliance that was slowly forming around their historical Capellan enemy. Or it could have been those ultra-radical Blakist crazies. They tried to kill Sun-Tzu Liao in my own palace a few years ago; I wouldn't put anything past them. I suppose Maltin might even have been acting on his own. But I'm not sure I believe in that kind of coincidence.

The conference had been in the planning stages since late 3059. We chose the world of Detroit as the site; Capellan aid had enabled the Magistracy to refurbish a 'Mech production facility there. A tour of the facility was to have been a highlight of the conference, meant to convey the benefits of Capellan friendship to Protector Jeffrey Calderon of the Taurian Concordat.

Poor Jeffrey had been ambivalent about the Capellan Confederation for months. He could see the advantage to his own state in a Capellan alliance, but found it almost impossible to trust Sun-Tzu Liao. He'd seen some of the messages the Liaos had sent to Thomas Calderon during the Clan war, purporting to prove that the Clan invasion was just another FedCom plot. He also knew that the Capellans were every bit as close to Concordat space as the FedCom, and that if they ever tried to take back the St. Ives Compact, they might not stop there. He allowed vigorous trade with the Confederation because it enriched his realm without entangling it—but a political alliance? That was another thing entirely.

Even the Magistracy's example, coupled with the strengthened ties between the Magistracy and the Concordat, weren't enough to overcome his mistrust in the end. He agreed to attend the Detroit Conference, principally as a personal favor to me. Sun-Tzu, I think, still had hopes that Calderon would change his mind and join us; but I had come to know Jeffrey better, and knew he would never risk tying his realm to an ally he feared would one day turn on it.

I didn't tell Sun-Tzu Liao this. The Magistracy had other business to transact with the Confederation, and the lack of backing from the Taurian Concordat meant that Sun-Tzu would need my realm all the more. Therefore, he was likely to accommodate any concessions I might demand. Or so I thought.

We originally set the conference for November of 3060, but postponed it by a month after the Blackwind Lancers attacked Sun-Tzu's traveling party on Hustaing. Not long afterward, Liao cancelled altogether; the Hustaing incident had snowballed into a full-blown crisis severe enough to require the deployment of SLDF peacekeeping troops on several St. Ives Compact worlds. Sun-Tzu, as First Lord of the new Star League, was responsible for overseeing the SLDF units—a duty that superseded any politicking to benefit his own realm.

Having gone to all the trouble to make the arrangements, I chose not to waste what might be the last chance to talk sense into Jeff Calderon about the Capellan alliance. The Protector's entourage and my own arrived at Detroit in the New Colony Region on 21 December 3060. The date seemed like a good omen at the time: old Terra's winter solstice, the turning of the year from winter to spring, a time of new beginnings.

The first few days of the conference went well enough. Ironically, I'd intended to begin the serious business by talking about stepping up our co-colonization efforts. I never got the chance. At a Christmas Eve reception, Colony President Sherman Maltin used a force of Colonial Marshals to take me and the Protector hostage. As ransom, he demanded full independence for the New Colony Region. Maltin's brief term of office had apparently given him a taste for power.

I never saw it coming, and from the look on his face, Jeffrey Calderon hadn't either. Maltin had a reputation as a fair-minded man and a capable administrator; nothing in his background suggested the kind of power-hunger that would lead

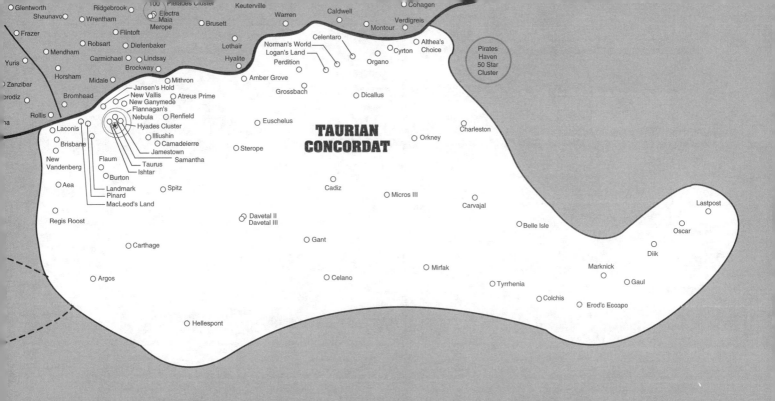
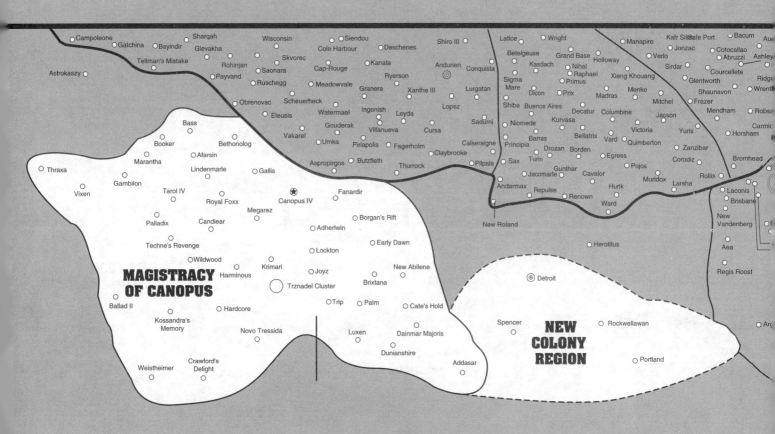

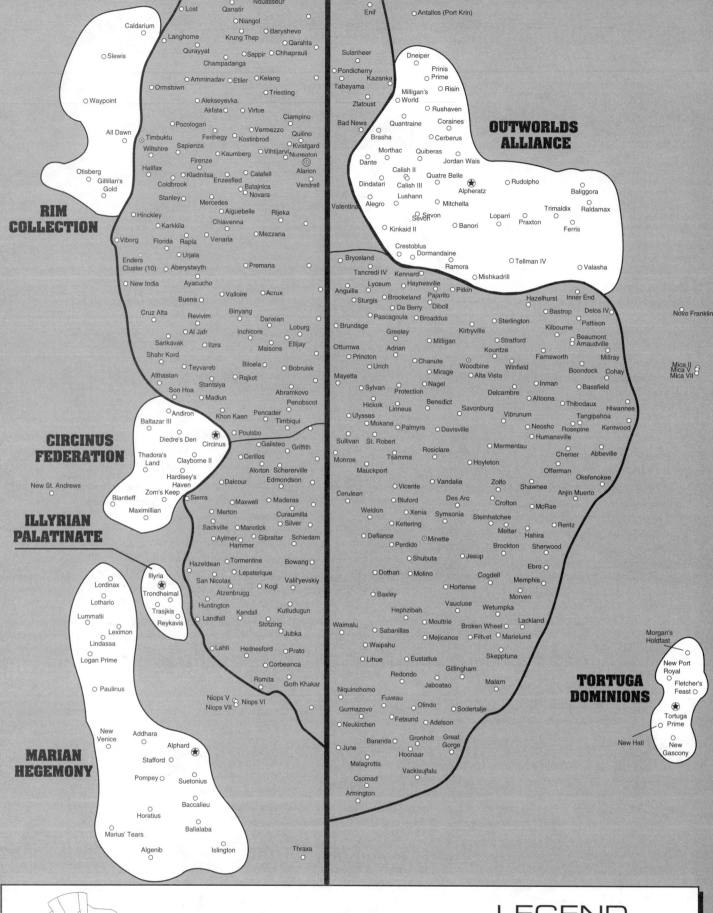

NEAR PERIPHERY KINGDOMS

LEGEND

8 PARSECS

40 PARSECS OR 130.4 LIGHT YEARS

SCALE: 1/8 INCH = 1 PARSEC = 3.26 LIGHT YEARS = 19,164,277,860,000 STATUTE MILES

MAXIMUM JUMP: APPROXIMATELY 30 LIGHT YEARS
FOR NAVIGATIONAL PURPOSES USE 9 PARSECS = 29.34 LY

© 3061 COMSTAR CARTOGRAPHIC CORPS

him to stage a military coup. But he'd done it, and done it damned well. The Detroit Conference had been intended as a meeting of allies, and things had been going relatively smoothly between the Magistracy and the Concordat, so we'd kept our military contingents down to small personal guard units. Taking the two of us hostage was a master-stroke; it enabled Maltin to keep both of our governments off-balance and afraid to send in the troops. The latter was essential for his scheme to succeed; formidable MechWarriors though the Marshals were, Maltin's loyalists couldn't have hoped to take on large numbers of Magistracy or Concordat troops. With Jeffrey and I at their mercy, they wouldn't need to.

Maltin seemed genuinely sorry that he'd been "forced" to take such steps to get what he wanted. I pointed out that he could have negotiated limited autonomy, but he merely shook his head and told me it would never have worked. The colonies had their own concerns, he said, many of them life-and-death, and all of them far removed from the government on distant Canopus and Taurus. In his mind, only complete independence would enable "his people" to carve out a viable existence. Maltin and Jeffrey Calderon spent a great deal of time arguing that point over the next several months. Meanwhile, other players on the chessboard were setting our rescue in motion.

Word of the coup had reached Sun-Tzu Liao relatively quickly, of course. More than likely he had an agent or three planted somewhere on Detroit to keep an eye on things. An independent New Colony Region, which would no longer be enriching either the Magistracy or the Concordat treasuries, didn't suit the Chancellor's plans; up to a point, he preferred strong and prosperous allies. In addition, as a formal ally of my own state, he couldn't afford not to act against this blatant affront to Canopian sovereignty. In short order, he dispatched my daughter Naomi to Detroit with a sizable force of MAF and Capellan troops.

The rescue party dropped on Detroit in February of 3061. Those Marshals who'd chosen not to back Maltin's coup remained neutral; their job, as one of them put it later, was to keep the peace between the colonists and deal with external threats to them, not to get involved in politics. Maltin's Marshals were aided by a few thrown-together units of independence-minded colonists, and gave Naomi's forces a difficult few months. The final outcome, however, was never much in doubt. Cutting-edge Capellan 'Mechs and sheer weight of numbers eventually prevailed over the Marshals' individual expertise and passion. By late June, the rescue party had surrounded Government House on Detroit, ready to storm the place and set us free.

They made their move on 28 June. My daughter's unit led the charge against the remaining pro-Maltin Marshals, who had dug in for a last stand. They knew they couldn't win, but were determined to go down fighting. The fierce battle claimed hefty casualties on both sides, including Protector Jeffrey Calderon. We thought he'd gotten caught in crossfire during the last, pitched room-to-room battle. But then the rumor mill started up, as people began to realize just how convenient Calderon's death was for the FedCom. Both of our deaths would have been even better, if the object was to spike the Capellan-Periphery alliance. But thanks to Naomi, I had the bad taste to survive.

Thanks to Sun-Tzu as well, which he knew when he sent the rescue force. The preponderance of Capellan troops in it was his way of reminding Naomi and I just what we owed, and to whom. So I now owe Sun-Tzu for my continued existence.

I suppose I'm properly grateful. I still don't trust Sun-Tzu any farther than I can throw him one-handed—but that's a personal judgment, not a political one. Politically, he has treated the Magistracy fairly since the start of our alliance. With Calderon gone, perhaps it will become what Sun-Tzu Liao desires. What I desire as well, if I'm honest.

Jeffrey Calderon left no heirs, and his older sister Janice is in no shape to claim the throne. Things are still shaking out in the Concordat, but it looks as though Lord Grover Shraplen of MacLeod's Land will be taking over. Ironic, that the man who most bitterly opposed so many of Jeffrey's accomplishments may be the architect of an accord with the Capellans. I can't say for certain how Shraplen will jump, but his loathing of the Davions is legendary. That alone might make him consider forging ties with the Capellans. Time, as it always does, will tell.

THE PERIPHERY

[The following file comes from a variety of sources, much of it funneled to me through ComStar ROM operatives in the Periphery as well as from my own agents there. Two principal realms to watch are the Magistracy of Canopus and the Taurian Concordat; the former is already in the Capellan Confederation camp, and the latter looks likely to fall that way. The Outworlds Alliance is also coming up on the radar screen; its economy has improved enough to employ most of its people, and Alliance President Mitchell Avellar is turning some of that newfound prosperity toward a military build-up. The Marian Hegemony and the Circinus Federation remain as aggressive as always, though we might turn that to our advantage in the near future. Finally, Periphery pirate activity remains a serious concern. —JC]

THE MAGISTRACY OF CANOPUS

—Excerpt from the unpublished memoirs of Magestrix Emma Centrella; 10 December 3061

How things can change in ten years. On this day in 3051, I was figuring out how best to approach my fellow Periphery state leaders in order to propose a Periphery-wide alliance against the Clans—and for good measure, against any Inner Sphere state unwise enough to send troops across our borders. I knew it would be a hard sell, especially to people like Caesar Sean O'Reilly of the Marian Hegemony and that bizarre little man who runs the Circinus Federation. Jumped-up tinpot dictators, both of them; but I knew they could do damage out of all proportion to their size and influence if I left them out of it. And now? Ten years later, instead of a Periphery alliance, I find myself and my realm in bed with the Capellan Confederation. The Clan threat has been driven away by the army of a reborn Star League. And I have thrown in my lot with an Inner Sphere state, in part to keep ancient history from repeating itself. The first Star League absorbed the Periphery after years of bloody conflict. This time around, the Magistracy is joining up before we get trampled. At least this way I can preserve my realm's independence. We're more useful to Sun-Tzu Liao as a sovereign state than as yet another Commonality; joining forces with his Confederation will keep this nation alive.

It is odd to be allied with the Confederation, given our often-unpleasant mutual history. This is, after all, the one Inner Sphere realm that prohibits Canopian pleasure circuses from operating within its borders, though I have promises that those restrictions will loosen. Traders of other goods and services have been granted only limited legal rights to operate in Capellan space, and that less than a year ago. Not exactly friendly behavior. Still, Sun-Tzu has loosened things up quite a bit from his mother's reign. He reopened diplomatic ties in 3052, almost before Romano Liao's body was cold. It took the Canopian–Taurian Concordat Alliance four years later to really make him sit up and take notice, however. The ink had hardly dried on the Treaty of Taurus before the Capellan representative on Canopus was weighing in, warning us that the Confederation would not tolerate any Canopian aggression. We sent him packing by mid-3057; being blustered and stormed at every day by a has-been MechWarrior finally got to be more than I could stomach.

Meanwhile, I continued my diplomatic efforts among our Periphery neighbors. The Clans remained a potential threat, and I've never believed in keeping all my ammo in one bin. What I'd accomplished with the Concordat, I intended to achieve with other realms, principally the Outworlds Alliance. They'd never been worth much economically or militarily in the past, but under competent leadership the Alliance was beginning to show definite signs of improvement. I was also concerned about the Marian Hegemony, whose marauding excuses for army units were launching increasing numbers of raids on Canopian worlds. Caesar Sean was getting back at me for an assassination attempt, which he mistakenly believed I had ordered. With Taurian military aid slow in coming, the Magistracy needed additional allies.

In May of 3058, we got one. Sun-Tzu Liao came to Canopus IV—not at the head of a conquering army, but virtually alone, with an unexpected proposal.

FRIENDS IN STRANGE PLACES— THE CAPELLAN ACCORD

Sun-Tzu's arrival with a single battalion and a couple of Death Commandos was unprecedented, as was the subject he had come to discuss. Within minutes of walking into the royal hall, he placed his cards on the table. He had learned of our troubles with Hegemony raiders, who had been making inroads into Canopian space using mysteriously acquired, cutting-edge

military equipment. To enable us to fight them off, he was willing to give the Magistracy badly needed technology, as well as the personnel to teach us how to make the most of it. He also offered his accompanying battalion for immediate assignment wherever I saw fit (an offer I immediately accepted). What he wanted in exchange seemed fairly simple: Magistracy Armed Forces troops to help him retake former Capellan worlds.

I'm naturally suspicious of any deal that sounds too good. And I was doubly suspicious of this offer at first; though we subsequently learned differently, at the time we had r e a s o n to suspect that the Capellan Confederation was the power surreptitiously providing the Marian Hegemony with its newtech 'Mechs. Still, the sheer surprise of it made me listen. Looking back, I'm glad I did.

As we later discovered, the Confederation had nothing to do with the Hegemony raids. Sun-Tzu personally led a force of Magistracy troops, with my daughter Naomi at their head, to Campoleone—the Free Worlds League planet from which the Hegemony operation was being run. The Word of Blake was behind it, and had carefully laid trails of evidence pointing to both the Capellans and the Free Worlds League. As to why, who knows? The Word of Blake has more factions than a BattleMech has moving parts, and they don't always tell each other what they're doing. I'm sure the Blakist operative who tried to assassinate Sun-Tzu Liao during his Canopus visit didn't have the approval of Precentor Blane or St. Jamais. Luckily for Sun-Tzu—and us—she failed.

With my suspicions proved unfounded, I chose to accept the Liao proposal. Sun-Tzu proved as good as his word, if a tad slower than I might have liked. He immediately sent technicians and advisers to help build a 'Mech production facility on Detroit, in the New Colony Region that we shared with the Taurian Concordat. I spotted the ulterior motive behind that choice right away. Sun-Tzu was already looking beyond the Magistracy to a three-way alliance that included the Concordat. The ties between that realm and my own meant that a large part of his work was already done; planting a shiny new 'Mech factory right under Protector Jeffrey Calderon's nose was simply added inducement. In the meantime, the facility and its eventual output stood to enhance the MAF with cutting-edge tech. The improvements would be a godsend in our dealings with the Hegemony—and if they also bolstered Sun-Tzu's military capability through his use of Magistracy troops, well, what else are allies for?

My daughter Danai initially opposed the alliance. She never had much use for the Capellan Confederation, or its Chancellor. The Capellan state, militarily weak by comparison to its Inner Sphere neighbors, looked to her like a poor bet. But she was always loyal, and gracefully accepted her assignment to command MAF units within Capellan borders. Not long afterward, Sun-Tzu Liao chose Danai's First Canopian Cuirassiers to join the Inner Sphere's anti-Clan campaign. A Periphery unit fighting the Clans as part of a new Star League Defense Force—quite an irony, that. I suppose some might call it even more ironic that Danai died battling the Clans. I call it fitting. Death in battle is a risk every MechWarrior takes, and Danai was a MechWarrior before anything else. Though the mother in me misses her bitterly every day, the ruler has somewhat fewer regrets. Danai would have led the Magistracy well, but Naomi may do an even better job. She always did have a finer grasp than Danai of the delicate dance we call politics. Her apparent personal feelings for Sun-Tzu worry me a bit, but she's only twenty-two years old. She has time to get over them.

Naomi is leading the MAF troops in Capellan space now, shaping up into a far better military commander than I'm sure she ever thought she could be. Her masterful handling of the situation on Detroit just a few months ago testifies to her ability. She'll make an excellent Magestrix when the time comes (though I don't plan to step down for quite awhile yet). On other fronts, the Canopian Institute of War is finally up and running, enriched by the presence of several Liao military advisors among its faculty. The Hegemony raids are tapering off; without Word of Blake backing and facing a stronger MAF, Sean O'Reilly appears to have lost his taste for teaching us a lesson. Consequently, I've been able to redeploy the Green Mountain Boys merc unit back to Detroit. Had they been there during the Christmas Eve Coup, Jeffrey Calderon might still be alive.

THE TAURIAN ALLIANCE

The unexpected death of the Taurian Protector on Detroit this past year put Lord Grover Shraplen in charge of the Concordat. Though Shraplen initially opposed the treaty between our nations, he's smart enough to see the benefits of continuing the alliance, especially as a bulwark against potential Davion aggression. However, I can't say he's exactly been warm and friendly toward our representatives. The alliance may be politically convenient, but Shraplen doesn't have to like it. His suspicious attitude will only pour fuel on the fire of those in both our realms who never cared for the alliance to begin with. They're not a problem yet, being distinctly in the minority. However, I'm likely to have my hands full making sure they stay that way.

Fear of the Davion bogeyman may also drive the Concordat into the Capellan embrace, even though Lord Shraplen doesn't much trust anyone outside his own state. Not that there's much chance of a Davion attack anytime soon, to my mind. Katrina Steiner-Davion is still consolidating her hold over the FedCom, and governing it along with the Lyran Alliance will keep her busy for quite awhile. As for the former Prince Victor, he seems oddly disinclined to take his throne back. Were he inclined toward military adventurism, the FedCom throne is the first prize he'd aim for. At best, the Concordat would be a very, very distant second.

SECESSION IN THE COLONIES

Colony President Sherman Maltin's attempted coup this past year tore the lid off a much larger problem than either the Protector or I had anticipated. Every colonial population has its share of free spirits, as well as those who believe that the locals can run things better than faraway seats of government. But that independence fever would develop so strongly and so quickly, with such significant support from the Colonial Marshals, was an unpleasant surprise.

In retrospect, it should have been clearer that closer ties with House Liao might spark such trouble. The Capellan alliance, especially the prospect of its expansion, frightened Maltin and quite a few other people in the colonies. The colony president apparently assumed that the alliance would lead to Capellan absorption, and took drastic steps to keep the New Colony Region from becoming a Capellan protectorate. Ironically, his bid for independence greatly increased the likelihood of the very occurrence he'd hoped to prevent. So long as Jeffrey Calderon was in charge, the Concordat was unlikely to join forces with the Capellan Confederation. With Calderon gone and a rabid anti-Davion installed in his stead, an alliance with House Davion's bitter enemy suddenly looks more attractive. Lord Grover Shraplen has so far made no final decisions, but Capellan representatives to the Taurian capital are getting a respectful hearing. It may be only a matter of time before all three of our nations are linked in a triple alliance.

The coup attempt had additional fallout as well. Magistracy citizens and political factions originally opposed to joint Canopian-Taurian colonization efforts can now point to Maltin—a Taurian—as exemplifying the hazards of cooperation with a rival realm. The involvement of some Colonial Marshals in the coup is particularly disturbing, as the Marshals were formed to keep the peace between often mutually suspicious Canopian and Taurian colony populations. That they would abrogate their sworn duty and turn on the leaders of both states is a profound shock, and inflames the fears of those who saw them from the beginning as a potential rogue army within Magistracy borders. Clearly, I have my diplomatic work cut out for me, both in the New Colony Region and inside the Magistracy proper. Which means I won't have as much time as I'd like to keep up talks with the Outworlds Alliance, or any of the other Periphery realms where we Canopians have made friendly overtures.

It's almost 3062, and I'm nowhere near the place I expected to be a decade ago. But the place the Magistracy has come to is a good one, with immense advantages for this realm. What the next ten years will bring, I won't venture to guess. I only know one thing; it's likely to be an interesting ride.

THE TAURIAN CONCORDAT

—Excerpt from Protector Grover Shraplen's inaugural address, 2 September 3061

"The Taurian Concordat stands now on the brink of a new beginning, though it is not one that most of us would have chosen. You all know me; you know that many times in the past I have opposed the policies and decisions of our late Protector, Jeffrey Calderon. And you also know that no opposition could outweigh my loyalty to the man we all believed would serve as our ruler for decades to come. That I now stand here in his place is an honor I never sought, brought about by a tragedy I would have given anything to prevent. Still, we must go on. We must do what is best for the Concordat, as Jeffrey Calderon always tried to do. With your help, and the freely offered aid of Privy Councillor Janice Calderon, I intend to do exactly that.

"In 3056, Protector Jeffrey Calderon forged a historic alliance with our sister nation, the Magistracy of Canopus. Though I hesitated to support this unprecedented move at the time, fearing that the Magistracy might gain ascendancy over our realm, time has shown the Protector's bold move to be a wise one as well. The Concordat and the Magistracy have enriched each other through diplomatic contacts, technological and artistic exchanges, and favorable trading practices. I therefore see no reason why we should not continue to honor the Treaty of Taurus, in all of its particulars. Indeed, the success of the Canopian alliance has prompted me to seriously consider another, similar partnership—not with another Periphery state, but with the Capellan Confederation.

"Many of you may find the notion of strengthening ties with an Inner Sphere nation alarming. Just a few short months ago, I would have agreed with you. But there are good reasons—serious reasons—for considering such a step at this point in our history. I am unfortunately not at liberty to disclose specifics, but evidence points strongly to Davion involvement in the Protector's death. House Davion has always opposed a strong Taurian Concordat, and has historically resorted to various means of keeping us weak. In our nation's earliest years, border raids and planetary assaults were the methods of choice; more recently, during the reign of Protector Thomas Calderon, the Davions adopted an intimidation strategy designed to cripple us economically by forcing us to allocate disproportionate resources to our military. With the assassination of Protector Jeffrey Calderon, the Steiner-Davions hoped to destabilize the Concordat. They may even have hoped that new leadership would drive a wedge between us and the Magistracy. And they certainly hoped to prevent our allying with House Liao, traditionally among their own bitterest enemies.

"They have accomplished none of those things. Make no mistake; I have not yet agreed to ally this nation with the Capellan state, nor will I do so without due consideration of the risks as well as the benefits. The Liaos as well as the Davions have betrayed us in the past, and I would not lightly ask the people of the Concordat to make common cause with them. But there is historical precedent for doing so. Not all the lords of House Liao did us wrong, and the current chancellor may yet prove a genuine friend to this state. Thus far he has done well by our Canopian allies; we have their example to look toward, and might reasonably hope for equal gain should we throw in our lot with this foe of the Davions. Certainly the cowardly Davion attack on Taurian sovereignty demands a strong response; one way or another, we will deliver one.

"I regret to tell you that Davion perfidy extends beyond the murder of our late Protector. The New Colony Region remains highly unstable in the wake of the coup attempt by former Colony President Sherman Maltin, and we have barely begun our search for the Davion agitators who helped whip up secessionist fever in that area. We must therefore presume that Davion agents are still operating freely on New Colony worlds, where they will no doubt take advantage of the very unrest they helped create. We also do not yet know how far the Davions' claws have sunk into the Colonial Marshals, many of whom supported Maltin's illegal bid for power. There is reason to believe that Maltin himself was suborned by Davion agents, either wittingly or unwittingly. I have ordered an immediate and thorough investigation, the results of which will be shared with the public once we get an idea of just how deep the Davion conspiracy runs.

"In the meantime, this government will step up recruitment of new Colonial Marshals whose loyalty we can trust. To ensure the safety of the colonists until the new marshals are trained and equipped, I have ordered several units of the Taurian Defense Force to the New Colony Region. They will remain there until they are no longer needed, and will defend our citizens against the Davion agitators in their midst as well as against external threats. I regret that I must declare martial law in effect on Taurian colony worlds and among Taurian populations on jointly held planets; until we have rooted out the enemy, however, such stern measures are unfortunately necessary.

"We will survive this crisis, and we will continue to prosper despite the best efforts of our foes. The unfortunate end of Jeffrey Calderon's tenure heralds the beginning of a new era for the Concordat—one in which unlooked-for friends will help us triumph over an old and crafty enemy. As we have done throughout our history, the Concordat will turn adversity into victory. I humbly ask all of you to aid me in that great endeavor."

—Personal letter from Grover Shraplen to his eldest daughter, Lady Marilla, who became ruler of MacLeod's Land upon her father's ascension to the Protectorship

5 September 3061

Dear Marilla,

Finally, I've managed to escape from the whirlwind of official duties long enough to write to you. I hope you are settling in well on MacLeod's Land; I have no doubt that our homeworld will prosper under your intelligent guidance. For my own part, I could wish myself anywhere but where I am. Does that sound strange, after all the times you've heard me grouse that I could do a better job of running the Concordat than poor old Thomas Calderon's youngest son? They're right, those old tales that tell us to be careful what we wish for. For years I dreamed of the things I'd do differently were I the Protector. Now I am, so I guess we'll finally find out if I'm right.

I truly curse the Davions—for murdering young Jeffrey, for interfering in our affairs yet again, and for thrusting me into a position I now find I don't really want. All of this realm's troubles, present and future, are mine now. I intend to make the Davions regret every sleepless night I expect to suffer. This Capellan alliance might be just the thing to do that. I am thinking seriously about it; those things I said in my inaugural address weren't just playing to the press, or carving out maneuvering room for negotiations. Though we'll likely need the latter; House Liao has not always been a friend to this realm, and I've heard Chancellor Sun-Tzu isn't much more stable than his mother was. Making him First Lord of their precious new Star League

just proves what fools the Inner Sphere House Lords are. Luckily for us, they've all been too preoccupied with the Clans to pay the Periphery states much mind.

That brings up another reason to join the Capellans. The Clan invasion is over, I hear—really over, not just a stopgap treaty like Tukayyid. That means the new Star League will be free to turn its eyes in our direction … and despite any jingoistic propaganda you may have heard, the TDF can't hope to stand for long against an Inner Sphere army determined to annex the Periphery. So far, the unrest in the Federated Commonwealth has worked in our favor; now we need to take advantage of the Davions' troubles to shore up our own position. The Capellans can give us military equipment—the same cutting-edge technologies they've been sharing with the Magistracy of Canopus, hopefully in large enough numbers to outfit the expanding TDF. Lord knows we could use the materiel, especially with the New Colony Region as unsettled as it is. Of course, we'll probably have to break off our diplomatic relations with the St. Ives Compact if we want to be friends with Sun-Tzu Liao. He's a touch obsessed with reclaiming all of what used to be Capellan territory, including St. Ives. Though with things heating up in that region of space, our embassy in the Compact will be a small loss. Our best bet may be to string the Capellans along for a few months, see how they do militarily and keep watching how they treat the Magistracy. Then I'll have a clearer idea of whether or not to take Chancellor Liao up on his proposals.

The Magistracy is another problem. With the Colonial Marshals understrength, it wouldn't surprise me if the Canopians tried to expand their control in the New Colony Region. I'm not sure I trust Emma Centrella; that woman is too clever by half. I don't agree with the fringe elements who see the Treaty of Taurus as part of a Canopian plot to absorb us; the Magistracy isn't strong enough, for one thing, and large portions of the MAF are off in Capellan space now, anyway. But I can well believe the Canopians might try to exploit the unsettled situation in the colonies. According to our late Protector's private papers, Magestrix Emma wasn't satisfied with the pace of our joint colonization efforts. She wanted a bigger and faster return on her investment. Now a chance to expand Magistracy power in the NCR has fallen into her lap. I can't believe she would pass it up. So we'll have to counter any Canopian moves in that direction, but subtly enough not to offend them. The Magistracy alliance has done a lot of good for the Concordat, and I've no wish to throw it aside. At most, I'd like to slow things down a little. Give us some breathing room, to be sure that what we agreed to in the Treaty of Taurus is really the best thing for the Concordat.

Take military aid, for example. Helping the Canopians build 'Mech factories is all well and good, but those resources might better have been turned toward guarding our backs against the Davions. Especially now. Perhaps Capellan aid can fill that gap—if not to us, then to the Magistracy. With the Capellans building their factories for them, they won't be pestering us to do it. We can use our funds and our expertise to safeguard our own borders, as we should have been doing all along. And we can make sure that what's ours in the colonies stays ours.

And then there's the military aid we've been giving the Outworlds Alliance, which may yet come back to haunt us. I told Jeff Calderon at the time that we'd no business sending advisors and whatnot to improve the Alliance military's performance, never mind how many able-bodied workers for the colonies we got out of it. Recent events have proved me right. Mitchell Avellar appears to have listened to the factions who've been calling for a massive military build-up; over the past few months, they've finally been getting their way. Our people did too good a job, and now the Alliance thinks it can take on the universe. The Alliance has shown no overtly hostile intent so far, but Davions are thick on the ground in the business community, and Avellar can't afford to alienate them. If the Davion mining concerns and such pull out, the Alliance economy will head straight back to hell. With that kind of dependence, the Outworlds Alliance is essentially a FedCom client state. Who knows what the Davions might be able to push President Avellar into, as soon as they get their own house in order?

I know, it sounds as if I'm seeing Davions under the bed ... but I don't think I'm exaggerating their influence. Victor Davion is the real wild card; the conquering hero, come home to find himself deprived of his realm. They say he disbanded his army in April, but I'm not sure I believe that. If he leads troops against his sister, good for us; if he turns his attentions elsewhere, we may be in very deep trouble. The one thing I'm sure he won't do is sit on his hands. Davions don't do that. I suppose I'm foolish to worry overmuch, however; all I can do is watch, wait and try to prepare the Concordat for the worst-case scenario. Beyond that, losing sleep over my worries will only make me a less effective leader. So I guess I'll mull a little wine the way your mother used to, turn in for the night and hope I can manage to sleep until morning.

Don't hesitate to be in touch if you need any advice from your old father, by the way. I may be beset with troubles, but sometimes other people's are the best antidote. Take care, and let me hear from you soon.

—Dad

[When Shraplen wrote this letter, you had not yet become Precentor Martial of ComStar. Since your acceptance of that position, Protector Grover Shraplen has become remarkably friendly toward the Word of Blake. They'd already made inroads among the New Colony worlds, where a lot of people were impressed enough with their mystical mumbo-jumbo to see them as the "real" ComStar. Just three weeks ago, the Protector invited the highest-ranking Blake precentor in the New Colony Region to come to Taurus for "discussions." Word is that he's thinking of granting the Blakists an exclusive contract for HPG maintenance, and cutting ComStar out. It hasn't happened yet, but it's looking increasingly likely. —JC]

OTHER PERIPHERY POWERS

[Rather than run down every Periphery state, this report focuses on those whose activities are of most potential interest or worry to the Star League. The Outworlds Alliance material comes via a ComStar ROM agent in that realm; the field report following comes from a member of the Explorer Corps. I've split the field report into two parts, one on the Marian Hegemony and the Circinus Federation, the other on bandit activity. —JC]

THE OUTWORLDS ALLIANCE
—Excerpt from the diary of Mitchell Avellar, President of the Outworlds Alliance

12 December 3061

Christmas and the New Year are approaching fast, and I can't help but wonder what 3062 will have in store for the Outworlds Alliance. I know what many of my advisors would say. They foresee continued prosperity, driven by the cranking up of our war machine, followed by heightened political influence in direct proportion to the size and strength of the Alliance mili-

tary. For once, they're doubtless thinking, the rest of the Periphery will have to stop treating us like a poor relation. It's true, we're not as poor as we were. In the five years since Dad left things to me in 3056, the Alliance economy has rebounded even faster than I thought it would. I was sure my Long Road program would take at least a decade to show results, especially since so much of it depended on the Federated Commonwealth.

Luckily, we finished our negotiations with FedCom business interests before Prince Victor went off to fight the Clan war. So far, Duchess Katrina—or is it Archon Princess now?—has declined to tamper with those arrangements. Most of the FedCom companies we approached were only too happy to give Alliance-owned business groups the responsibility of reopening and refurbishing their facilities here; all it cost them was a little start-up capital, and now many of those firms are turning a profit. Some of my advisors, though, saw cause for worry in Katrina's takeover of the FedCom. They wonder if she'll try to shut things down here, and don't want to wait around to find out. They've been after me to turn more of our resources toward a strong military almost since I first took office; the FedCom's change of government was just another excuse. But I doubt we have much to worry about on that front. Katrina is half a Steiner, and they're nothing if not receptive to business concerns. As long as the deals with us remain profitable, Katrina will do nothing to upset the owners of private FedCom companies.

The real worry is the Capellan Confederation. I neither like nor trust Chancellor Liao's machinations with the Magistracy of Canopus and the Taurian Concordat. An alliance with both of them would give House Liao a huge sphere of influence in the Periphery. I don't think Sun-Tzu Liao will threaten us directly, at least not yet; we're not a rich enough prize. But I'd like to avoid Liaoist aggression in the future, and also keep Sun-Tzu's Periphery friends out of the Alliance's hair. We've barely begun to climb out of the economic pit; it would be nice to finish what we've started.

So I gave in to the military boosters a few months ago, and the build-up is going well. The advisors from the Taurian Concordat were a huge help in upgrading our ground forces. I expect them to be close to par with our air corps by the end of next year. I can't help but worry about the long-term costs, though. Building and maintaining an army, to say nothing of the military-industrial complex necessary to keep it equipped, is expensive. Part of me believes that those resources would be better devoted to the civilian economy. After all, how many 'Mechs and tanks and planes and bombs and guns does one small nation need?

I also wonder how this newly expanded and outfitted Alliance Military Corps will be used. I intend only to defend my realm against potential aggressors ... but some other president, sometime in the future, may opt for a war of expansion. A successful one would certainly enrich the Alliance in the short run with the resources of the planets we conquered. But there are drawbacks to growing too big, quite apart from the moral implications of such action. We might easily overextend ourselves, or get so unwieldy that we balkanize. The latter has already been a problem, though not as much as it was a few years ago. The Separatist political faction still hasn't found a charismatic leader around which to jell, and the recent ascendancy of the strong-military party has taken some of the energy from their jump sails. Ongoing economic improvements have been a big help, too. It's hard to get people talking secession when they have plenty of money in their pockets.

Above all, the Alliance must keep expanding economically. Insofar as the military machine we're creating will help us do that, it's a good thing. I'll just have to make sure it doesn't become a monster, swallowing up too many of our available resources. And we'll need a stronger military to fend off enemies who may consider us worth bothering with as we grow richer. Pirate and bandit raids, always our worst problem, will only intensify. Our neighbor states may become troublesome as well, though I intend to keep up good relations with as many as I can. The Taurian Concordat is already nervous about the military build-up; the new Protector is oversensitive about potential threats to his realm. I'll have to reassure the Taurian ambassador the next time he starts asking probing questions. Our trade contacts with the Taurians are too important to jeopardize.

Fortunately for several local planetary economies, the end of the Clan war doesn't seem to have affected Explorer Corps operations much. With no need to concentrate solely on finding the Clan homeworlds, they appear to be shifting toward general exploration—which means that the Alliance worlds they've been using as launching and base sites are likely to continue in those capacities. That's good news for all of my people who have jobs because of the Corps' presence. ComStar in general has been a godsend to the Outworlds Alliance; the education they provided to so many Alliance citizens throughout the 3030s and '40s has been a key to our current revival. I can't say I have much use for their mystic-minded counterparts, the Word of Blake. Blake representatives have come nosing around a few Alliance worlds, but most get sent packing fairly quickly. We're a free-thinking lot out here; spiritual mumbo-jumbo doesn't impress the average Alliance citizen much. Results do.

I only hope the results of our shift to a more militarized economy are as promising as some of its backers believe. For better or worse, we're committed to it now. It will be interesting to see where it takes us … .

THE MARIAN HEGEMONY AND THE CIRCINUS FEDERATION

Field Report 1002459
From: Adept Garrison McLeod, Islington Observation Post, Marian Hegemony
To: Demi-Precentor Karol Stanislav, Commander, Rimward Exploration Theater

The following field report covers recent activities in the Marian Hegemony and the neighboring Circinus Federation, as well as bandit activities throughout Explorer Corps operations areas.

The Hegemony and the Word of Blake

I regret to report that the Word of Blake has finally won out in its struggle with ComStar for dominance in the Marian Hegemony. You will recall that six months ago, Caesar Sean O'Reilly finally made good on his threats to take the Alphard HPG station under his personal control. He then staffed it with Word of Blake personnel, among them members of the radical Toyama and Sixth of June sects, effectively freezing ComStar out of the Hegemony capital. The Word of Blake spent the ensuing half-year pressing for even greater influence throughout the Hegemony, and this past week they finally got it. The Caesar issued a formal declaration making ComStar persona non grata within Hegemony borders, and simultaneously announced the start of HPG construction on the planets of Lothario and Pompey. Needless to say, these new facilities will be under Word of Blake control.

They will not, however, be under the sway of the ultra-radicals. Relations between the Caesar and the most fanatical Blakist sects appear to have cooled somewhat since 3058, when the Toyama covertly supplied high-tech 'Mechs to the Marian state. The abrupt end to that operation and the death of its principal architect, Precentor Demona Aziz, seem to have given O'Reilly second thoughts about the competence of his allies, and he has since turned his attentions toward the more centrist elements of the Word of Blake. Any diminishing of the fanatics' power, especially of the Sixth of June, must be regarded as welcome.

Capellan Relations

Previously cordial relations with the Capellan Confederation have soured markedly, partly because of the Liao-Magistracy alliance and partly because of Sun-Tzu Liao's personal involvement in exposing the Blakists' Hegemony operation. The latter particularly infuriated the Caesar, who reportedly referred to the Capellan Chancellor as "that stinking little slant-eyed rat," and considered cutting off the Confederation's germanium supplies. Ultimately, however, Caesar O'Reilly settled for jacking up the price of the vital element for Capellan traders. So far, Sun-Tzu Liao has gone along with this, likely because he does not have the available forces at the moment with which to take the germanium he needs. Should that change, however, the Marian leader has made a bad enemy.

The Lothian League

Unrest in the former Lothian League, a problem ever since the Hegemony's conquest of that realm in 3054, has grown worse since the most recent Periphery report compiled by ComStar (January 3059). Much of the upsurge in Lothian resistance can be traced to appearances by a woman who may be Elena Logan, younger daughter of Dame Lorelei Logan and heir-presumptive to the League since the death in battle of Liesel Logan. This individual greatly resembles Elena Logan and exhibits the Logan family's MechWarrior skills.

Whether or not she is the genuine article remains to be proved, but the League citizens who have seen her believe in her. Throughout the past year, she has turned up at gatherings of various resistance groups and even at the occasional public rally, calling for all good League citizens to fight the Marian occupation and pledging to restore the Logan family to its rightful place. She invariably disappears before Marian authorities can move in, and has reportedly been involved in breaking several prominent dissidents out of jail. Rumor has it that "Elena Logan" is knitting together the Lothian League's disparate resistance groups into a unified opposition force, whom she intends ultimately to lead against the Marian garrison troops. In recent weeks, the Legion has been hard-pressed to hold its own against the rising unrest; the situation has apparently forced the Caesar to abandon his rumored designs on the tiny Illyrian Palatinate.

Two months ago, Caesar Sean abruptly transferred his son and heir, Julius O'Reilly, from the First Marian Legion to the Second and sent him to the former League capital of Lordinax. There appear to be several reasons for this move, chief among them to "toughen up" his eldest son by forcing him to deal with civilian insurgents. That strategy, however, appears to have backfired. Exposure to the Lothians' plight has made Julius O'Reilly sympathetic to their cause, and deepened his conviction that the Lothian conquest was wrong. Should he live long enough to succeed his father, Julius may well lift the occupation and restore the League's freedom.

The persistent coldness between the Caesar and his heir, coupled with Caesar O'Reilly's rumored involvement in his own father's death, suggest a second motive behind Julius' transfer. Highly suspicious of his son's growing popularity, the Caesar may be hoping that Lothian dissidents will kill Julius and thereby remove a potential threat to his own power.

New Colony Machinations

The New Colony Region, already unsettled by secessionist fever and martial law, has become a prime target for Marian Hegemony and Circinus Federation raiders. The Federation and the Hegemony are acting in concert, their joint operations apparently proposed by Caesar Sean in lieu of the Federation's earlier proposal for a joint invasion of the Illyrian Palatinate. Units from the two nations do not work well together, however, reflecting the high level of mistrust between their governments.

The Circinus Federation has had somewhat greater success than its partner in the NCR, which helped blunt formerly widespread criticism of President "Little Bob" McIntyre's administration. McIntyre's build-up of the Federation military with his own loyalists largely did the rest. The president now has far tighter military control over the state than he did just three years ago, completing the transformation of the Federation from a democracy to a dictatorship. Existing dissent is greatly subdued; former leading voices among the Federation's planetary governors have either been silenced by the military or are afraid of attracting the attention of their increasingly paranoid and irrational chief executive. The Black Warriors, until recently equally divided between loyalists and potential rebels, has since fallen firmly into the loyalist camp. Though the dissident Lord Captain

Michael Cirion still holds his company command rank, observers believe it is only a matter of time before Major Fritz Donner, leader of the loyalist faction, amasses enough power to dismiss Cirion in spite of the Lord Captain's family connections. *[As much as I hate the notion of building up these jumped-up pirate kingdoms, I think we ought to look seriously at providing their NCR activities with some sort of backing. Not enough to make either of them genuine powers in the region, but enough to force the Magistracy and the Concordat to concentrate military resources in colonial territory. Every MAF and TDF unit kept busy on a New Colony world is one less unit Sun-Tzu Liao can call on for his own expansionist designs, particularly in the St. Ives Compact. Any aid would have to be extremely covert, of course, especially given your position as overall commander of the SLDF. Maybe we can kick ideas around sometime soon. —JC]*

BANDIT ACTIVITY

The end of the Clan war halted the influx of AWOL mercenary units who fled to the Periphery rather than fight on the Clan front lines. Most of those who arrived during the early years of this decade, however, have since carved out territories for themselves or joined up with established pirate bands, and few of them show any signs of leaving. In addition, the virtual destruction of Clan Smoke Jaguar's warrior caste has driven most of the few survivors to banditry. Small Jaguar units eke out a precarious existence in the Periphery, raiding isolated planets. Fortunately for Periphery citizens, the Jaguars have so far refused to ally with Inner Sphere pirate bands, whom they regard as worse than dezgra.

A few Jaguar units have turned up recently in Port Krin and other cities on Antallos, a known pirate haven. They have called attention to themselves by destroying several small pirate bands, though no one has yet been able to determine their reasons for doing so. The Jaguars have yet to go after larger bands such as Vinson's Vigilantes, but many locals believe they will do so before long. Meanwhile, various organized-crime interests on Antallos have attempted to enlist Jaguar MechWarriors as hired muscle. So far, they have found no takers.

Other Jaguar warriors have allegedly gone to ground on the independent world of Astrokazsy, reportedly drawn to the planet by rumors of its past history as a storage site used by the original SLDF. The Star League tie makes it a place of redemption for them, and they are said to be engaged with dezgra units from other Clans in a battle for control of the Star League caches there. The presence of those other dezgra Clan units' may be the source of persistent rumors that the Great Houses of the Inner Sphere field-test top-secret new designs in Astrokazsy's wilderness.

The New Belt Pirates are still operating in the Wolf Clan occupation zone, but may not be for much longer. The decimation of the Crusader Wolf Touman in the Refusal War allowed the pirates to increase their raids against Wolf-held worlds throughout 3058 and into early 3059, but the Crusader Wolves have stepped up campaigns against them over most of the past two years. Wolf Khan Vladimir Ward, in violation of the standard Clan

people of the victimized border worlds, who blame the Cats for taking up the time and attention of the Combine's leaders and military. If not for the "dirty Clanners," they believe, the Coordinator would immediately send his best units to wipe the pirates off the map.

Meanwhile, in a public-relations gesture designed to win over the citizens of the Federated Commonwealth, Archon Katrina Steiner-Davion has doubled the price on the heads of Fuchida's Fusiliers. This rogue merc unit turned pirate band has spent its entire existence raiding FedCom worlds, after refusing orders from its FedCom employer to fight on the Clan front lines in 3051. The Fusiliers increased their border raids shortly after the Archon assumed control of the FedCom, apparently assuming that she would have her hands full sniffing out pro-Victor loyalists in the AFFC. So far, the pirates' gamble has paid off. With the sharp rise in the bounty, however, the Fusiliers' luck may be running out.

NOTABLE PERSONALITIES

—Prepared by Jerrard Cranston, from field reports by agents in the Periphery

The following individuals are most likely to influence events in the Periphery in the near future, for better or for worse.

MAGESTRIX EMMA CENTRELLA

Rank/Position: Magestrix of the Magistracy of Canopus
Year of Birth: 3008 (age 53)

Profile:
At 53 years of age, Emma Centrella retains much of the beauty and charm that have helped make her one of the most talented diplomats among Periphery state leaders. Highly intelligent and completely committed to the good of her realm, the Magestrix must be counted among Sun-Tzu Liao's most valuable allies (whether or not Sun-Tzu realizes that). Emma's stormy relationship with her mother, Magestrix Kyalla Centrella, taught her the game of politics and court intrigue; had she not excelled at it, she would not have survived Kyalla Centrella's attempt to assassinate her in 3039. By 3040, Emma had built a sufficient power base to take the Canopian throne away from her unstable parent. She has since led the Magistracy to a position of unprecedented prosperity and influence, exemplified by the historic alliance with the Taurian Concordat. It and her alliance with House Liao best represent the bold gambles for which she is renowned.

The Magestrix appears to have taken the recent death of her eldest daughter in stride. Unlike most other Periphery rulers, she recognized the threat posed by the Clans and tried

practice of assigning such dishonorable duty to solahma units, allegedly uses bandit-hunting expeditions as training exercises for new Wolf units, and also for units from other Clans acquired in the so-called Harvest Trials. The New Belt Pirates are unlikely to hold out for long against the full weight of the Wolf Clan troops, and will probably head back to the Periphery before next year is out.

Vance Rezak and his Band of the Damned continue to make trouble along the Draconis Combine border, in accordance with Rezak's personal war against his former homeland. The DCMS, preoccupied with the difficulties of integrating the Nova Cats into the Combine, has yet to deal decisively with the pirates. The pirate raids have not endeared the Nova Cats to the

to do something about it. She does not appear to blame the Star League or the Inner Sphere for Danai's loss, but instead has turned her energies toward grooming Naomi Centrella to step into the heir's role.

NAOMI CENTRELLA

Rank/Position: Commander of Canopian forces in Capellan space
Year of Birth: 3039 (age 22)

Profile:

Not quite twenty-three years old, Naomi Centrella never expected to become the likely heir to the Magistracy of Canopus. Since being thrust into the spotlight, Naomi has handled herself with poise and grace unusual in someone so young. Gifted with her mother's charm and diplomatic instincts, Naomi Centrella is likely to make her a worthy successor.

Though widely regarded as a less skilled MechWarrior than Danai, Naomi has still shown considerable ability as a military leader during the past few years. She currently serves as overall commander of the MAF units stationed in Capellan space, and by all accounts is doing a masterful job. She appears to have high personal regard for Sun-Tzu, and the rumor mill is running overtime with speculation that Naomi Centrella will soon replace Isis Marik in Sun-Tzu's affections. I'm not certain how much credence to give this, but the two of them have been spending more time together lately. Naomi Centrella's feelings for Sun-Tzu appear to be genuine; whether he returns them, or would do anything about it if he did, remains to be seen. How Magestrix Emma might react to a match between Sun-Tzu and Naomi is anyone's guess.

PROTECTOR GROVER SHRAPLEN

Rank/Position: Protector of the Taurian Concordat
Year of Birth: 2986 (age 75)

Profile:

Grover Shraplen inherits a government whose policies he generally opposed. The new Protector's abrupt change in status and responsibilities has forced him to moderate his views, however, particularly with regard to the Treaty of Taurus and several of Jeffrey Calderon's reforms. Shraplen has publicly indicated complete support for the Canopian alliance, and so far shows no inclination to reinstate the civilian conscription of

builders enacted in Protector Thomas Calderon's day. However, Shraplen's fears of a Davion-led conspiracy to undermine the Concordat have prompted him to beef up the military budget. Military spending remains lower than it was during Thomas Calderon's reign, but is expected to rise steadily over the next several years.

Known for his eloquence as well as his loyalty to the Concordat, Shraplen is regarded as an elder statesman by most Taurian citizens. Should he decide to lead his nation into an alliance with the Capellan Confederation, his personal prestige will make such close ties to an Inner Sphere state reasonably palatable to the people. Until the death of Jeffrey Calderon, Shraplen's distrust of House Liao ran almost as deep as his anti-Davion feelings. His conviction of Davion involvement in the Calderon assassination, however, has made the Federated Commonwealth Enemy Number One.

PRESIDENT MITCHELL AVELLAR

Rank/Position: President of the Outworlds Alliance
Year of Birth: 3034 (age 27)

Profile:

Still a few years shy of thirty, the young president of the Outworlds Alliance has gained considerable experience in ruling a nation over the past several years. He has dealt ably with the Separatists and other factions in the Alliance government who questioned his ability to rule because of his youth, and his popularity among the citizens has grown by leaps and bounds as the Alliance's battered economy continues to improve. It remains to be seen what his nation's recent military build-up will do, both to its hope for prosperity and to Mitchell's own influence. His formidable intelligence, however, has enabled him to turn the Outworlds Alliance from a basket case to a going concern in a little over five years. This remarkable achievement suggests that not much is beyond Mitchell Avellar's capabilities.

As yet, Avellar has shown no signs that he intends to use the expanding Alliance Military Corps against his neighbors. However, the build-up is still in progress, and the pro-military voices are among the loudest in the Alliance government. Therefore, we can't rule out the possibility of aggressive moves by the Outworlds Alliance sometime in the future.

INDEX